LEEDS BECKETT UNIVERSITY
LIBRARY
DISCARDED
TELEPEN
71 0129114 5

Design of Thermal Loads for Building Structures

To Madeleine My Love

Design of Thermal Loads for Building Structures

Practical Building Services Design – Volume 2

K.J.V. Fowler
F.C.I.B.S., F.Inst.R., M.ASHRAE

George Godwin
London and New York

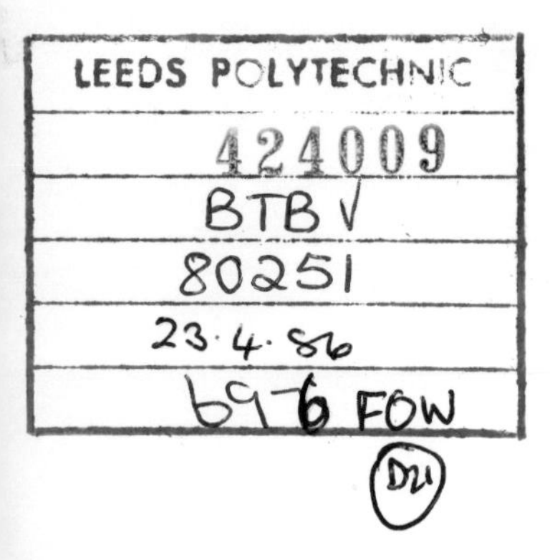

George Godwin
an imprint of:
Longman Group Limited
Longman House, Burnt Mill, Harlow
Essex CM20 2JE, England
Associated companies throughout the world

Published in the United States of America
by Longman Inc., New York

First published 1985

British Library Cataloguing in Publication Data

Fowler, K.J.V.
Practical building services design.
Vol. 2: Design of thermal loads for building structures
1. Buildings—Environmental engineering
I. Title
696 TH6021

ISBN 0-7114-5799-9

Printed in Great Britain by Bath Press, Avon

Contents

Preface

Volume 1 develops a logical process whereby outdoor design conditions may be calculated the world over and thence shows how indoor design conditions may be selected to correspond with the outdoor conditions so calculated.

The theory of psychrometry is touched upon sufficiently to show its thermodynamic derivations, with greater emphasis given to the practical aspects usable in the design of air-conditioning systems.

In developing the conclusions of Volume 1, the existing methods, codes of practice, data and recommendations propounded by various recognised authorities were examined and correlated into design practices which, in one or other respect, are common to all of them. Volume 2 progresses a stage further into the design procedures by dealing with the calculations of the thermal loads of buildings and enumerating the constituents of such loads.

The process used in Volume 1 of analysing and comparing the procedures and data published by the principal authorities of the building services industry, is repeated in Volume 2 and extended to show that marked differences can occur between the calculated results of the several methods in common use.

These differences are due to the fact that, whilst in general the methods of calculation are common to the authorities, the data tabulated by each for use in the calculations show considerable variations, or are lacking in some respect.

The authorities concerned are all of international standing. They have developed their design procedures and data over periods of years and largely independently, wherein lies the main reason for the differences between them.

The present volume makes a consensus of published data, and fills the information gaps that exist in order to provide a comprehensive manual for the calculation of building thermal loads.

The next will show how the calculations are used in the design of the several forms of air-conditioning systems that are in current use.

Acknowledgements

We are grateful to the following for permission to reproduce copyright material:

McGraw-Hill Book Company for our Fig. 3.9 and Tables 6.2 and AII.2 from the *Carrier Corporation Handbook of Air Conditioning Design*; The Chartered Institution of Building Services for our Figs. 3.10, 3.11, 3.12 and Table 3.11 from *CIBS Guide A1*, Tables 3.6, 5.1, 5.2, 5.3, 5.4, 5.5, 5.6 and 5.7 from *CIBS Guide A3*, and Tables 4.1 and AVII.1 and Formulae 3.1 and 3.2 from *CIBS Guide A6*; the Controller of Her Majesty's Stationery Office for our Fig. 3.1 from Kew data sheets (1954), and Tables 3.7, 3.8 and 3.9 from Building Regulations Parts F and FF; Pilkington Glass Limited for our Figs. 3.7 and 3.8 and Table AII.1 from *Thermal Transmission of Windows.*

Note added in proof

The Chartered Institution of Building Services on 13th February 1985 became the Chartered Institution of Building Services Engineers.

Introduction

The present volume of the series is a practical guide to the preparation of thermal load calculations that must be made prior to commencement of the detailed design and layout of air-conditioning and heating systems.

As will become apparent from the text, the various bodies recognised as reference authorities by building services engineers, show some variance in the design data published in their handbooks and guides to practice. Also, in some instances, the necessary information is incomplete or does not exist, thus requiring designers to make arbitrary assessments.

There is no question that the data that are presented by the authorities is well-founded but, having been derived and developed independently over periods of years mainly from subjective test and experiment, it is inevitable that diversity in the results will have occurred. These have been examined, and correlated in this second volume into forms and methods intended for ease of use but with sufficient detail and accuracy to reduce the need for interpolation and judgment. In addition, the information gaps are filled wherever possible.

During the discussion reference is made occasionally to various systems of air conditioning. Without some qualification these references may leave the reader at a disadvantage and, therefore, this introduction is further used to illustrate and briefly describe, by a series of monographs, the main forms of air conditioning in current use.

Energy conservation in the design of these systems is a present-day imperative and some of the means whereby this may be achieved are included in the sketches.

For the present, these are intended as no more than indicators for the references made in the text.

Data, formulae and calculations are expressed in both SI units and Imperial (conventional) units. Generally SI is shown as the primary form followed by the Imperial equivalent in brackets. However, in some instances where appropriate to the discussion, the reverse order is used.

1 Self-contained unit systems

(a) Wall- or window-mounted type

Suitable for individual offices.
Relatively noisy.

One-piece air conditioner with outdoor protruding compressor/condenser section and indoor section incorporating fan and motor, cooling coil, electric heater, air filter and controls.

No central plant.

Requires large aperture through wall or window.

Manual start, automatic run. Power supply 13 amp or 20 amp according to size of unit.

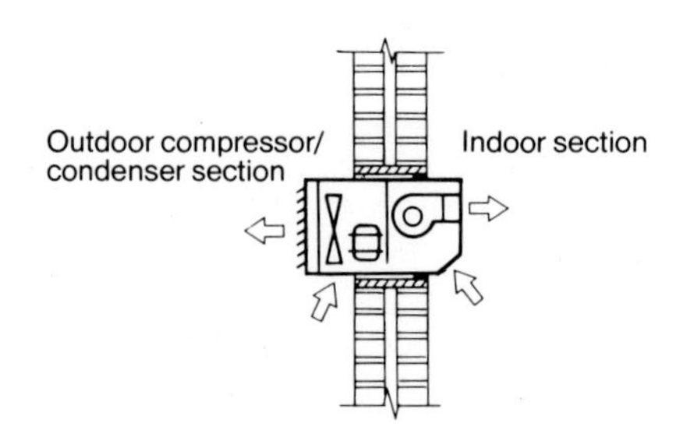

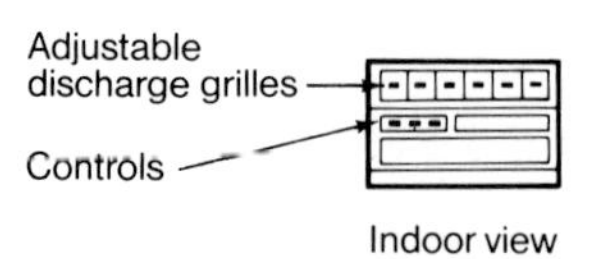

Indoor view

(b) Console, floor-mounted type

Suitable for individual offices.
Quieter than (a) but more expensive.

One-piece air conditioner with air- or water-cooled condenser section and indoor section incorporating fan and motor, cooling coil, electric or hot-water heater, air filter and controls.

No central plant for air-cooled version with electric heater but large wall aperture required.

Water-cooled version and hot-water heating require water source and/or boiler plant.

Manual start, automatic run. Power supply 13 amp or 20 amp according to size of unit.

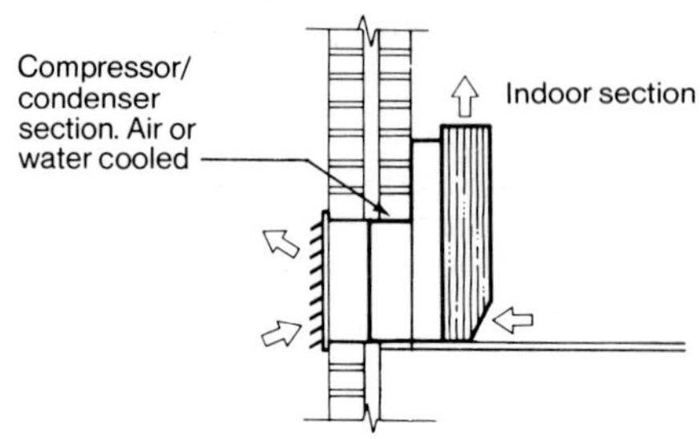

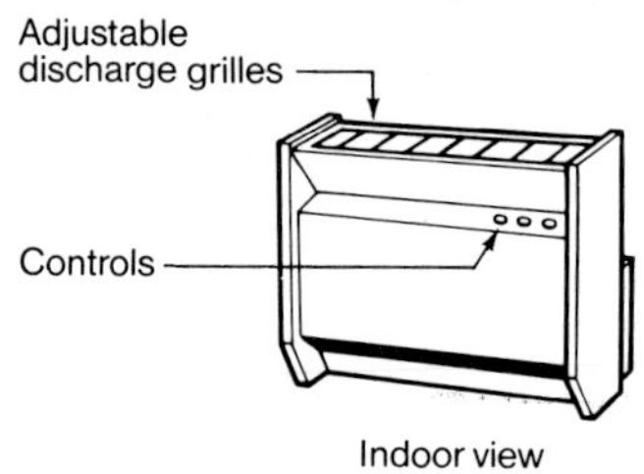

Indoor view

(c) Split-unit type

Suitable for individual offices.
Quiet running.

Two-piece air conditioner comprising indoor and outdoor sections linked with bundled pipe and power lines.

Outdoor compressor/condenser section air-cooled. Can be mounted on ground, wall or roof.

Indoor section incorporates fan and motor, cooling coil, electric or hot-water heater and in-built or remote controls. Can be floor, wall or ceiling mounted.

No central plant for electric heater version. Hot-water heating requires boiler plant.

Small (63 mm (2½ in.) dia.) hole through wall required for connecting lines.

Manual start, automatic run. Power supply 13 amp or 20 amp according to size of unit.

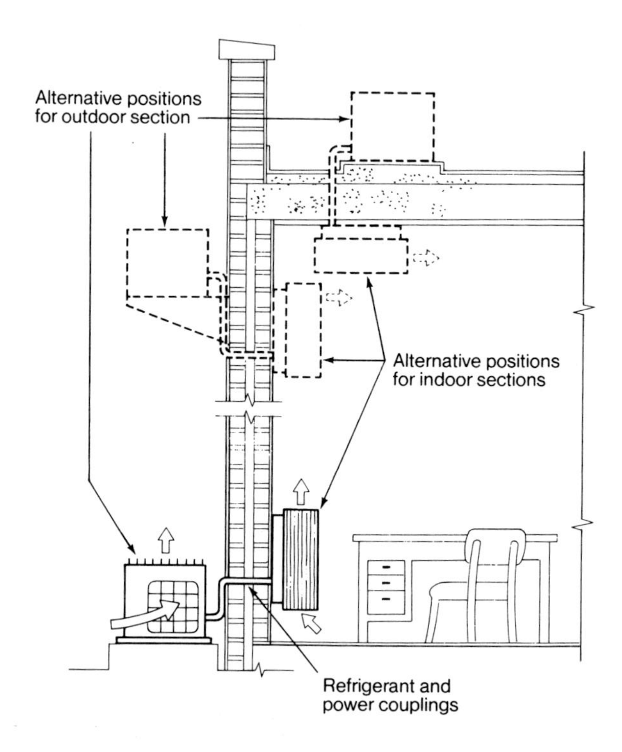

All unit types are available in 'Heat-pump' form

2 Fan-coil unit systems

Applicable to multi-storey offices, hotels, etc.

Individual air-conditioning units incorporating fan and motor, cooling coil, electric or hot-water heating coil, air filter and in-built or remote controls.

Central plant required for chilled water to units and boiler plant for units with hot-water heating.

Can be used with two-pipe or four-pipe water systems

Two-pipe system with electric heating supplies chilled water for cooling purposes.

Two-pipe system with hot-water heating supplies hot or chilled water with changeover from winter to summer.

Four-pipe system supplies hot and chilled water continuously to provide for variable temperatures in individual rooms.

When used in the UK with a central ventilation plant, the two-pipe system will operate with cold water all year and cold air in summer, warm air in winter. The four-pipe version will operate with hot and cold water as required and cold air all year.

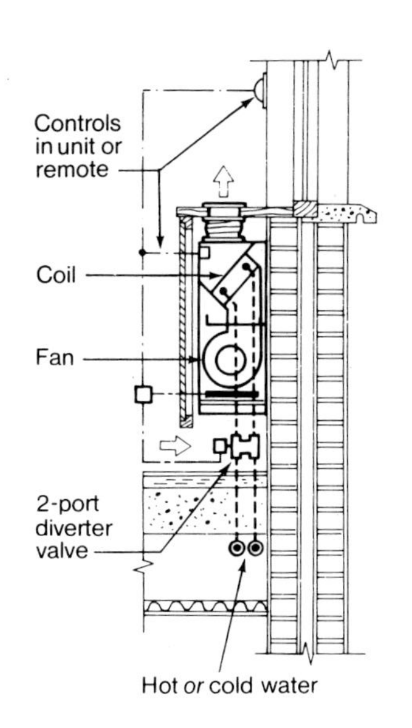

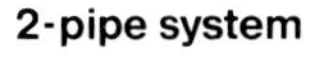

2-pipe system

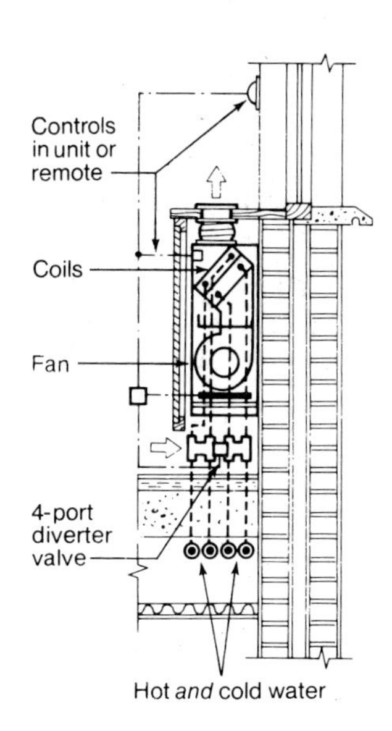

4-pipe system

Units can be floor mounted, either free-standing or in purpose-made enclosures.

High-level units are sited in suspended ceilings or in corridor bulkheads.

Controls are in-built or remote and units can be controlled singly or in groups.

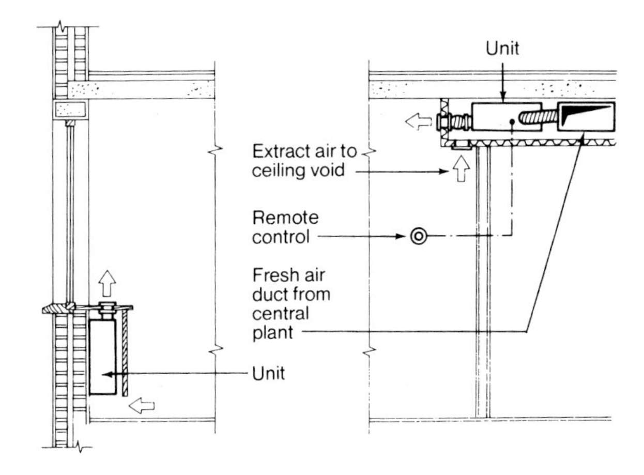

Alternative unit arrangements

Fresh air for ventilation purposes can be from a central plant or can be drawn directly into the units through perimeter walls.

The voids above ceilings or bulkheads are used to convey the vitiated air back to the central plant for partial recirculation or discharge to atmosphere. The central plant is similar to that used for induction systems.

The system is quiet in operation and can be designed for fully automatic starting and running and for energy conservation.

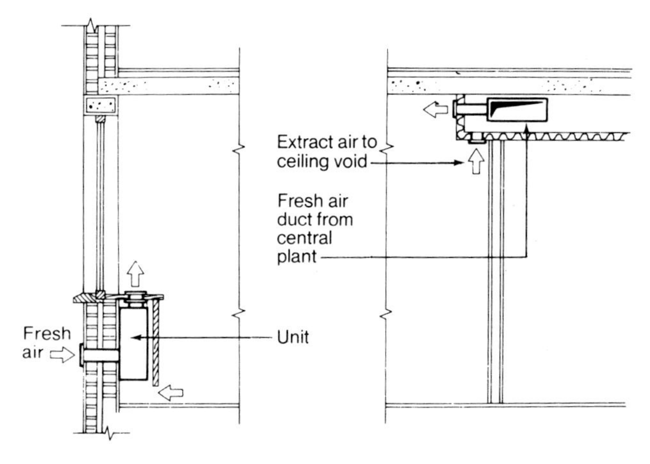

Alternative fresh-air arrangements

3 Induction unit systems

Applicable to multi-storey offices, hotels, etc.

Individual air-conditioning units incorporating high-velocity air ejector nozzles, cooling coil, heating coil, air filter and in-built or remote controls.

High-velocity conditioned air enters the acoustic manifold and is ejected through the nozzles. The ejected primary air induces secondary air from the room to pass through the heating and cooling coils to provide heating or cooling as may be required.

Can be used with two-pipe or four-pipe water systems.

Two-pipe system supplies hot or chilled water with changeover from winter to summer or, in the UK, chilled water all year with cold air in summer and warm air in winter.

Four-pipe system supplies hot and chilled water continuously, to provide for variable temperatures in individual rooms, and cold air all year.

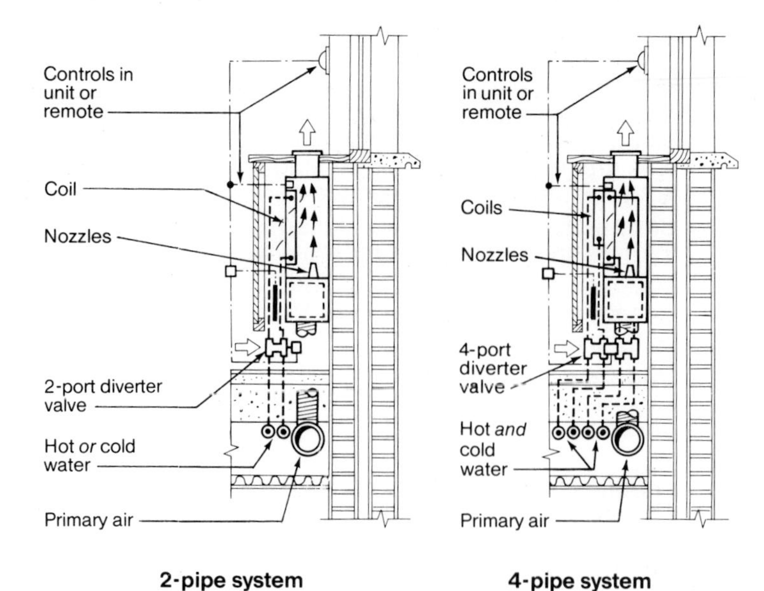

2-pipe system **4-pipe system**

Units can be floor mounted or at high level either free-standing or in purpose-made enclosures and suspended ceilings.

Floor-mounted versions have in-built controls. Remote controls are used for high-level arrangements. Units can be controlled singly or in groups.

In each case it is customary to use suspended ceilings or corridor bulkheads to convey vitiated air back to the central plant for partial recirculation or discharge to atmosphere.

Unit
Extract air to ceiling void
Primary air duct
Remote control
Unit
Primary air duct

Alternative unit arrangements

Central plant is required for chilled and hot water to the units and to supply the conditioned primary air.

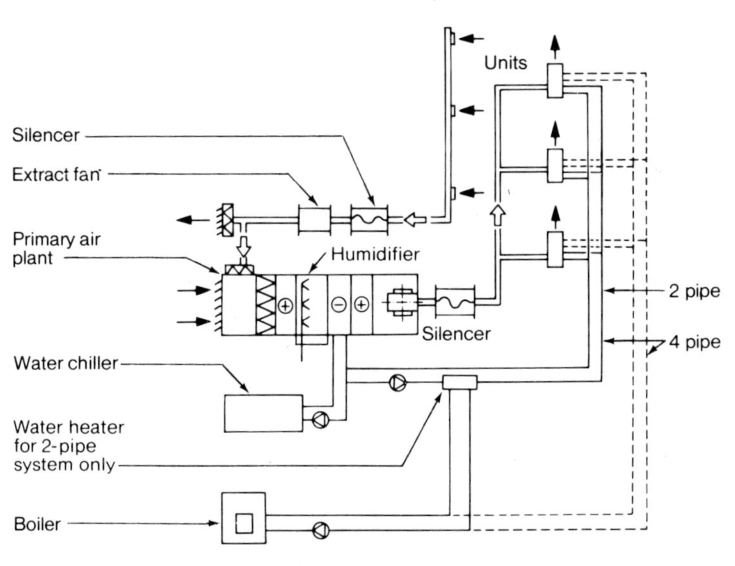

Diagrammatic of air and water systems

The system is quiet in operation and can be designed for fully automatic starting and running and for energy conservation.

4 Variable-air-volume (VAV) systems

Suitable for multi-storey offices, particularly inner-zone areas.

The VAV system of air conditioning uses a series of acoustically lined units within which air, supplied at a constant temperature, is varied in volume in order to maintain the required room temperatures.

The units are usually mounted above suspended ceilings but floor-mounted arrangements are possible.

The units can be controlled singly or in groups.

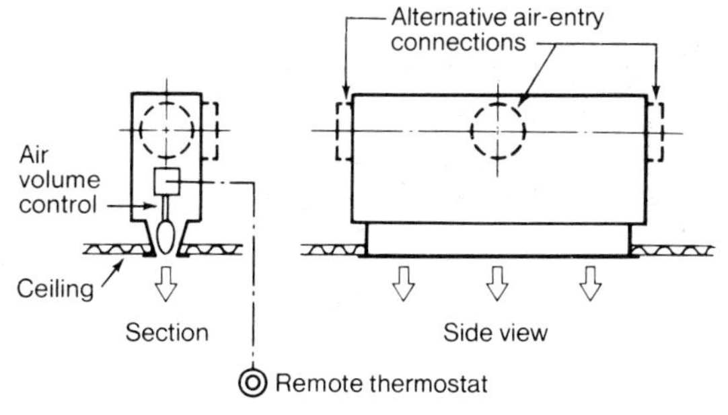

Detail of VAV unit

One method of application is for the units to be used for ventilation and cooling and for the heating to be provided by radiators or convectors arranged at the perimeter walls of the building.

The supply air consists of a mixture of fresh and recirculated air which is conditioned at a central plant.

Vitiated air is extracted from the building via ceiling intake grilles or through the lighting fittings.

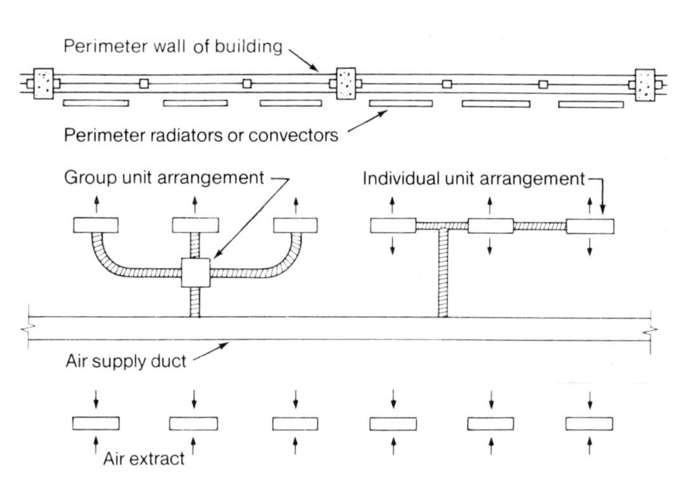

Arrangement with perimeter heating

An alternative application is to use heater batteries attached to the VAV units to replace the perimeter heating.

This arrangement renders the system self-contained and results in additional usable floor space.

The supply and extract-air arrangements are as for the first alternative described above.

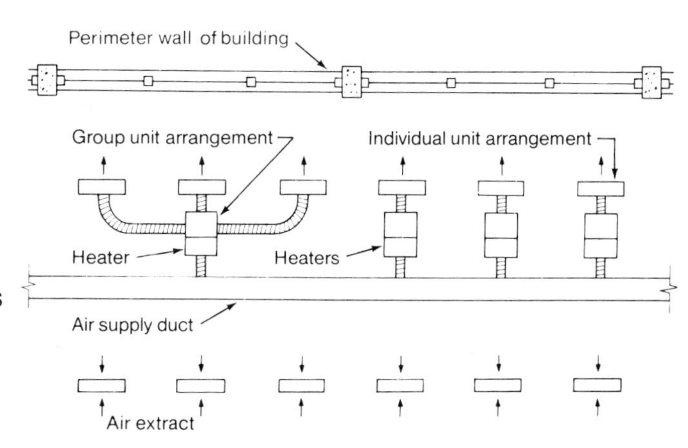

Arrangement with unit heaters

A central air plant is required, to the arrangement shown in the diagrammatic, together with refrigeration plant for cooling purposes and a boiler plant for the perimeter heating or the unit heaters.

The system is very quiet in operation and can be designed for fully automatic starting and running and for energy conservation.

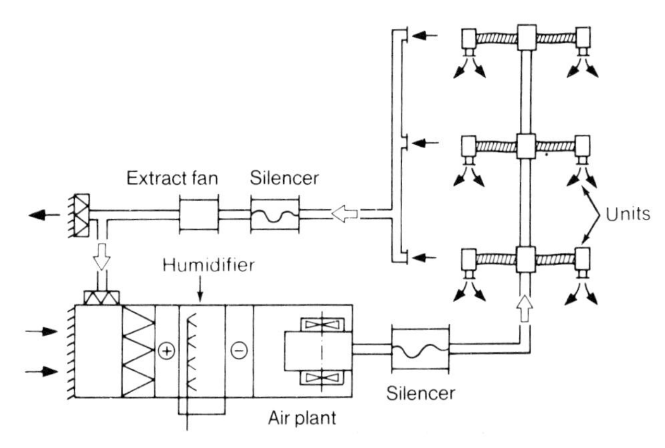

Diagrammatic of air plant

5 Dual-duct systems

Applicable to multi-storey offices, hotels, etc.

Individual air-conditioning units incorporating high-velocity hot and cold supply air ducts with mixing valve and constant-pressure valve.

High-velocity conditioned hot and cold air enter the acoustic mixing box through separate duct branches.

A motorised mixing valve automatically selects the correct blend of hot and cold air to maintain the room temperature required by the controlling thermostat.

A constant-pressure valve ensures that the volume of air delivered to the room remains constant.

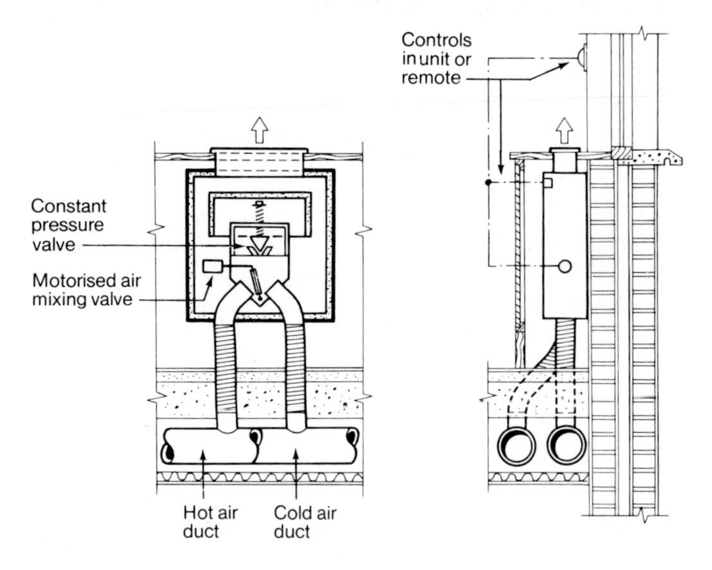

Front section and end view of dual-duct air conditioner

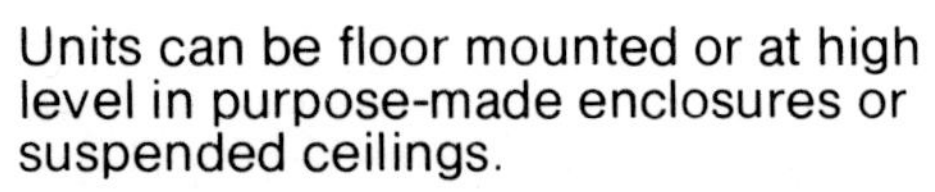

Units can be floor mounted or at high level in purpose-made enclosures or suspended ceilings.

Floor-mounted versions have in-built controls. Remote controllers are used for high-level arrangements. Units can be controlled singly or in groups.

In each case it is customary to use suspended ceilings or corridor bulkheads to convey vitiated air back to the central plant for partial recirculation or discharge to atmosphere.

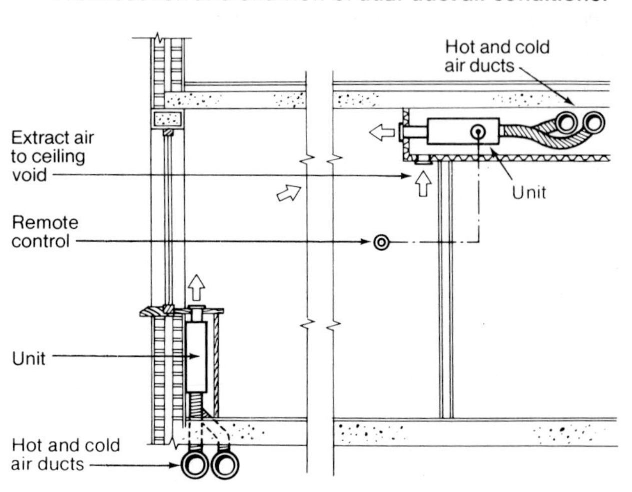

Alternative unit arrangements

A central plant is required to condition the air and to circulate the hot and cold air streams to the units.

The system is very quiet in operation and can be designed for fully automatic starting and running and for energy conservation.

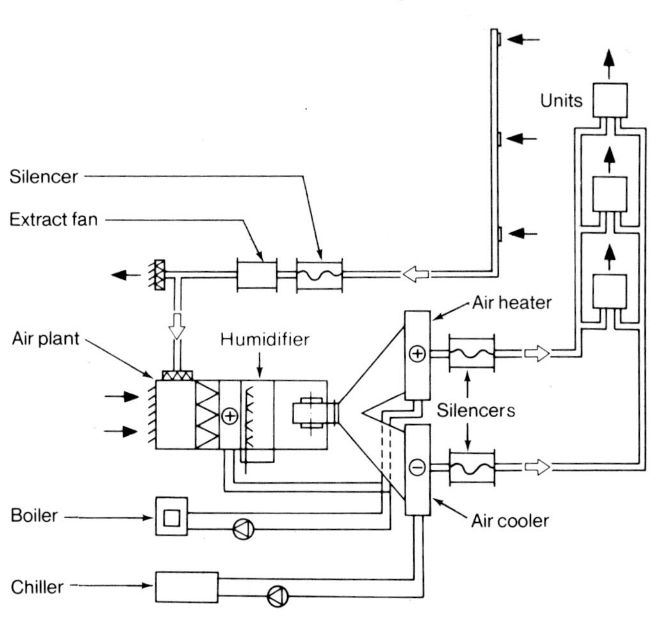

Diagrammatic of air and water systems

6 Versatemp systems

Suitable for office suites, multi-storey offices and hotels, etc

'Versatemp' is a proprietary name for a system of air-conditioning units which operate as 'heat pumps' for heating purposes.

There are other similar forms marketed by several manufacturers.

The system comprises individual self-contained air conditioners incorporating an hermetically sealed refrigeration assembly, a fan and motor, two heat exchangers 'A' and 'B', an air filter and in-built or remote controls.

Water at a constant nominal temperature (24 °C (75 °F)) and constant flow rate is circulated through heat exchanger 'B' in each unit.

For **cooling** purposes the refrigerant reversing valve is in position 1.

Heat removed from the room air at heat exchanger 'A' is rejected into the water circuit at heat exchanger 'B'.

For **heating** purposes the reversing valve is in position 2 and the unit is now acting as a 'heat pump'.

Heat is extracted from the water at heat exchanger 'B' and is transferred through the refrigeration circuit to the room air via heat exchanger 'A'.

The changeover from cooling to heating is effected automatically by the unit controls.

Units can be floor mounted, either free-standing, in purpose-made enclosures, or beneath raised floors.

High-level units are sited in suspended ceilings or in corridor bulkheads.

Fresh air for ventilation can be from a central plant or drawn directly into the units through perimeter walls.

The voids above ceilings or bulkheads are used to convey the vitiated air back to the central plant for partial recirculation or discharge to atmosphere.

Controls are in-built or remote.

No insulation is required on pipes or ducts.

Somewhat noisy in operation.

A central plant is required to the arrangement shown in the diagrammatic.

The system can be designed for fully automatic starting and running and incorporates inherent energy conservation.

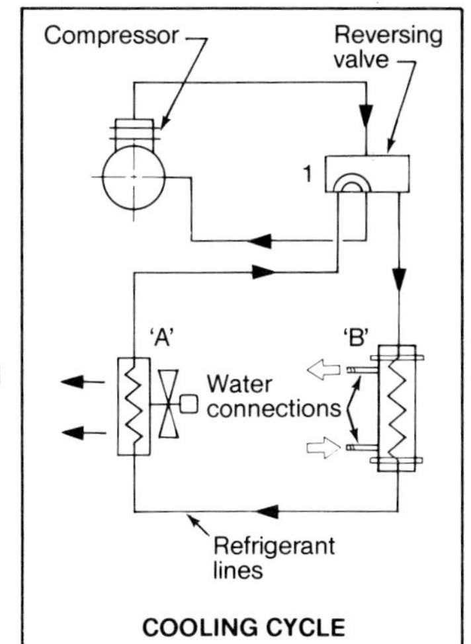

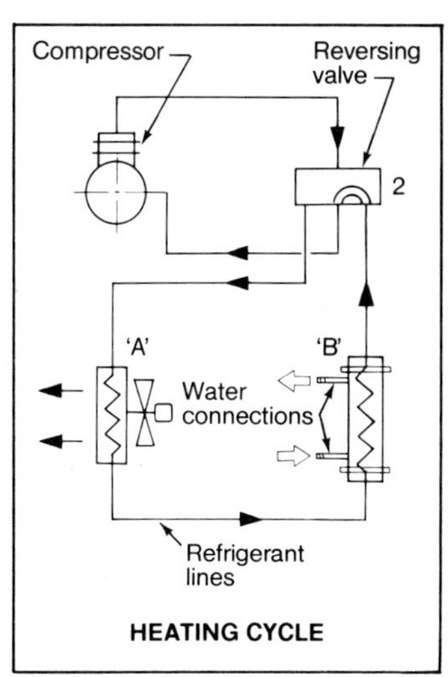

Diagrammatics of refrigeration circuit in unit

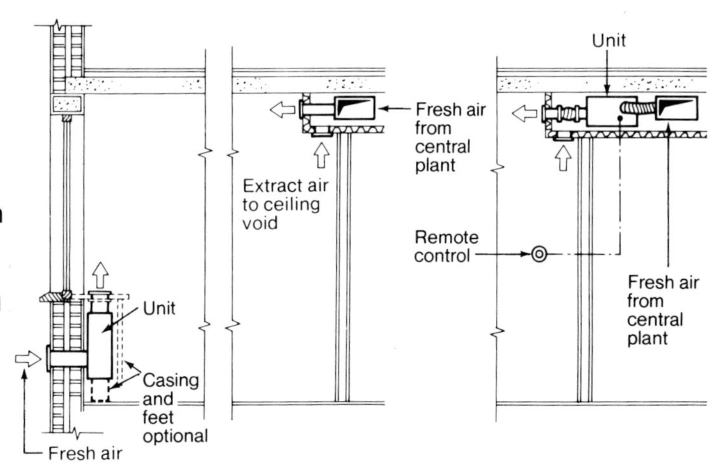

Alternative unit arrangements

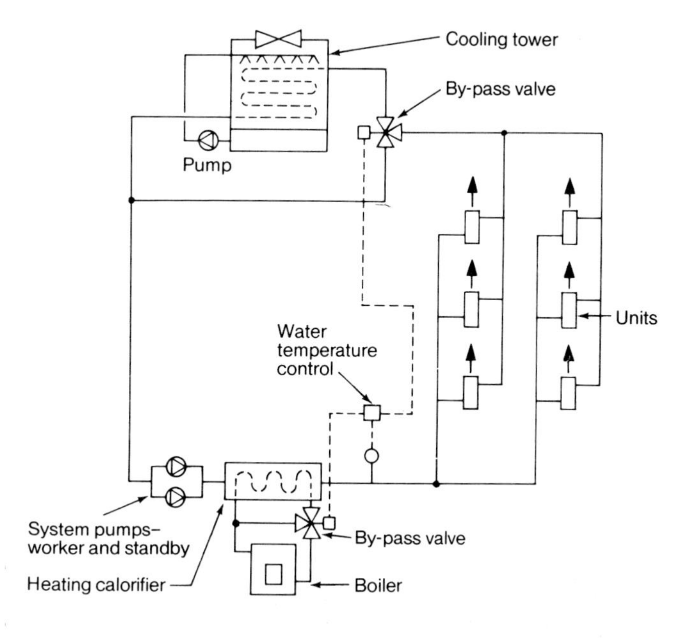

Diagrammatic of water circuit

7 Energy conservation systems

(a) Air-to-air heat pumps

What is usually termed a refrigeration plant is used in reverse form to provide heated air for circulation into a building.

Outdoor air is blown across a heat exchanger 'A' through which the refrigerant of the refrigeration circuit passes.

From the air low-grade heat is transferred to the refrigerant which is compressed to a high-temperature gas by the compressor.

Heat is then transferred from the refrigerant gas to the air which is drawn across heat exchanger 'B' and discharged to the building.

Approximately one-third of the heat generated comes from the compressor and two-thirds from the outdoor air.

Hence for 1kW of electrical power 3kW of useful heat are produced which renders the system cheaper to run than equivalent oil- or gas-fired systems.

Also, if a reversing valve is introduced into the refrigeration circuit (as indicated in the Versatemp diagrams), then the plant can be used for cooling purposes as well as heating.

(b) Air-to-water heat pumps

The principle is the same as (a) above except that heated (or chilled) water is produced for circulation to the building.

(c) Energy wheel

The supply air to a building and the air extracted from it are passed across the halves of a rotating absorbent wheel. Heat and moisture from the extract air are thereby transferred to the supply air instead of being discharged to waste.

Up to 80% of the heat in the extract air can be reclaimed by this method.

Other similar methods for air-to-air heat reclaim are:

(i) Run-around circuit.
This uses heat exchangers in the supply and extract air systems with a pumped water circuit connecting them.
The two air systems can be separated.

(ii) Heat-pipe circuit.
This uses a combined heat exchanger within which a gas/liquid refrigerant circulates to transfer heat between the supply and extract air systems.
No pump is required but the two air streams must be adjacent to each other.
There is no moisture transfer with these circuits as is the case with the energy wheel.

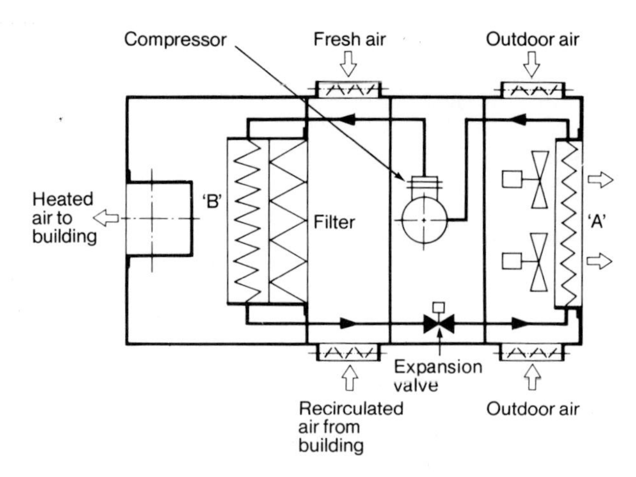

Diagrammatic of air-to-air heat pump plant

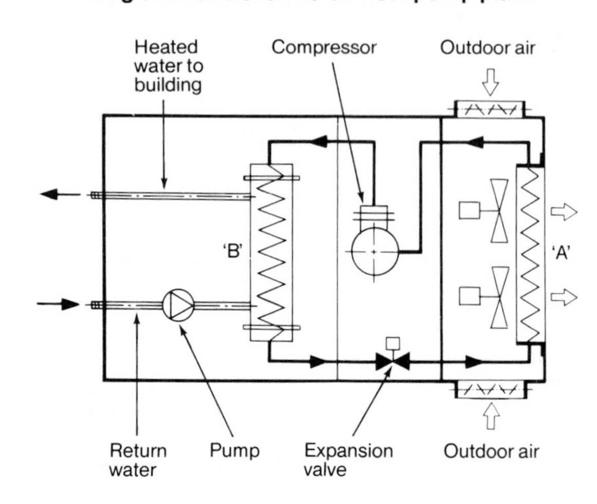

Diagrammatic of air-to-water heat pump plant

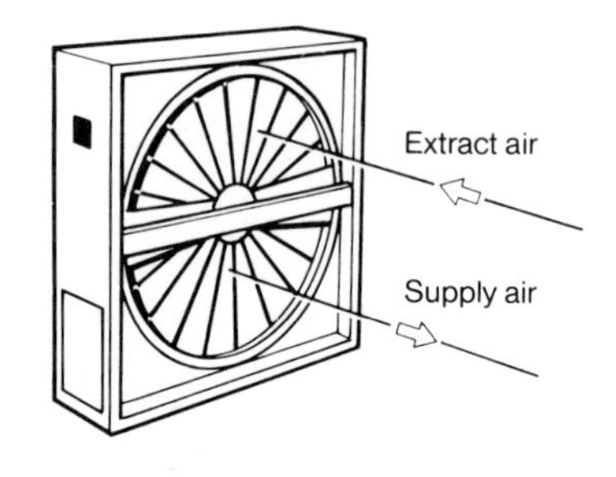

Energy wheel

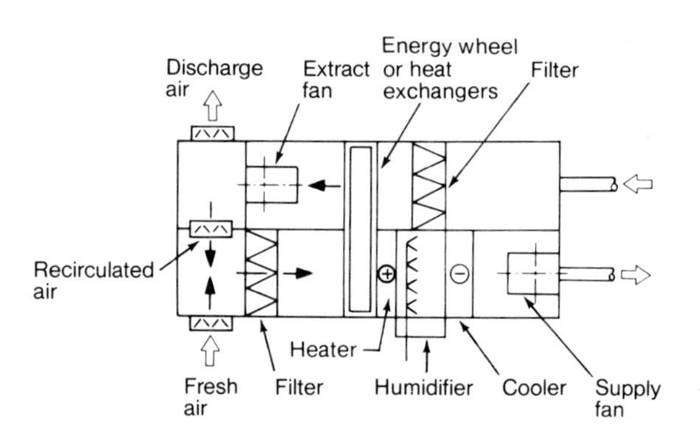

Arrangement of air plant

1 Thermal load calculations

The calculation of the thermal loads (heat gains and heat losses) of buildings is an arbitrary process due to the fact that the data used are based almost entirely upon field, laboratory or analogue trials made by numerous establishments over the past 50 years or so.

The results of this research have then been variously interpreted, applied and progressively updated so that reference to handbooks and institutional guides shows such variation in the data presented that uncertainty must arise in the choice of the authority to be adopted and disparities become evident in the results when comparative cooling load calculations are made.

In the UK three authorities are referred to in the design of building services, namely:

1. The Chartered Institution of Building Services (CIBS).
2. The American Society of Heating, Refrigerating and Air-conditioning Engineers (ASHRAE).
3. The Carrier Air-conditioning Company (Carrier).

A comparison of selected data from their respective guides and handbooks will illustrate these disparities.

Table 1.1 Outdoor design temperatures for London in the UK and Riyadh in Saudi Arabia; degrees Celsius dry-bulb (DB) and wet-bulb (WB) temperatures

	CIBS DB/WB	*ASHRAE DB/WB*	*Carrier DB/WB*
London			
Summer	29 °C/20 °C	28 °C/20 °C	*
Winter	−4.5 °C/*	−4.5 °C/*	*
Riyadh			
Summer	44 °C/28 °C	43 °C/25.5 °C	*
Winter	4 °C/*	3 °C/*	*

* Not quoted

Table 1.2 Indoor design temperatures for London and Riyadh; °C dry-bulb (DB) temperature and % relative humidity (RH)

	CIBS DB/RH	*ASHRAE DB/RH*	*Carrier DB/RH*
London			
Summer	20–22 °C/50%	*	*
Winter	19–20 °C/50%	*	*
Riyadh			
Summer	27–28 °C/40–45%	22.8–26.1 °C/20–70%	23.5–26 °C/45–50%
Winter	22 °C/45%	20–23.6 °C/20–70%	23.5–24.5 °C/30–50%

* Not quoted

* 25.5 °C room temperature is used since ASHRAE provides data at this condition only; CIBS and Carrier provide data over a range of room temperatures.

Table 1.3 Heat emissions from humans; watts of sensible heat (SH) and latent heat (LH) at 25.5 °C* (78 °F) room dry-bulb temperature

	CIBS *SH/LH*	*ASHRAE* *SH/LH*	*Carrier* *SH/LH*
Office worker	72.5/67.5	75/75	63/69
Theatre occupant	67.5/47.5	60/40	61.5/41

Table 1.4 Fresh-air ventilation rates; litres of air per second per square metre of occupied floor area

	CIBS *litres/sec/m²*	*ASHRAE* *litres/sec/m²*	*Carrier* *litres/sec/m²*
Offices			
Partitioned	1–1.8	3.8–10.2	1.27
Open-plan	2.8–4.6		1.27
Boardrooms	6.7–10	*	6.35
Theatres	*	*	3.5–7 litres/sec/person

* Not quoted

Consider, for example, figures quoted for outdoor and indoor design temperatures, heat emissions from humans and fresh-air ventilation rates (see Tables 1.1, 1.2, 1.3 and 1.4).

From these tables it is apparent that, in order to design a theatre in Riyadh, a UK engineer and an American engineer would be obliged to look elsewhere for the missing data and their calculations of these load components would produce conflicting results.

These disparities are not confined only to the data tabulated by the three authorities; in addition, there are marked differences in the methods proposed by each of them for making cooling load calculations, again producing conflicting results.

The three methods are examined at length in Chapter 2 with the aim of selecting one of the bodies as the standard design authority.

2 Comparison of cooling load design methods

In this chapter, and in Appendix I (p. 135), detailed comparisons are made of the design procedures of the CIBS, ASHRAE and Carrier as set out in their respective guides and handbooks. These latter are listed below and referred to in the calculation procedures that follow.

2.1 CHARTERED INSTITUTION OF BUILDING SERVICES

Section A of the CIBS *Guide*:

A2, 1982	Weather and solar data
A3, 1980	Thermal properties of building structures.
A5, 1979	Thermal response of buildings.
A7, 1971	Casual gains.
A9, 1979	Estimation of plant capacity.
A9, 1983	Supplement to A9, 1979.

All data in the CIBS *Guides* are presented in SI units only.

2.2 AMERICAN SOCIETY OF HEATING, REFRIGERATING AND AIR-CONDITIONING ENGINEERS

1981 *Fundamentals Handbook*:

Chapter 26	Air-conditioning cooling load.
Chapter 27	Fenestration.

In the *Fundamentals Handbook*, data, calculations, etc. are presented in both SI units and imperial units. In the ASHRAE calculations SI units are used.

2.3 CARRIER AIR-CONDITIONING COMPANY

Handbook of Air-conditioning System Design, Part 1:

Chapter 3	Heat storage, diversity and stratification.
Chapter 4	Solar heat gain thru glass.
Chapter 5	Heat and water vapor flow thru structures.
Chapter 7	Internal and system heat gain.

The Carrier *Handbook* presents imperial units only. Therefore, these are used in the Carrier methods of calculation, with conversions made for comparison with the other authorities.

2.4 COMPARISON OF THE THREE DESIGN METHODS

Study and application of the methods proposed by the three authorities for the calculation of heat gains into buildings, show random differences in the resulting cooling loads such that the method to be used must largely be a matter of choice.

Of the direct gains, that due to solar transmission will comprise some 60 to 70% of the total. Therefore, it is instructive to compare the results that the three methods produce in the calculation of this load component.

2.5 SOLAR HEAT GAIN CALCULATIONS

An appropriate exercise for the purpose is contained in Example 4 of Chapter 26 of the ASHRAE *Fundamentals Handbook* from which the following are extracted.

> 'Determine the solar heat gains through the south and west windows of a building of medium-weight construction located in 32 °N latitude at 12.00, 14.00 and 16.00 hours in the month of August.
>
> 'South windows, double-glazed clear glass with 6.35 mm air space; area 9.29 m^2 (100 ft^2); no shading.
> 'West windows, single grey-tinted glass; area 9.29 m^2 (100 ft^2) with interior light-coloured venetian blinds.'

2.5.1 ASHRAE method (SI units)

Solar load, $Q = A(SC)(SHG)(CLF)$

	ASHRAE reference	*South*	*West*
A (area)	—	9.29 m^2	9.29 m^2
SC (shading coefficient)	Ch. 27, Table 28	0.82	
	Ch. 27, Table 34		0.53
SHG (solar heat gain factor)	Ch. 26, Table 11	350 W/m^2	
	Ch. 26, Table 11		691 W/m^2
CLF (cooling-load factor)			
12.00 hours	Ch. 26, Table 13	0.52	
	Ch. 26, Table 14		0.17
14.00 hours	Ch. 26, Table 13	0.58	
	Ch. 26, Table 14		0.53
16.00 hours	Ch. 26, Table 13	0.47	
	Ch. 26, Table 14		0.82

Solar load *Q*			Watts
South	12.00 hours	$= 9.29 \times 0.82 \times 350 \times 0.52 =$	1386
	14.00 hours	$= 9.29 \times 0.82 \times 350 \times 0.58 =$	1546
	16.00 hours	$= 9.29 \times 0.82 \times 350 \times 0.47 =$	1253
West	12.00 hours	$= 9.29 \times 0.53 \times 691 \times 0.17 =$	578
	14.00 hours	$= 9.29 \times 0.53 \times 691 \times 0.53 =$	1803
	16.00 hours	$= 9.29 \times 0.53 \times 691 \times 0.82 =$	2790

2.5.2 Carrier method (Imperial units)

Solar Load, $Q = A$ (SC)(SHG peak)(SF)

	Carrier reference	*South*	*West*
A (area)		100 ft^2	100 ft^2
SC (shading coefficient)	Ch. 4, Table 16	0.80	0.53

	Carrier reference	South	West
SHG peak (peak solar heat gain interpolated and corrected for glass area)	Ch. 3, Table 6	82.8 Btu/ft²/hr	192.3 Btu/ft²/hr
SF (storage factor 100 lb/ft²)			
12 hr operation			
12.00 hours	Ch. 3, Table 11	0.64	
14.00 hours	Ch. 3, Table 11	0.70	
16.00 hours	Ch. 3, Table 11	0.63	
12.00 hours	Ch. 3, Table 11		0.20
14.00 hours	Ch. 3, Table 11		0.44
16.00 hours	Ch. 3, Table 11		0.72

Solar load Q			Btu/hr	Watts
South	12.00 hours	$= 100 \times 0.80 \times 82.8 \times 0.64$	= 4239	1241
	14.00 hours	$= 100 \times 0.80 \times 82.8 \times 0.70$	= 4637	1358
	16.00 hours	$= 100 \times 0.80 \times 82.8 \times 0.63$	= 4173	1222
West	12.00 hours	$= 100 \times 0.53 \times 192.3 \times 0.20$	= 2038	597
	14.00 hours	$= 100 \times 0.53 \times 192.3 \times 0.44$	= 4484	1313
	16.00 hours	$= 100 \times 0.53 \times 192.3 \times 0.72$	= 7338	2149

2.5.3 CIBS method (SI units)

In Section A9 of the CIBS *Guide*, two methods are used based upon internal conditions of either Inside Air Temperature (t_{ai}) or Dry Resultant Temperature (t_c).

The dry resultant temperature method is recommended by the CIBS. Therefore, this is used in the calculation below but, in the summary on p. 14, the values according to the air temperature control method are also shown.

Solar load, $Q = A(S_c)(S_a)$

	CIBS reference	South	West
A (area)		9.29 m²	9.29 m²
S_c (shading coefficient for medium-weight building)			
South	Table A9.22	0.775	
West, blinds at 45 °	Table A9.23		0.755
S_a (cooling load factor interpolated)			
12.00 hours	Tables A9.22, A9.24	267.2	
14.00 hours	Tables A9.22, A9.24	262.8	
16.00 hours	Tables A9.22, A9.24	145.4	
12.00 hours	Tables A9.23, A9.25		105.2
14.00 hours	Tables A9.23, A9.25		243.8
16.00	Tables A9.23, A9.25		354.2

Solar load Q			Watts
South	12.00 hours	$= 9.29 \times 0.775 \times 267.2 =$	1924
	14.00 hours	$= 9.29 \times 0.775 \times 262.8 =$	1892
	16.00 hours	$= 9.29 \times 0.775 \times 145.4 =$	1047
West	12.00 hours	$= 9.29 \times 0.755 \times 105.2 =$	738
	14.00 hours	$= 9.29 \times 0.755 \times 243.8 =$	1710
	16.00 hours	$= 9.29 \times 0.755 \times 354.2 =$	2484

2.5.4 Summary of solar heat gain loads

		ASHRAE	*Carrier*	*CIBS*	
				t_c	(t_{ai})
		W	*W*	*W*	*W*
South window	12.00 hours	1386	1241	1924	(1433)
	14.00 hours	1546	1358	1892	(1409)
	16.00 hours	1253	1222	1047	(780)
West window	12.00 hours	578	597	738	(642)
	14.00 hours	1803	1313	1710	(1488)
	16.00 hours	2790	2149	2484	(2161)

Examination of the values of solar heat gain attributable to the three authorities leads to the conclusion that there is no pattern sufficient to provide a guide to the adoption of one or the other method except, perhaps, that the Carrier values are generally the lowest.

2.6 CALCULATION OF TOTAL DIRECT GAINS

To take the comparison a stage further, a more detailed calculation is shown in Appendix I (p. 135) of all the direct heat gains that occur in normal building applications.

The constructional example used is a typical module in a multi-storey building depicted in Fig. 2.1 and having the characteristics listed in Appendix I (p. 135).

In Appendix I the design methods of the three authorities have been applied to the module in order to produce comparative overall loads. Each method of calculation has been followed separately with notes and references given to the relevant sources of data.

An analysis of the calculated loads is shown in Table 2.1.

These calculations of all the components of a cooling load show that the disparity between the methods of the three authorities remains as great as in the case of the previous direct solar gain calculation. Hence, to make the choice of method to be used, consideration must be given to factors in addition to a comparison of the numerical values of the calculated loads.

2.7 QUALITATIVE COMPARISON

Combining a qualitative appraisal of the design methods of the three authorities with the quantitative ones already made, produces the relative merits shown in Table 2.2.

The Carrier method shows advantages in all respects and, in the preface to their *Handbook of System Design*, the statement is made that 'it embodies all the

Fig. 2.1 Typical building module

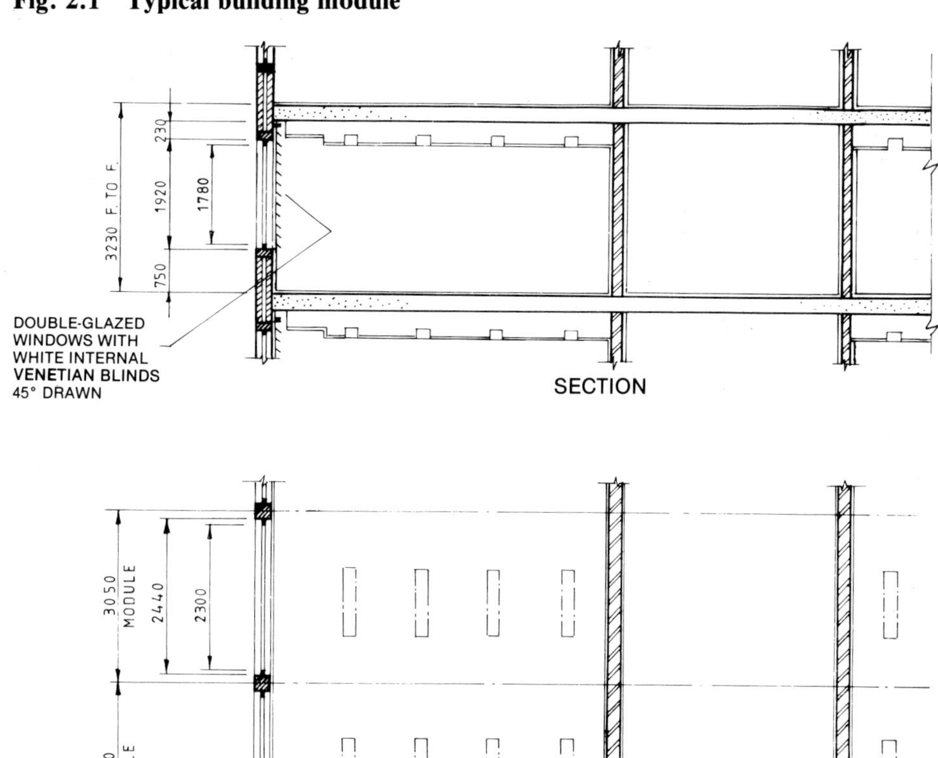

Table 2.1 Comparative cooling load components

	ASHRAE (W)	*Carrier (W)*	*CIBS (W)*
Window solar gain	1119	970	1093
Window conduction	83	89	
Mean gain			−97
Cyclic gain			74
External wall conduction	12	30	
Mean gain			−4
Cyclic gain			−2
Internal wall conduction	27	27	31
Lighting gain	375	235	275
Occupant gain	107	150	167
Totals	1723	1501	1537

Table 2.2 Comparative merits of cooling load calculations

	ASHRAE	*Carrier*	*CIBS*
Magnitude of calculated loads	Highest	Lowest	Average
Areas of application	N latitudes, generally	Universal, N and S latitudes	N latitudes, UK mainly
Ease of use	Relatively complicated	Relatively simple	Complicated
Data documentation	Good	Good	Fair
Explanation of use	Good	Good	Poor
Textual errors and amendments	Several	None	Several
Source references	Extensive	Extensive	Extensive

knowledge and experience gained over the past fifty years by the pioneer in the field, Carrier Air-conditioning Company'.

This is a self-emulative statement, but there is no question that it is substantiated by the thousands of air-conditioning systems, designed in accordance with the Carrier *Handbook*, which have been successfully installed and operated.

However, experience with the Carrier method of design has shown that there are some gaps to be filled and improvements that can be made in its application. Hence, the design procedures which follow seek to extend and amplify existing methods and data.

2.8 BASIC PROCEDURES

The present discussion is concerned with the basic procedures for calculating cooling loads in buildings of a commercial nature: offices, hotels, apartment blocks and similar constructions.

These basic procedures will be relevant to other applications but, in specialist cases such as computer rooms, laboratories, etc. there will exist additional load components to be taken into account. For example, in a laboratory, heat will be emitted from process equipment, furnaces, etc., and gas appliances and fume cupboards will give rise to abnormal loads in the form of sensible and latent heat emissions and to high ventilation rates. Such specialist factors may form large additions to the basic cooling loads so that, for safe accuracy of calculation in these cases, manufacturer's precise data should be used.

Returning to the basic components of the cooling loads imposed on building structures, these fall into two categories of heat transfer, namely:

(a) Direct to the conditioned areas, comprising

Sensible heat from:

- solar radiation through external glazing;
- conduction through external surfaces;
- conduction through internal surfaces;
- illumination and equipment.

Sensible and latent heat from:

- the building population;
- food and other combustion processes;
- air infiltration.

(b) Indirect to the circulatory systems, comprising
  Sensible heat from:
    circulating fans and pumps;
    distribution ducts and pipes.
  Sensible and latent heat from:
    air circulation processes.

It should be noted that the (a) and (b) components are to some extent mutable, i.e. exposed packaged air plants will be subject to solar and conduction heat gains; extensive duct and pipe runs within the conditioned areas may require consideration (particularly with regard to possible condensation); air circulation systems (fume cupboards, etc.) may be located within the conditioned areas, etc.

However, for purposes of discussion, it is reasonable to accept the basic load components as listed and they are dealt with in detailed form in Chapter 4.

Firstly the bases of the design specification must be defined and this follows in Chapter 3.

3 Design specification

At the outset of the calculation of the thermal loads of a building it is necessary first to establish a specification of the various elements of the design against which the calculations are to be made. These elements are:

Temperatures	– outdoor and indoor.
Population	– rates, sex and activities.
Illumination	– rates, type and configuration.
Ventilation	– rates and application.
Infiltration	– rates and sources.
Fenestration	– arrangement, shading and transmission values.
Structure	– construction weights and transmission values.
Noise levels	– background and equipment sources.

Whenever possible actual data should be obtained relating to these various aspects of the design or, lacking these, a suitable reference source should be used.

It is in resorting to this second alternative that problems arise since, as has been demonstrated, published data is either equivocal or does not exist. This leaves the engineer with the choice of using his own judgment or working to a consensus of the available data.

The latter is the logical course, but it is a process which is too tedious for use on a day-to-day basis but, where appropriate, it has been applied to data published by the CIBS, ASHRAE and Carrier in the derivation of the procedures and information which follow.

3.1 OUTDOOR DESIGN TEMPERATURES

Optimum temperatures are used for summer and winter design purposes expressed in degrees Celsius* or degrees Fahrenheit, dry-bulb and wet-bulb. The optimum levels are based upon dry-bulb values likely to be equalled or exceeded for 1% of the *nett hours* of the relevant design seasons, thus:

* Modern usage uses the term degrees Celsius rather than degrees Centigrade. The values are the same, expressed in °C.

Summer	– June to September in the Northern hemisphere.
	December to March in the Southern hemisphere.
Winter	– December to February in the Northern hemisphere.
	June to August in the Southern hemisphere.

The term 'nett hours' relates to the period for which the plant will be required to operate: 10 to 12 hours daytime for office applications; 16 hours for residences and apartments; 24 hours for hotels.

Such optimum outdoor design conditions may be calculated using the CIBS 'Approximate Method B' in the extended form (described in Volume 1 of this series) in conjunction with the *Tables of Temperature, Relative Humidity and Precipitation, M.O. 617 A – F* published by the London Meteorological Office.

Based upon data extracted from these tables the 'Approximate Method B' is applied as given in the following subsections.

3.1.1 Summer

(a) The month is selected which has the *highest average monthly maximum dry-bulb* temperature.
(b) That highest average monthly maximum dry-bulb temperature is chosen as the *summer* design *dry-bulb* temperature.
(c) For the same month, a vapour pressure is derived from the *average daily maximum dry-bulb* temperature and the *average daily minimum relative humidity*.
(d) That vapour pressure is associated with the design dry-bulb temperature to produce the *summer* design *wet-bulb* temperature.

Typical extracts from the *M.O. 617* meteorological tables for London, New York and Johannesburg appear in Fig. 3.1 (p. 20). Note that the temperatures are given in degrees Fahrenheit.

The CIBS 'Approximate Method B' procedure is illustrated by application of the meteorological data for the three localities in Table 3.1.

Table 3.1 Representative calculations of summer outdoor design conditions

	London	*New York*	*Johannesburg*
Average monthly maximum dry-bulb temperature	82 °F (27.8 °C)	96 °F (35.6 °C)	87 °F (30.6 °C)
Month	July	July	January
Average daily maximum dry-bulb temperature	71 °F (21.7 °C)	82 °F (27.8 °C)	78 °F (25.6 °C)
Average daily minimum relative humidity	57%	58%	50%
Vapour pressure at	71 °F/57% RH = 14.96 mbar	82 °F/58% RH = 21.65 mbar	78 °F/50% RH = 16.38 mbar
Wet-bulb temperature at	82 °F/14.96 mbar	96/21.65 mbar	87/16.38 mbar
Screen*	= 66 °F (19.02 °C)	= 76 °F (24.4 °C)	= 69 °F (20.6 °C)
Sling†	= 65 °F (18.4 °C)	= 75 °F (23.9 °C)	= 68 °F (20.0 °C)

* Measured on a static screen thermometer.
† Measured by a whirling hygrometer. Sling values should be used in air-conditioning design.

In rounded figures the *summer* design conditions would be specified as:

London	28 °C DB/18.5 °C WB sling, in July (82 °F DB/65 °F WB).
New York	36 °C DB/24 °C WB sling, in July (96 °F DB/75 °F WB).
Johannesburg	30.5 °C DB/20 °C WB sling, in January (87 °F DB/68 °F WB).

Fig. 3.1 Typical extracts from London Meteorological Office tables M.O. 617

(a) London (Kew) 51°28′N. 00°19′W. 18 ft

	Temperature (°F)						Relative humidity (%)		Precipitation (in.)		
	Average daily		Average monthly		Absolute		Average of observations at		Average monthly fall	Maximum fall in 24 hr	Average no. of days with 0.10 in. or more
	Max.	Min.	Max.	Min.	Max.	Min.	07.00	13.00			
January	45	36	53	22	57	9	89	81	1.8	1.6	6
February	46	36	54	24	62	11	87	73	1.5	0.9	5
March	49	37	60	26	68	17	87	63	1.7	0.9	5
April	55	40	67	31	80	26	85	62	1.5	1.2	5
May	63	46	75	35	87	30	81	58	1.7	1.8	5
June	68	51	80	42	88	37	78	57	2.1	2.4	5
July	71	55	82	47	90	43	80	57	2.2	2.3	6
August	70	54	81	45	94	41	85	61	2.2	1.8	6
September	65	50	75	38	92	31	90	64	1.9	1.6	5
October	57	45	65	32	83	25	91	70	2.7	1.4	7
November	49	39	58	28	63	20	90	78	2.2	1.3	7
December	46	37	54	25	59	11	88	81	2.3	1.5	7
Year	57	44	85*	19†	94	9	86	67	23.8	2.4	69
No. of years	30	30	35	35	76	76	15	15	35	51	80

(b) New York 40°43′N. 74°00′W. 314 ft

	Temperature (°F)						Relative humidity (%)		Precipitation (in.)		
Period	Average daily		Average monthly		Absolute		Average of observations at		Average monthly fall	Maximum fall in 24 hr	Average no. of days with 0.01 in. or more
1869–1949	Max.	Min.	Max.	Min.	Max.	Min.	07.30	12.00			
January	37	24	57	7	68	−6	72	60	3.7	3.4	12
February	38	24	56	7	73	−14	70	58	3.8	3.2	10
March	45	30	69	17	84	3	70	55	3.6	3.6	12
April	57	42	80	30	91	12	68	53	3.2	3.7	11
May	68	53	87	42	95	34	70	54	3.2	4.2	11
June	77	60	92	52	97	44	74	58	3.3	3.9	10
July	82	66	96	59	102	54	77	58	4.2	3.8	12
August	80	66	94	57	102	51	79	60	4.3	5.0	10
September	79	60	90	47	100	39	79	61	3.4	6.2	9
October	69	49	80	36	90	27	76	57	3.5	9.4	9
November	51	37	70	24	75	7	75	60	3.0	3.6	9
December	41	29	60	12	69	−13	73	61	3.6	3.2	10
Year	60	35	98*	2†	102	−14	72	58	43.0	9.4	125
No. of years	46	46	30	30	77	77	57	28	50	50	50

(c) Johannesburg/Germiston 26°14′S. 28°09′E. 5463 ft

	Temperature (°F)						Relative humidity (%)		Precipitation (in.)		
Period	Average daily		Average monthly		Absolute		Average of observations at		Average monthly fall	Maximum fall in 24 hr	Average no. of days with 0.04 in. or more
1932–1950	Max.	Min.	Max.	Min.	Max.	Min.	08.00	14.00			
January	78	58	87	51	91	42	75	50	4.5	3.6	12
February	77	58	85	50	91	45	78	53	4.3	4.0	9
March	75	55	82	47	88	41	79	50	3.5	3.0	9
April	72	50	79	38	85	30	74	44	1.5	1.9	4
May	66	43	75	32	78	22	70	36	1.0	2.9	3
June	62	39	69	28	76	19	70	33	0.3	0.7	1
July	63	39	71	27	74	19	69	32	0.3	1.1	0.9
August	68	43	77	30	79	20	64	29	0.3	0.8	0.9
September	73	48	82	36	86	27	59	30	0.9	1.9	2
October	77	53	87	41	90	32	64	37	2.2	1.4	7
November	77	55	87	44	93	35	67	45	4.2	2.9	10
December	78	57	87	47	92	42	70	47	4.9	3.5	11
Year	72	50	89*	24†	93	19	70	41	27.9	4.0	70
No. of years	19	19	19	19	18	18	17	17	18	18	18

*Average of highest each year †Average of lowest each year ‡Standard of time: GMT

3.1.2 Winter

(a) The month is selected which has the *lowest average monthly minimum dry-bulb* temperature.
(b) That lowest average monthly minimum dry-bulb temperature is chosen as the *winter* design *dry-bulb* temperature.
(c) The winter design dry-bulb temperature so selected is associated with the *average daily maximum relative humidity* for the same month to produce the *winter* design *wet-bulb* temperature.

Applying the appropriate meteorological data for the same three localities produces the results shown in Table 3.2.

Table 3.2 Representative calculations of winter outdoor conditions

	London	*New York*	*Johannesburg*
Average monthly minimum dry-bulb	22 °F (−5.5 °C)	7 °F (−14 °C)	27 °F (−3 °C)
Month	January	January	July
Average daily maximum RH	89%	72%	69%
Sling wet-bulb temperature at	22 °F/89% RH = 21 °F (−6 °C)	7 °F/72% RH = 6 °F (−14.5 °C)	27 °F/69% RH = 24 °F (−4.5 °C)

The *winter* design conditions would be specified as:

London	−5.5 °C DB/−6 °C WB, in January (22 °F DB(21 °F WB).
New York	−14 °C DB/−14.5 °C WB, in January (7 °F DB/6 °F WB).
Johannesburg	−3 °C DB/−4.5 °C WB, in July (27 °F DB/24 °F WB).

In Appendix II of Volume 1 these conditions and others are tabulated and they appear to varying extents in the CIBS, ASHRAE and Carrier manuals. Relevant extracts are shown in Table 3.3.

3.2 INDOOR DESIGN CONDITIONS

Whereas outdoor design conditions are specified in terms of dry-bulb and wet-bulb temperatures, indoor design conditions are related to dry-bulb temperatures, percentage relative humidity and rates of air movement.

3.2.1 Dry-bulb temperatures

These should be quoted as a base level with a tolerance of + or − 1.1 °C (2 °F) for normal applications; this to allow for the inevitable variations that will occur through the volume of a room and for fluctuations resulting from the action of the controlling thermostat.

Table 3.3 Comparison of outdoor design temperatures

Locality	*Volume 1, Appendix II*		*CIBS 1982, Section A2*		*ASHRAE 1981 F, Chapter 24*		*Carrier Part 1, Chapter 2*	
	Month	*°C DB/WB*	*Month*	*°C DB/WB*	*Month*	*°C DB/WB*	*Month*	*°C DB/WB*
London								
Summer	July	28/18.5	July	29/20	*	28/20	*	*
Winter	Jan.	–5.5/–6		–4.5/*	*	–4.5/*	*	*
New York								
Summer	July	36/24	July	34/24	*	33/23	July	35/24
Winter	Jan.	–14/–14.5	*	–9/*	*	–12/*	*	–17.5/*
Johannesburg								
Summer	Jan.	30.5/20	Jan.	31/21	*	29.5/21	*	*
Winter	July	–3/–4.5	*	1/*	*	–0.5/*	*	*

* Not quoted

Notes to the table

1. The CIBS summer temperatures were calculated using their 'Approximate Method B'. Winter dry-bulb temperatures were selected in accordance with the recommendations of *Post-war Building Studies No. 33* used by the CIBS.
2. The CIBS summer wet-bulb temperatures are static screen values, whereas sling values should be used since they refer to moving air as measurable with a whirling hygrometer. None of the three authorities quotes winter wet-bulb temperatures.
3. Calculations made using these design temperatures should have no increments added for overload capacities.

Closer tolerances may be required for special applications such as standards rooms, and wider tolerances may be necessary with some forms of air-conditioning systems which embody relatively coarse temperature control, e.g. the various types of self-contained room air conditioners.

3.2.2 Relative humidity

The specification of relative humidity should also include a tolerance around a base level; the base level being selected according to the type of glazing to be used, i.e. single, double, etc. in order to limit the likelihood of condensation.

All authorities agree that, within fairly wide limits, relative humidity is not a major factor in acceptable standards of comfort. Therefore, for comfort applications, the following nominal standards should be specified:

With single-glazing 35% RH ± 10% RH
With multi-glazing 50% RH ± 10% RH

Concerning these specified levels, the following points should be noted:

(a) The tolerance is 10% RH and not simply 10%, there being a significant difference between the two notations.

(b) Relative humidity is the term which is generally used and understood but, in their revised *Guide*, the CIBS has introduced *percentage saturation* as a definition of the moisture content of air. There is only a marginal numerical difference between the two so that, unless exceptional accuracy is required, the relative humidity term and scale may be safely retained.

(c) In localities having severe winter design conditions (e.g. New York −14 °C and Ottawa −29.5 °C dry-bulb temperatures) multi-glazed windows will doubtless be used, but the lower levels of RH should be specified with only a negative tolerance, i.e. 35% RH + 0 −10% RH.

As has been demonstrated, the indoor design conditions recommended by CIBS, ASHRAE and Carrier are inconsistent and incomplete so that the design engineer, in many cases, is obliged to make a choice or an estimate. However, it is useful and entirely logical for a consensus to be made of the recommendations of the three authorities and that the outcome should include some correlation with outdoor design temperatures. This empirical process, which is described in Chapter 2 of Volume 1, results in the nomogram of Fig. 3.2. The method of using the chart is shown in the figure.

3.2.3 Rates of air movement

Rates of air movement should be related to indoor design temperatures: at the upper temperature levels a perceptible air movement will add freshness to the comfort response, but a similar rate at the lower temperatures will become a draught.

Again there is no close coherence in the recommendations of the authorities, but order can be introduced into the discord by using the consensus procedure. This is also described in Chapter 2 of Volume 1 and Fig. 3.3 is the chart that has been derived from the process.

Concerning the air movements under discussion, these refer to terminal velocities from the sources of air input and not to velocities through the cross-sections of treated spaces.

3.3 POPULATION RATINGS

It is of importance that the population aspects of buildings should be clearly understood and specified since the associated cooling loads can be of magnitudes ranging from 10% of the total load, in the case of office applications, to 80% for cinemas, theatres, etc. The aspects concerned are the numbers of individuals to be considered; their age-groups, sex and activities.

3.3.1 Population numbers

These should be established by reference to the project authority (client, developer, architect, etc.) or by a head count from drawings or site survey.

3.3.2 Age-group and sex

Assuming that the population consists of normally healthy individuals, their heat emissions (metabolic rates) will vary to the following approximate ratios:

Adult males − 1.0
Adult females − 0.85
Children − 0.75

3.3.3 Activity

The heat emission from healthy individuals depends upon their activity; for example, an assembly room may be usable for committee meetings or for dancing, the metabolic rates for these activity levels being 102 and 249 W per person, respectively, for mixed adult communities.

The foregoing information is frequently unavailable so that it becomes the responsibility of the design engineer to specify the population details. To assist him, representative data are tabulated in Table 3.4 (p. 26).

Fig. 3.2 Nomogram for selection of indoor design conditions

Use of the chart

Summer: Plot maximum outdoor design conditions for locality concerned.
Proceed vertically (downwards or upwards) to base line A, B and horizontally to intersect with indoor temperature curve 1,2.
Read indoor design conditions at intersection.

Winter: Plot minimum outdoor design conditions for locality concerned.
Proceed horizontally to base line C,D,E and vertically to intersect with indoor temperature curve 2,3.
Read indoor design conditions at intersection.

Examples:

Locality	*Outdoor design conditions*	*Indoor design conditions*
1. London (Kew)		
(a) Summer	28 °C DB/19 °C WB	22 °C DB/45% RH
(b) Winter	– 5.5 °C DB/ – 6 °C WB	20 °C DB/35% RH
2. New York		
(a) Summer	36 °C DB/24 °C WB	24.5 °C DB/50% RH
(b) Winter	– 14 °C DB/ – 14.5 °C WB	23 °C DB/35% RH

Note: The winter indoor design conditions of curve 2,3 are for single-glazed windows wherein a reduced relative humidity is required to avoid surface condensation.

When multi-glazing is used the relative humidity can be increased to the nominal level of 50%.

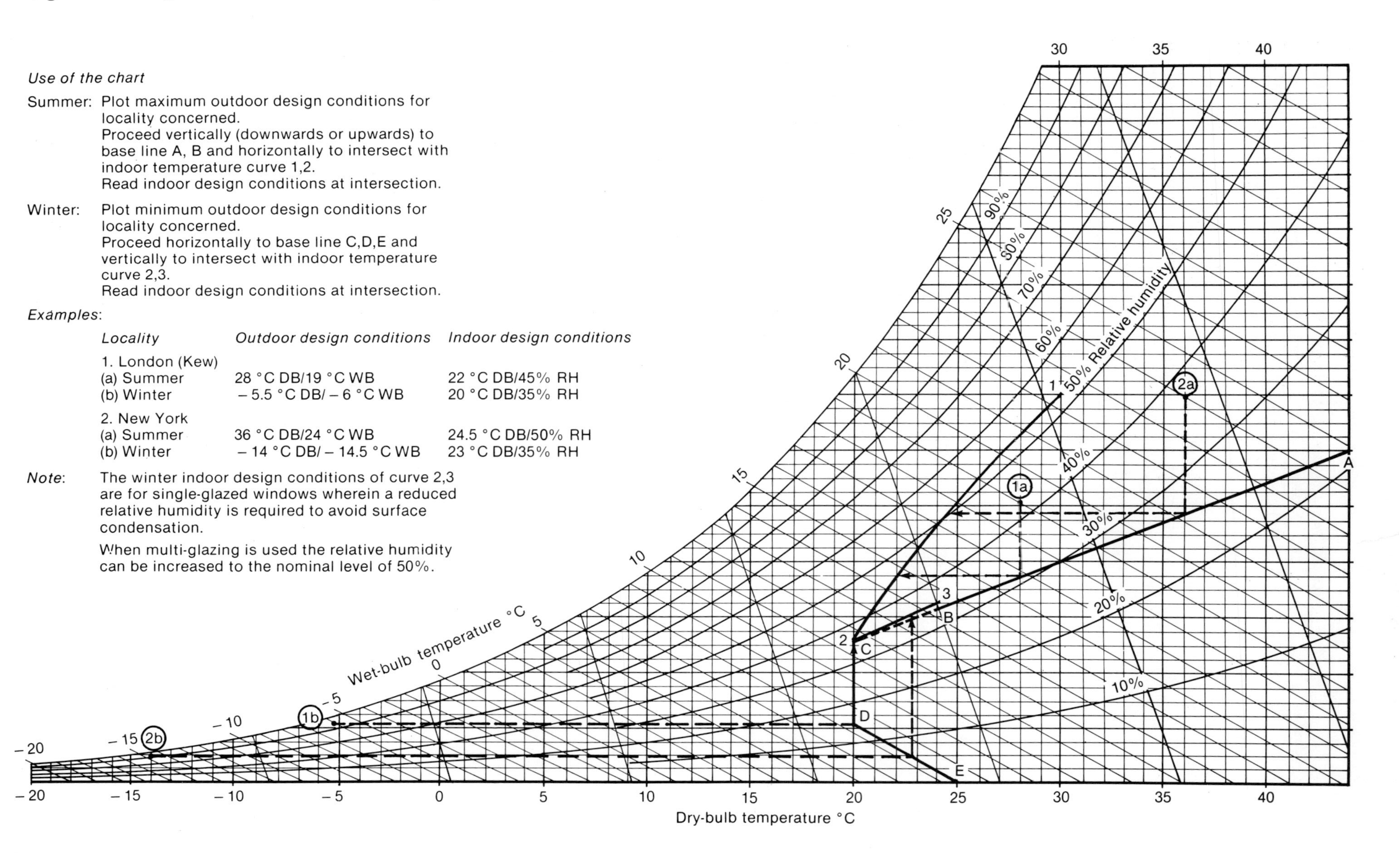

Fig. 3.3 Chart of room air velocity

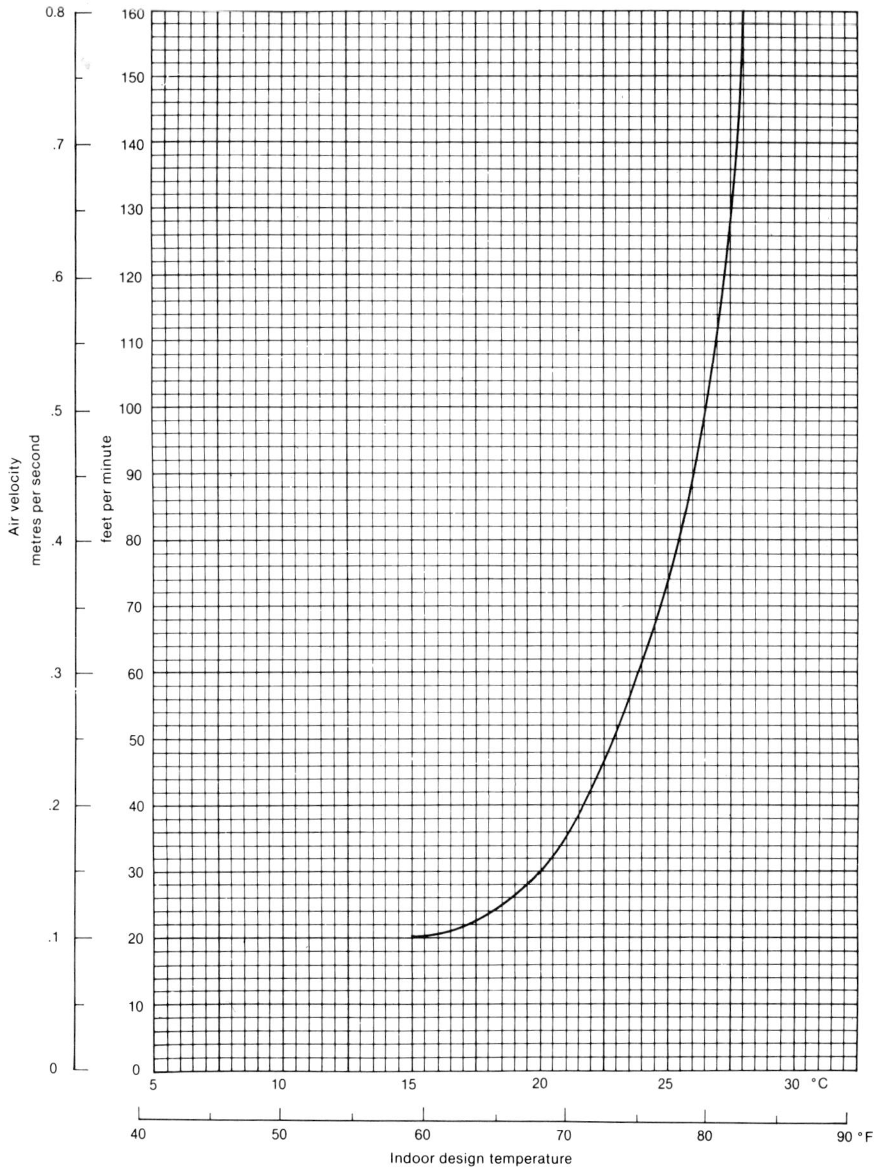

Column 1 of Table 3.4 lists the room applications; column 2 gives the range of floor areas of the relevant spaces likely to be occupied by one person; column 3 recommends a nominal floor area per person from the range; column 4 suggests the likely activity to be associated with the type of room.

The areas concerned are gross wall-to-wall areas excluding furniture and fittings and, in the case of theatres, excluding adjuncts such as the stage, boxes and lobbies.

3.4 ILLUMINATION RATINGS

The information required for specification of the illumination ratings within buildings relates to the type of lighting to be used, the total of the installed wattage and the configuration of the lighting fittings.

3.4.1 Illumination type

This denotes whether the lighting is incandescent, fluorescent or a combination of each; the type and efficiency of the lamps and the arrangement of the starting gear.

Table 3.4 Populated areas and activities

Application 1	Floor area/person (m^2) Range 2	Nominal 3	Activity 4
Offices			
General	5.5 – 8.5	7.00	Seated, working
Private	7.5 –11.0	9.25	Seated, working
Directors	9.5 –14.0	11.75	Seated, working
Executives	14.0 –23.0	18.50	Seated, working
Meeting rooms			
Staff	2.0 – 3.0	2.50	Seated, working
Management	3.75– 5.5	4.50	Seated, working
Directors	5.5 – 8.5	7.00	Seated, working
Eating rooms			
Staff	1.5 – 2.5	2.00	Seated, eating
Management	2.0 – 4.0	3.00	Seated, eating
Directors	3.0 – 5.5	4.25	Seated, eating
Hotels, etc.			
Bedrooms	4.5 – 9.25	7.00	Seated, at rest
Public rooms	1.5 – 2.5	2.00	Walking, dancing
Restaurants	1.5 – 3.25	2.50	Seated, eating
Bars	1.5 – 2.5	2.00	Standing
Lounges	2.0 – 5.5	3.75	Seated, at rest
Auditoria, etc.			
Theatres	0.5 – 1.0	0.75	Seated, at rest
Cinemas	0.5 – 1.0	0.75	Seated, at rest
Concert halls	0.55– 1.1	0.80	Seated, at rest
Churches	1.0 – 2.0	1.50	Seated, at rest
Art galleries	2.0 –11.0	6.50	Walking slowly
Museums	4.0 –14.0	9.00	Walking slowly
Sales areas			
Shops	1.0 – 5.5	3.25	Walking, working
Supermarkets	2.0 – 4.5	3.25	Walking, working
Dept. stores			
Basements	1.5 – 5.0	3.25	Walking, working
Ground floors	2.0 – 6.0	4.00	Walking, working
Upper floors	2.0 – 9.0	5.50	Walking, working
Banks	7.5 –11.0	9.25	Seated, working
Apartments	9.5 –14.0	11.75	Seated, at rest

In the case of incandescent (tungsten) lights, the heat equivalent is equal to the electrical input, having first appeared as approximately 10% of visible light and 90% as heat generated directly within the lamp; of this some 80% is dissipated by radiation and 10% by convection and conduction.

In fluorescent fittings, the heat equivalent varies with the lamp efficiency and the ballast losses that occur in the starting gear. The power input is converted into approximately 25% of visible light and 75% of heat which dissipates in the proportions of 25% by radiation and 50% by conduction and convection. The ballast losses appear directly as heat the extent of which depends upon the lamp rating, rapidity of start and the line voltage. The proportions of these ballast losses can vary between 1.0 and 2.0; an average factor being 1.25.

3.4.2 Total installed wattage

This states the overall power input to the lighting fitting including the ballast factor, if applicable. For a given level of illuminance (lux or lumens per square metre) the power input will depend upon the type of fitting and diffuser; the height of the fitting above the plane of illuminance; the surface reflectance, etc.

3.4.3 Configuration of the fittings

The configuration and arrangement of the lighting fittings will determine the proportions of the heat equivalent of the power input which will appear as sensible heat – direct to the conditioned areas or indirect to the circulatory air and water systems.

The magnitude of the cooling load due to the illumination of buildings is generally second only to the solar heat gains and, in some instances, the solar load may be exceeded by the illumination load.

For normal office applications the heat gains from the lighting will be about 20% of the total direct gains. Hence, whenever possible, the necessary data concerning the lamps and fittings to be used should be obtained from the manufacturer.

3.4.4 Empirical data for illumination loads

It is customary for the power output from the installed lighting to be specified as a wattage rating per square metre (m^2) or per square foot (ft^2) of the gross occupied floor area. The chart in Fig. 3.4 expresses these ratings for standard-type light fittings as a function of the illuminance (lux) levels. Whilst it is empirical in origin, the chart is sufficiently accurate for use in normal applications in the absence of manufacturer's data.

Fig. 3.4 Heat output equivalents of luminance levels

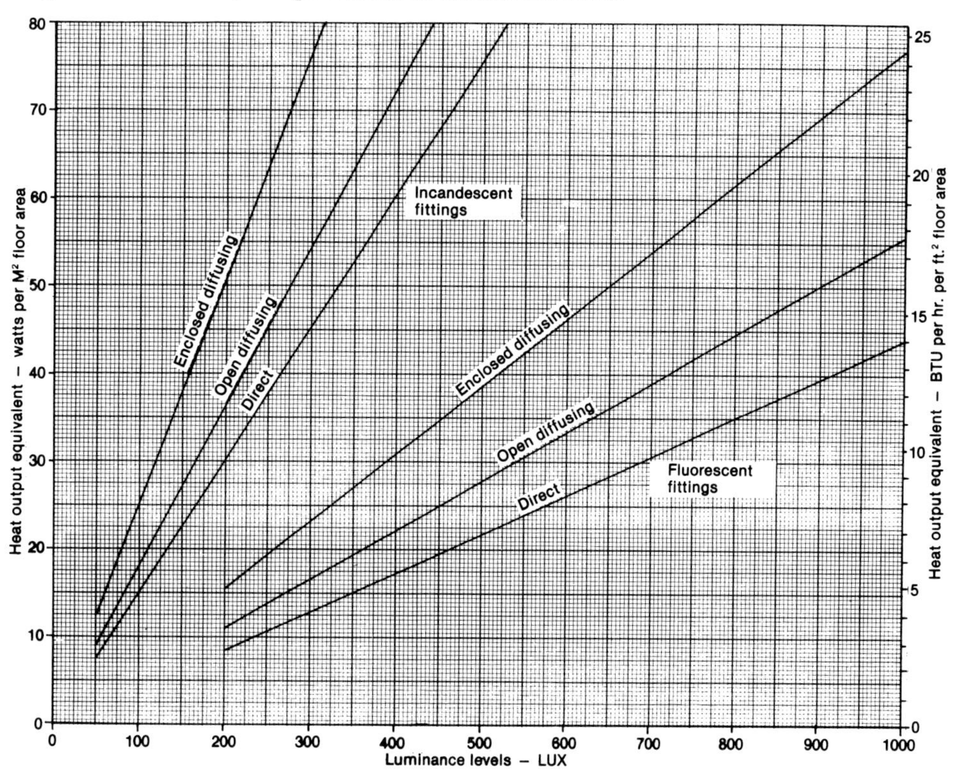

3.5 VENTILATION RATINGS WITH AIR CONDITIONING

3.5.1. Fresh-air ratings This refers to the rate at which outdoor air should be mechanically circulated through the occupied spaces of buildings in order to maintain an odour-free environment.

These rates are variously expressed as:

(a) Air changes per hour – the number of times per hour that the volumetric air content of a space is changed.

(b) Volumetric rate per occupant – litres per second, litres/sec (or cubic feet per minute, cfm) per person.

(c) Volumetric rate per square metre, m^2 (or per square foot, ft^2) of the gross floor area of an occupied space, the gross area referring to the wall-to-wall space, including that occupied by furniture, etc.

The air change method is unsuitable since the rate will vary with the height of the space concerned and will become excessive in cases where the floor-to-ceiling height is greater than 3 m. Therefore in most handbooks, ventilation rates are expressed in terms of alternatives (b) and (c) with the recommendation that the greater of the two should be used. This leads to some confusion, particularly since there is little agreement in the rates proposed by the handbooks. This is evidenced in Table 1.4 (p. 10) which gives extracts from the proposals of the CIBS, ASHRAE and Carrier on the basis of litres/sec/m^2 of occupied floor area – alternative (c) above.

A more satisfactory and logical approach is to combine the methods of the (b) and (c) alternatives, i.e. to relate the fresh-air supply rate per unit of occupied floor area to the floor area allocated to each occupant. This can be done empirically by an analysis of published data; in this case, of the CIBS, ASHRAE and Carrier.

The ventilation standards recommended by each of these authorities use air volume rates per person and per unit of floor area, classified according to the extent that smoking is likely to occur, thus: 'no smoking', 'some smoking' and 'heavy smoking'.

If the salient values of the CIBS, ASHRAE and Carrier recommendations are plotted against the 'nominal' areas of Table 3.4, patterns appear through which curves can be drawn of unit area air flow rates versus floor areas per person for each of the smoking categories noted above.

This procedure is shown in Fig. 3.5(a) with the authority reference and notation points indicated and, in Fig. 3.5(b), the curves are reproduced in uncluttered form and with scales of air change rates added for three dimensions of room heights: 2.6 m (8 ft 6 in), 3.0 m (10 ft 0 in) and 4.6 m (15 ft 0 in).

From Fig. 3.5(b) the following representative readings can be extracted:

1. Floor area 9.3 m^2 (100 ft^2) per person with some smoking: 1.3 litres/sec/m^2 (0.25 cfm/ft^2) of fresh air would be required. This would provide 12 litres/sec (25 cfm) per person and an air-change rate of 1.75 per hour, assuming a room height of 2.6 m (8 ft 6 in).
2. Floor area 0.7 m^2 (7.5 ft^2) per person in a room height of 3 m (10 ft 0 in) and no smoking: 5.7 litres/sec/m^2 (1.12 cfm/ft^2) of fresh air would be required resulting in a rate of 4.0 litres/sec (8.5 cfm) per person and an air change of 6.7 per hour.
3. Floor area 2.5 m^2 (27 ft^2) per person; room height 2.6 m (8 ft 6 in); heavy smoking: 5.2 litres/sec/m^2 (1.02 cfm/ft^2) of fresh air would be required giving 13 litres/sec (27.5 cfm) per person at an air-change rate of 7.2 per hour.

Fig. 3.5(a) Derivation of chart of fresh-air flow rates

Fig. 3.5(b) Chart of fresh-air flow rates v. floor area per person

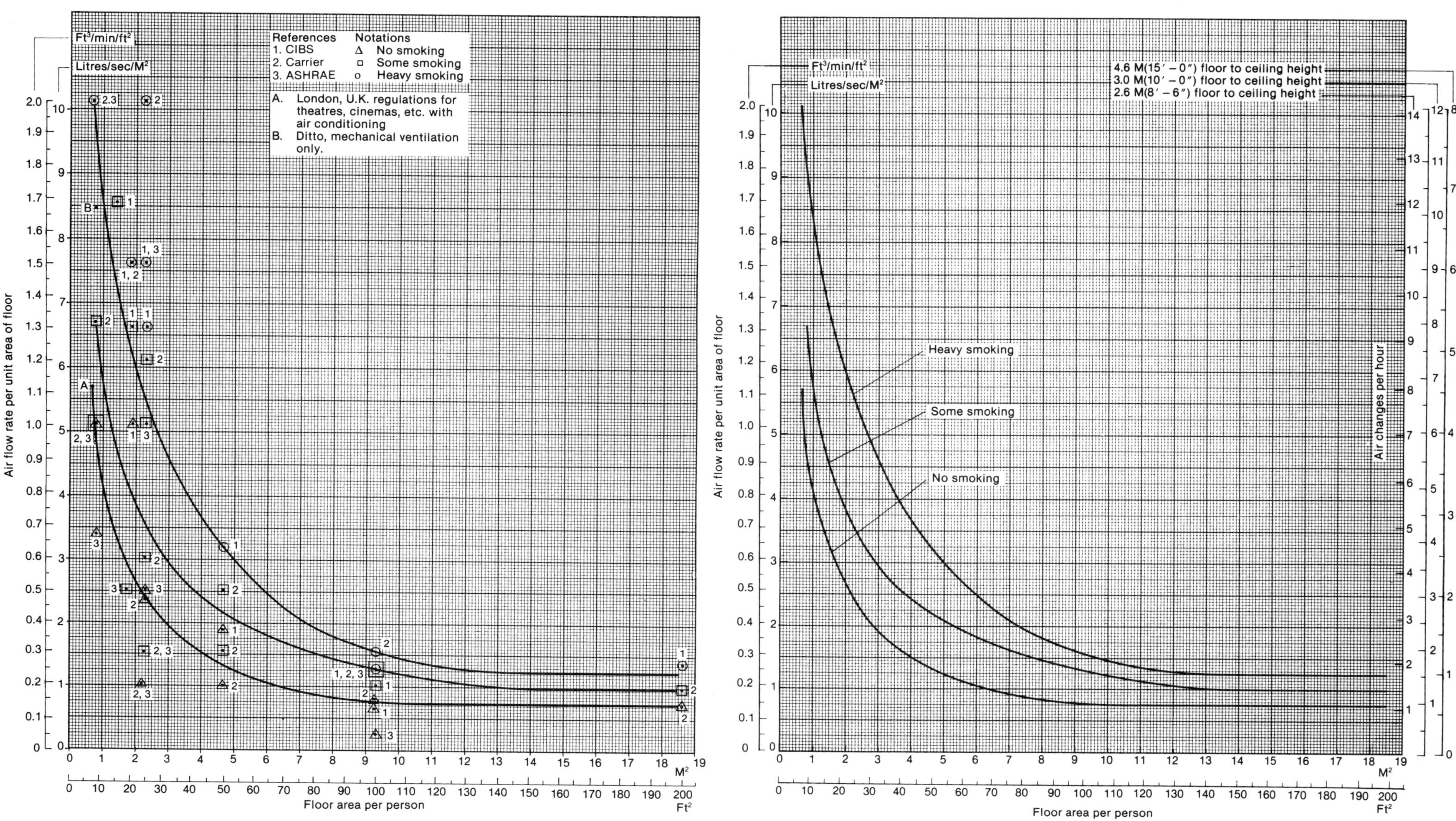

3.5.2 Extract-air ratings

To maintain the circulation rate a proportion of the fresh-air input to a building must be extracted and discarded, the balance of the input being used for pressurisation of the building to offset the natural infiltration that will occur to varying extents – particularly in cold weather.

It is customary to leave 1 to 1.5 air changes per hour of the fresh air within the building for pressurisation purposes, the rate depending upon the application: for the lower fresh-air rates, 1.0 air change/hr would be used and 1.5 air changes/hr for the higher rates. Thus, for the selections (1–3) made above, the following would apply:

1. (a) 1.75 air changes/hr fresh-air input, 1.0 air change to remain for pressurisation.
   Extract air rate = 0.75 air changes/hr
   = 43% of the fresh-air input
   = 0.56 litres/sec/m^2 (0.11 cfm/ft^2).
2. (a) 6.7 air changes/hr fresh-air input, 1.5 air changes to remain for pressurisation.
   Extract air rate = 5.2 air changes/hr
   = 78% of the fresh-air input
   = 4.4 litres/sec/m^2 (0.87 cfm/ft^2).
3. (a) 7.2 air changes/hr fresh-air input, 1.5 air changes to remain for pressurisation.
   Extract air rate = 5.7 air changes/hr
   = 79% of the fresh-air input
   = 4.1 litres/sec/m^2 (0.8 cfm/ft^2).

3.6 VENTILATION RATINGS WITHOUT AIR CONDITIONING

As part of the design specification for a building to be air conditioned, it is frequently necessary to include ventilation ratings for ancillary areas such as toilets, kitchens and car-parks. Guidance in these respects is given in the following sections.

3.6.1 Toilets

City and council regulations in the UK generally specify that, for toilets which cannot be naturally ventilated, mechanical extract must be provided at the minimum rate of 3.0 air changes/hr; no specification is made concerning the fresh-air input rate.

To conform with the required standards of commercial buildings, these provisos are unacceptable, it being customary to ventilate all toilet and ancillary accommodation to higher specifications. The ancillary accommodation includes washrooms and lobbies, the latter being a ventilated space which must separate the toilet accommodation from adjacent working and circulation areas.

A further requirement, for odour control is that the extract-air rate should exceed the fresh-air supply rate. Thus, the following standards should be used:

	Extract air-change rate	*Fresh air-change rate*
Enclosed toilet accommodation	8.0–10.0/hr	6.0–8.0/hr
Windowed toilet accommodation	6.0–8.0/hr	5.0–6.0/hr
Lobbies	—	3.0/hr

3.6.2 Kitchens

Whereas the normal heat gains within buildings will range from 50 to 150 W/m^2, those in kitchens will vary between 200 and 2000 W/m^2. With such loads full air conditioning is generally either uneconomic or impracticable, particularly since a large proportion of the heat emitted from cooking equipment is radiant.

Thus, mechanical ventilation is used in order to limit the increase in temperature within the working areas above the outdoor air temperature, and to provide odour control. For the latter purpose, air is extracted at a rate in excess of the supply air.

The ventilation rates are recommended in guides and handbooks on an arbitrary air-change basis, varying between 20 and 60 per hour according to the reference authority selected, and without qualification of the quoted recommendation.

Figure 3.6 is an empirical chart which relates the air-change rates to the heat gain loadings per square metre of floor area. The following comments are relevant to the application of the chart:

(a) The whole of the extracted air should be through hoods above the cooking and wash-up equipment.

(b) Where spaces adjacent to kitchens are air conditioned, a cooling advantage can be obtained by drawing a proportion of the supply air from these spaces (via serveries, doors, etc.), but this proportion should not exceed 20% of the total supply quantity to the kitchen.

(c) When the heat gain loading exceeds 2 kW/m^2 floor area, conditions in the kitchen will tend to become uncontrollable. In these circumstances cooling should be applied on a 'spot' basis with direction control at localised heat sources. In this case the ventilation air quantities should be halved and the cooling should be provided on a recirculating air basis through plant equipped with two-stage filtration.

Fig. 3.6 Ventilation rates for kitchens

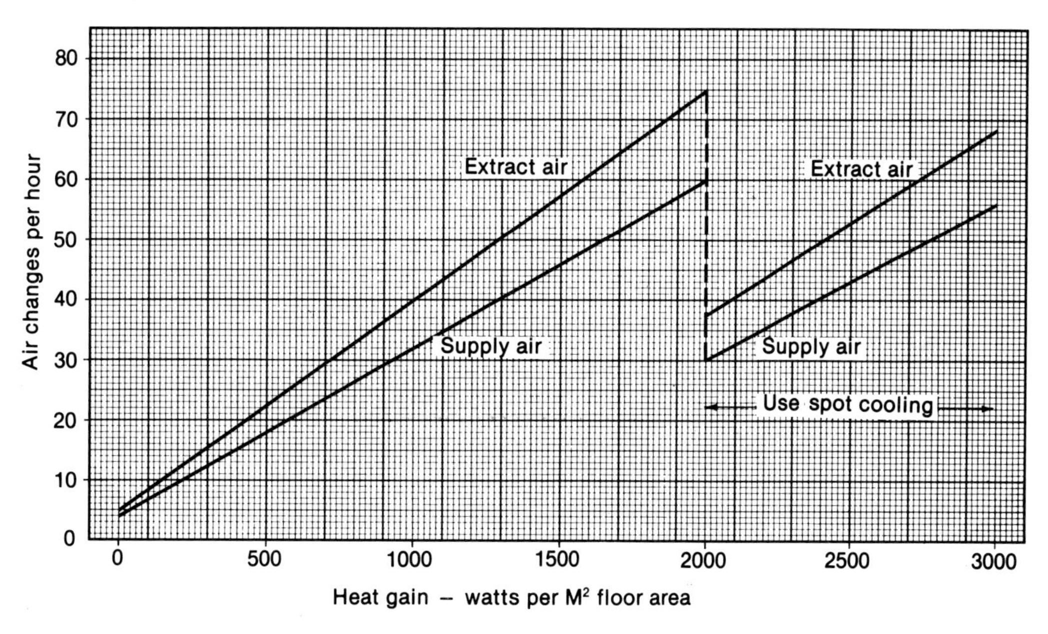

3.6.3 Enclosed car-parks

Preferably these should be naturally ventilated through stallboard vents distributed around the perimeter of the car-park.

To comply with statutory regulations in the UK the total area of the natural air vents should be not less than 2½% of the area of the car-park floor. Entrances may be included in this percentage area providing that closing doors or shutters are of lattice type.

If the full specification cannot be met, mechanical ventilation will be required to provide 3.0 air changes/hr each of supply and extract air. In completely enclosed car-parks where no natural ventilation is possible, mechanical supply and extract plant becomes mandatory. Each plant should comprise two sections, each capable independently of providing 3.0 air changes/hr and to incorporate automatic change-over in the event of the failure of one section.

In addition, a standby source of power must be supplied to the plants independent of the grid electricity supply.

3.7 INFILTRATION RATINGS

Infiltration (or perhaps air leakage is a more descriptive term) defines the airtightness of a building, a feature which, now that energy conservation is a recognised requirement, must be dealt with at the initial design stage and covered by an understandable specification.

Failure to take these precautions can undermine the capabilities of the heating or air-conditioning system and can impose severe running-cost penalties. The unconsidered use of recommended air-change rates is outmoded; for example the customary allowance of 1.0 air change/hr of infiltration in office buildings will in winter, increase the heat losses by some 50%.

Uncontrolled infiltration will be reduced to some extent in air-conditioned or ventilated buildings by the pressurisation effect which should be incorporated in accordance with the recommendations of Section 3.5.2 (p. 30), but for this to be effective, a full study should be made of all supply and extract-air systems (including toilets, kitchens, etc.) so that the results may be evaluated with the rates of infiltration specified.

Structural infiltration, through windows, doors, vents, etc. occurs in two main forms: by pressure differentials exerted through the structure by wind pressure; and due to imbalances between the internal and external air temperatures (stack effect). Leakage will also occur through the solid parts of the structural envelope but to such a minor degree that it is usually neglected.

The rates of infiltration are variously specified as:
(a) Airflow per unit area of the building openings.
(b) Airflow per unit length of crack clearance around closed windows and doors.
(c) Volumetric air changes per hour.

Infiltration effects can be expressed mathematically as, for example, by the CIBS formulae.

Infiltration around closed windows and doors:

$$Q = C(\Delta_p)^n \qquad [3.1]$$

where

Q	= volume flow rate of air per metre of window-opening joint	litres/sec
C	= window infiltration coefficient, defined as the volume flow rate of air per unit length of window-opening joint at a pressure differential of 1 N/m^2	litres/sec/m
Δ_p	= the pressure differential across the window	N/m^2
n	= an exponent which, for windows, is 0.63	

Infiltration due to stack effect:

$$\Delta_p = 0.043h(t_i - t_o) \qquad [3.2]$$

where

Δ_p	= pressure arising	N/m^2
h	= vertical distance between inlet and outlet openings	m
t_o	= outside temperature	°C
t_i	= inside temperature	°C

The combination, or resultant, of wind and stack-effect pressures may be above, below or equal to the atmospheric pressure depending on the sizes and characteristics of the building openings and the site of measurement within the building. The leakage rates will vary accordingly from infiltration to exfiltration and they will be further complicated by operating factors such as the opening and closing of entrance and internal doors, the movement of lifts, etc.

These factors are largely unpredictable at the design stage so that it becomes essential to apply limitations to the effects of infiltration at the outset. These limitations should comprise the use of well-sealed window-frames; gasketed window and external door openings; the use of entrance double doors and revolving doors in buildings exceeding five storeys above ground; automatic louvres, where permitted, over statutory smoke vents; etc.

These provisions added to the pressurisation effect should make it possible to reduce the extent of the infiltration and, thereby, to make specification simpler.

Based upon equations [3.1] and [3.2] above, and specimen testing, ASHRAE, Carrier and CIBS present data for the calculation of rates of infiltration. These are used in the calculations of air leakage through windows made below which, as far as possible, have been selected for similar window characteristics from the handbooks of these authorities. The airflow results have been used in conjunction with the typical module of Fig. 2.1 (p. 15) to produce air-change rates and heat gains and losses.

The ASHRAE data are based upon summer and winter wind speeds of 10 and 25 mph (4.5 and 11.2m/sec) respectively; Carrier use 7.5 and 15 mph (3.4 and 6.7 m/sec). The ASHRAE figures have been taken as being more representative and the Carrier rates adjusted to suit. Both relate to casement-type windows having 0.031 25 in. (1/32 in.) of crack width around the openable sections.

The equivalent data are not tabulated by the CIBS. Instead, a direct-reading nomogram is presented which is based upon wind speeds, building height and window coefficients.

In respect of Fig. 2.1, the openable section per module comprises a top-hung casement 2.44 m × 0.38 m (8 ft 0 in × 1 ft 3 in) giving a total crack length of 5.64 m (18 ft 6 in). The other relevant module details are as listed in Appendix I (p. 135), namely:

Module volume	=	48.36 m^3 (1700 ft^3)
Window area	=	4.68 m^2 (50.35 ft^2)
Window *U*-value	=	3.85 $W/m^2/°C$ (0.67 $Btu/hr/ft^2/°F$)
Wall area	=	2.98 m^2 (32.06 ft^2)
Wall *U*-value	=	0.49 $W/m^2/°C$ (0.08 $Btu/hr/ft^2/°F$)

Using these factors the comparative calculations appear as in Table 3.5.

From the three comparative sets of calculations it will be seen that disparity exists between the window leakage rates recommended by the three authorities resulting in hourly air-change rates varying, in the winter case, from 0.21 to 0.78. The mean value between these extremes is approximately 0.5 and this value is an upper limit which should be specified.

Table 3.5 Comparative calculations of air-change rates and heat transfer

	Summer (10 mph (4.5 m/sec) wind speed)	*Winter (25 mph (11.2 m/sec) wind speed)*
1. ASHRAE, Table 4 Ch. 22, 1981 *Fundamentals Handbook*		
Air leakage rates	0.2 litres/sec/m (0.13 cfm/ft)	0.77 litres/sec/m (0.50 cfm/ft)
Air leakage volumes	0.2 × 5.64 = 1.13 litres/sec (0.13 × 18.5 = 2.4 cfm)	0.77 × 5.64 = 4.34 litres/sec (0.5 × 18.5 = 9.25 cfm)
Air changes per hour	0.08	0.33
Sensible heat gain/loss due to infiltration	+ 7.6 W(+ 26 Btu/hr)	− 135 W(− 460 Btu/hr)
% of module heat gain/loss	0.40	22%
2. Carrier *Handbook*, Table 44, Part 1, Ch. 6		
Air leakage rates	0.6 litres/sec/m (0.4 cfm/ft)	1.85 litres/sec/m (1.2 cfm/ft)
Air leakage volumes	0.6 × 5.64 = 3.4 litres/sec (0.4 × 18.5 = 7.4 cfm)	1.85 × 5.64 = 10.4 litres/sec (1.2 × 18.5 = 22.2 cfm)
Air changes per hour	0.26	0.78
Sensible heat gain/loss due to infiltration	+ 23 W(+ 79 Btu/hr)	− 323 W(− 1103 Btu/hr)
% of module heat gain/loss	1.5	40%
3. CIBS *Guide*, Section A, Fig. A4.2		
Air leakage rates	0.12 litres/sec/m (0.08 cfm/ft)	0.5 litres/sec/m (0.32 cfm/ft)
Air leakage volumes	0.12 × 5.64 = 0.68 litres/sec (0.08 × 18.5 = 1.50 cfm)	0.5 × 5.64 = 2.82 litres/sec (0.32 × 18.5 = 6.0 cfm)
Air changes per hour	0.05	0.21
Sensible heat gain/loss due to infiltration	+ 4.7 W(+ 16 Btu/hr)	− 87.3 W(− 298 Btu/hr)
% of module heat gain/loss	0.30	15%

However, an air-change rate will, in alternative applications produce different volumes of airflow and, moreover, will not mean very much to a window manufacturer: it will be more understandable if quoted as a leakage rate through a closed window at a given pressure differential across the window.

From the typical examples above, an air-change rate of 0.5 per hour results in an airflow of approximately 7 litres/sec (15 cfm) related to the winter case of a wind speed of 25 mph (11.2 m/sec) which, in turn, represents a pressure of 75 Pa (0.3 in. w.g.). A leakage of 7.0 litres/sec through the overall window area of 4.68 m^2 is equivalent to 1.5 litres/sec/m^2 (0.3 cfm/ft^2) and this is a reasonable basis for application.

Therefore, the window specification would read: 'air leakage rate not to exceed 1.5 litres/sec/m^2 square metre of window area with a pressure differential across the window of 75 Pa'.

This will result in a summer air-change leakage (at 10 mph (4.5 m/sec) wind speed) of about 0.12 per hour and a heat gain of some 0.7% of the overall sensible heat gain to the space. Thus, when the specification is applied, the summer heat gain due to infiltration may be neglected.

In the foregoing calculations and the proposed specification, no account has been taken of the pressurisation effect discussed in Section 3.5.2. This is because any such pressurisation would, in the severe winter case, be only partially effective in offsetting the wind pressure equivalent of 75 Pa (0.3 in. w.g.). Therefore, it should be regarded as a capacity margin which will assist in the less severe circumstances at other times of the year and in retarding other forms of leakage which cannot easily be accounted for.

3.8 FENESTRATION

The performance specification of the fenestration of buildings (windows, rooflights and similar) relates to the coefficients of heat transfer by conduction and radiation: conduction due to indoor/outdoor temperature differentials, and radiation by solar impact or insolation.

3.8.1 Thermal transmittance coefficients (*U*-values)

The transfer of heat by conduction through glass and other fabrics of building structures may be either positive or negative in value (heat gains or heat losses). In the case of fenestration the heat transfer is calculated from the expression:

$$Q_c = A_f U_f (t_o - t_i) \qquad [3.3]$$

where

Q_c	= heat transmitted by conduction	W
A_f	= area of fenestration	m^2
U_f	= coefficient of transmittance of the fenestration assembly	W/m^2/°C
t_o	= outdoor air temperature	°C
t_i	= indoor air temperature	°C

The thermal transmittance coefficients of glass are sufficiently well documented for values to be specified by regulations, the latter being Part FF of The Building (First Amendment) Regulations 1978. Part FF4 states:

> 'The *U*-value of any window opening or rooflight opening shall be assumed to be 5.7 W/m^2/°C if it is single-glazed, 2.8 W/m^2/°C if it is double-glazed or 2.0 W/m^2/°C if it is triple-glazed irrespective of whether the light-transmitting material is glass or not . . .'.

These values are for glass alone taking no account of modifications due to the window-framing and wind speeds. In Table 3.6 below is reproduced a list of *U*-values for typical windows from Section A3 of the CIBS *Guide*.

Appropriate values from Table 3.6 should be specified, with particular attention to the provision of thermal breaks in metal frames. In the absence of such an insulating membrane, serious condensation on the internal surfaces of the frame will occur during cold weather and, in sunlight, stresses will be exerted in the glass due to uneven temperature distribution; with heat-absorbing glasses this can lead to fracture.

Table 3.6 *U*-values for typical windows

Window type	*Fraction of area occupied by frame (%)*	*U-value for stated exposure (W/m² °C)*		
		Sheltered	*Normal*	*Severe*
Single glazing				
Wood frame	10	4.7	5.3	6.3
	20	4.5	5.0	5.9
	30	4.2	4.7	5.5
Aluminium frame (no thermal break)	10	5.3	6.0	7.1
	20	5.6	6.4	7.5
	30	5.9	6.7	7.9
Aluminium frame (with thermal break)	10	5.1	5.7	6.7
	20	5.2	5.8	6.8
	30	5.2	5.8	6.8
Double glazing				
Wood frame	10	2.8	3.0	3.2
	20	2.7	2.9	3.2
	30	2.7	2.9	3.1
Aluminium frame (no thermal break)	10	3.3	3.6	4.1
	20	3.9	4.3	4.8
	30	4.4	4.9	5.6
Aluminium frame (with thermal break)	10	3.1	3.3	3.7
	20	3.4	3.7	4.0
	30	3.7	4.0	4.4

Note: Where the proportion of the frame differs appreciably from the above values, particularly with wood or plastic, the *U*-value should be calculated (metal members have a *U*-value similar to that of glass).

The exposure designations in Table 3.6 are interpreted as:

Sheltered – up to the third floor of buildings in city centres.

Normal – most suburban and rural buildings; fourth to eighth floors of buildings in city centres.

Severe – buildings on coastal and hill sites; floors above the fifth in suburban or rural districts; floors above the ninth in city centres.

3.8.2 Shading coefficients

The transfer of heat through fenestration is discussed more fully later; the relevant aspect here being the specification of the *shading coefficient*, or *solar gain factor* as it is termed by the CIBS. A general expression for heat transfer through glass due to solar radiation is:

$$Q_r = A_g I_{Dd} S_c \qquad [3.4]$$

where

Q_r	= heat transmitted by radiation	W
A_g	= area of glass	m²
I_{Dd}	= incident solar radiation, direct and diffuse	W/m²
S_c	= shading coefficient	—

The shading coefficient is a factor which requires to be specified at the design stage, being defined as the proportion of the solar radiation that is transmitted through a particular window configuration, i.e. whether of single bare glass construction, through double-glazing with blinds, etc.

Insolation consists of two components of solar radiation: *direct* radiation which reaches the earth's surfaces as a proportion of the solar heat intensity at the outer atmosphere, having been reduced in passing through the atmosphere; and *diffuse* radiation which is a proportion of the solar heat which has been absorbed and scattered during its passage through the atmosphere and partially reradiated to the earth.

Direct radiation will be transmitted through building fenestration only when the latter is directly irradiated, whereas diffuse radiation will occur and be transmitted in cloud conditions and through fenestration in shade.

Both forms of radiation will be modified to varying extents depending upon the configuration of the window assembly; the modification factor being termed the *shading coefficient*.

The modifications that occur take the form of a further reduction of the solar radiation in transmission through the fenestration and a change in the proportions of the short wavelength and long wavelength of the radiation transmitted. The short-wavelength component will be directly transmitted to the internal surfaces of the building whilst the long-wavelength radiation will be absorbed in the materials of the fenestration assembly and re-emitted by further radiation, and by convection and conduction. Comparative examples of these effects are:

Glazing assembly	*Total transmission (%)*	*Short wavelength (%)*	*Long wavelength (%)*
4 mm clear glass	98	94	4
4 mm clear glass with internal blind	55	11	44

Shading coefficients of fenestration assemblies relate mainly to the *solar optical* properties of the glass, the materials used in blinds and drapes, and the solar angle of incidence with the fenestration surface.

The angle of incidence has several variables (latitude, time of year, time of day and building orientation), but it is customary in the higher latitudes for calculations of shading coefficients to be made with angles of incidence approximately perpendicular to the plane of the surface under consideration, i.e. angles of incidence from 0° to 30°. In the lower latitudes around the equator, solar angles of incidence at the times of peak heat gain will tend towards the other end of the scale (50° to 80°) and, in these circumstances, it may be necessary to make check calculations.

The solar optical properties relevant to shading coefficients are the reflectance, absorptance and transmittance factors of the materials used in relation to solar irradiation; the most important being the reflectance factor, R, which is the capacity of a material for reflecting solar radiation and, thereby, reducing the amount of heat transmitted into a building.

The absorptance factor, A, represents the proportion of the solar radiation which is absorbed by the fenestration assembly (glass, blinds, etc.) some of which is then released internally to the building and some re-emitted externally; a partition factor, P, denotes the fraction which is released internally. The transmittance factor, T, is the component of the solar energy which is transmitted directly into the building.

Thus, a total heat gain factor, F, is the sum of the transmitted component, T, and the portion of the absorbed energy that is released internally, i.e.

$$F = T + PA \quad [3.5]$$

The *shading coefficient*, S, relates the total heat gain factor of a particular fenestration assembly to the total heat gain factor of a *notional pane of clear glass* 3 to 4 mm thick, the value of which is taken as 0.87:

$$S = F/0.87 \quad [3.6]$$

This is, perhaps, somewhat complicated in the explaining, but the meaning can be clarified by illustration and examples.

In Fig. 3.7 are reproduced data from one of the Pilkington series of booklets (*Thermal Transmission of Windows*) for two examples of window construction: a 4 mm sheet of clear glass and a 6 mm float sheet with an internal venetian blind. Calculations are appended to show the derivation of the shading coefficients in each case.

Figure 3.8 shows similar data for two Pilkington proprietary glasses: 6 mm bronze Spectrafloat 49/66 and 6 mm green Antisun 75/60.

From these two figures the following aspects should be noted:

(a) The solar optical properties are relatively constant at the lower angles of incidence but they diverge rapidly at incident angles above 50°.

(b) The absorptance factor is high for the glass and venetian-blind assembly and particularly for the blind itself. This explains the sense of overheating that can be experienced by persons seated in close proximity to this arrangement of window with the blinds drawn.

(c) The numerical notation of glasses (e.g. 49/66) indicates the percentage of light (49%) which is transmitted and the total heat gain factor (66%).

(d) A glass such as Spectrafloat can be regarded as being heat *reflecting*, whilst one such as Antisun is heat *absorbing*. This is evident from their respective values of reflectance and absorptance.

These characteristics should be considered in selecting glasses from the viewpoint of the overheating aspect of (b) above and the possibility of fracture, particularly when such proprietary glasses are to be used in combinations with others and with blinds.

(e) In addition to the solar optical properties of comparative types of glass, the light-transmittance factor is of major importance and must be considered. From Fig. 3.8 it will be seen that 75% of natural light is transmitted through the Antisun glass but only 49% in the case of bronze Spectrafloat.

(f) Glare through irradiated windows can be troublesome. It will be reduced through proprietary glasses to an extent corresponding with the light-transmittance factor but may remain a problem. It can be fully eliminated only by complete cut-off, as applicable with the use of blinds.

In Appendix II (p. 145) are listed shading coefficients for representative forms of window combinations. These are usable for general purposes but, when proprietary forms of glass or solar reflecting blinds and curtains are to be used, precise data should be obtained from the manufacturer.

Fig. 3.7 Solar optical properties of 4 mm sheet glass, and 6 mm float glass with internal venetian blind

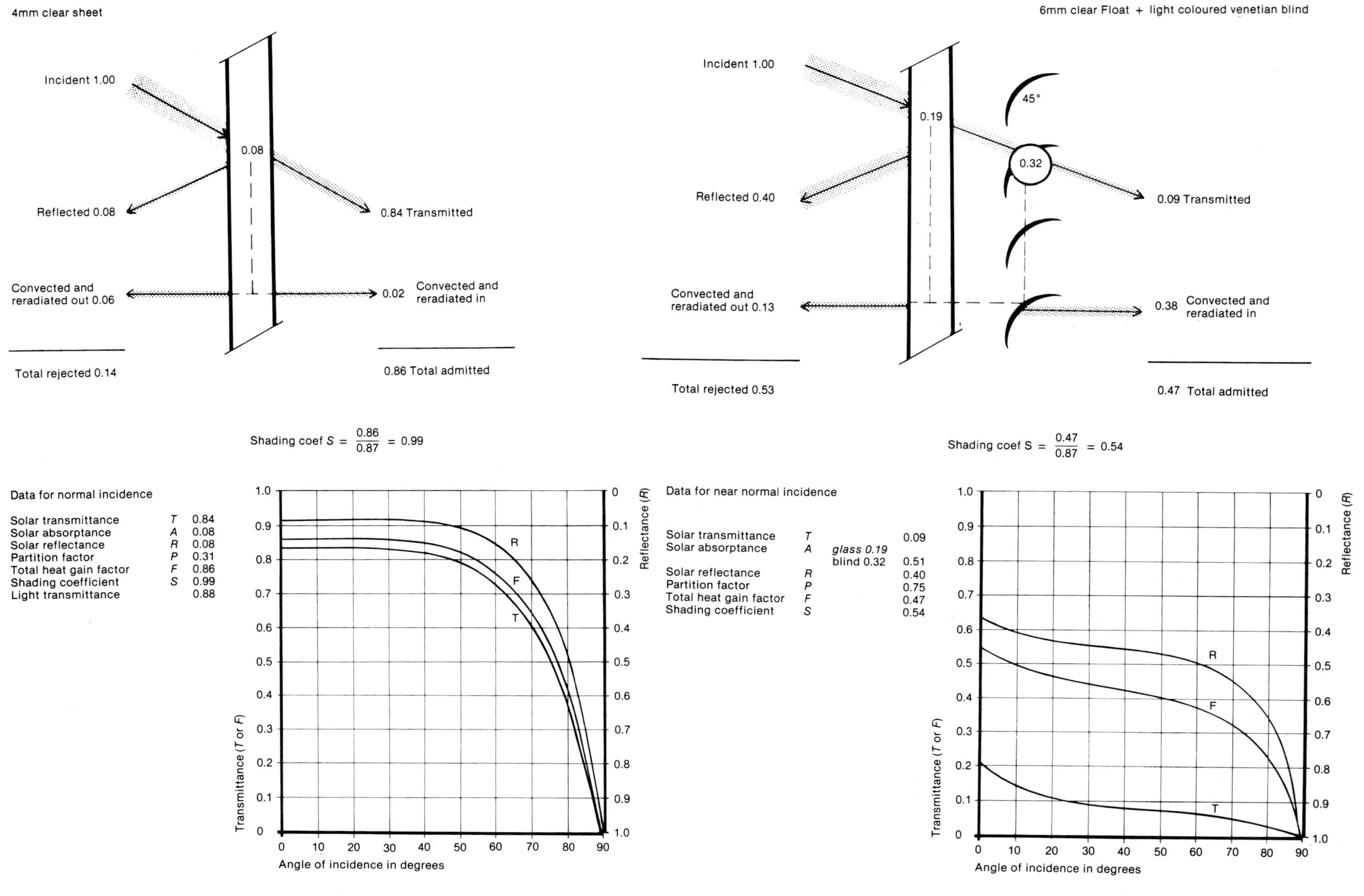

Data for normal incidence

Solar transmittance	T	0.84
Solar absorptance	A	0.08
Solar reflectance	R	0.08
Partition factor	P	0.31
Total heat gain factor	F	0.86
Shading coefficient	S	0.99
Light transmittance		0.88

Data for near normal incidence

Solar transmittance	T		0.09
Solar absorptance	A	*glass 0.19* blind 0.32	0.51
Solar reflectance	R		0.40
Partition factor	P		0.75
Total heat gain factor	F		0.47
Shading coefficient	S		0.54

Fig. 3.8 Solar optical properties of 6 mm bronze Spectrafloat and 6 mm green Antisun glasses

6mm 'Spectrafloat' 49/66 (bronze)

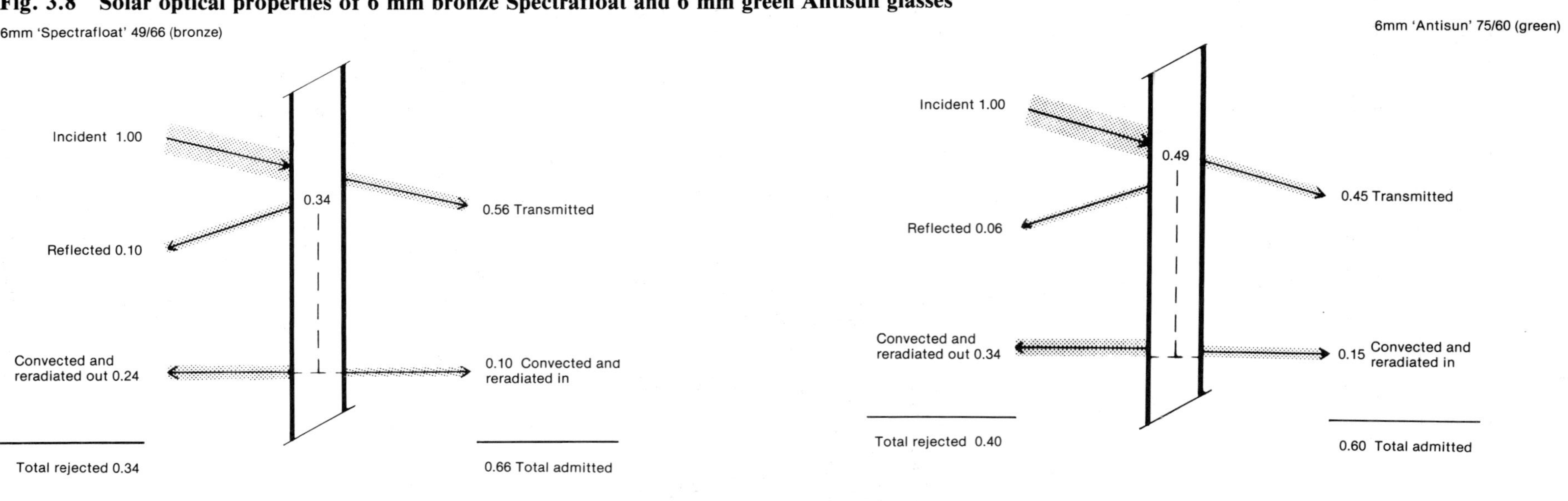

Shading coef $S = \frac{0.66}{0.87} = 0.76$

Data for near normal incidence

Solar transmittance	*T*	0.56
Solar absorptance	*A*	0.34
Solar reflectance	*R*	0.10
Partition factor	*P*	0.31
Total heat gain factor	*F*	0.66
Shading coefficient	*S*	0.76
Light transmittance		0.49

6mm 'Antisun' 75/60 (green)

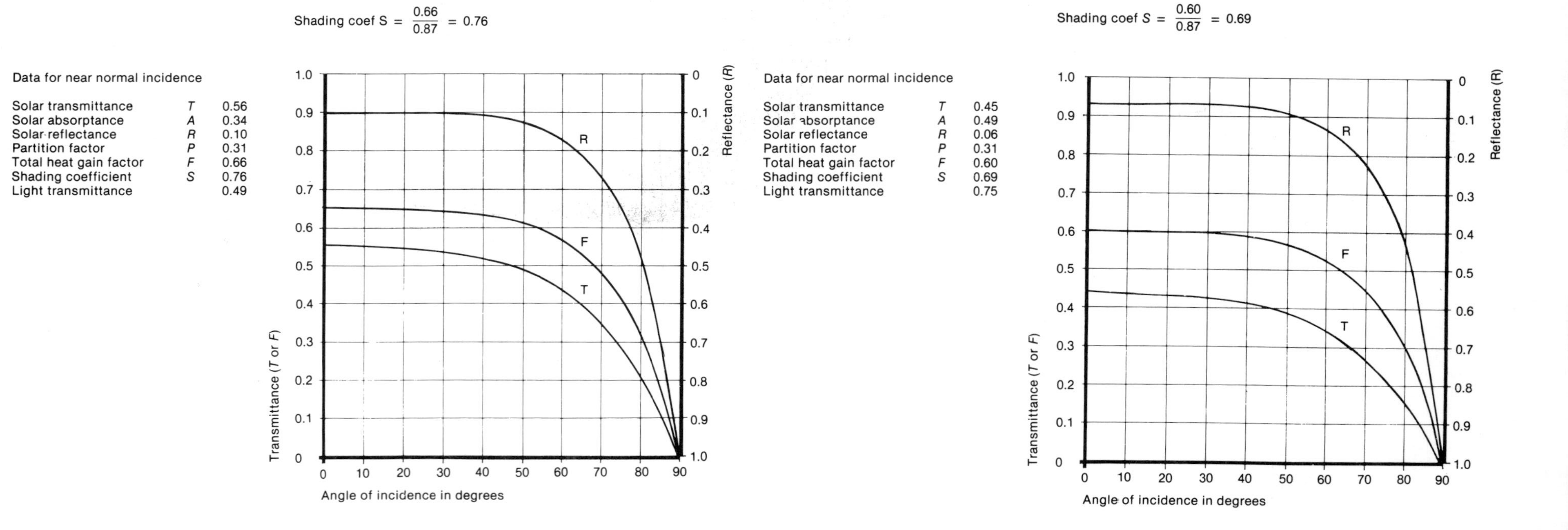

Shading coef $S = \frac{0.60}{0.87} = 0.69$

Data for near normal incidence

Solar transmittance	*T*	0.45
Solar absorptance	*A*	0.49
Solar reflectance	*R*	0.06
Partition factor	*P*	0.31
Total heat gain factor	*F*	0.60
Shading coefficient	*S*	0.69
Light transmittance		0.75

3.9 BUILDING STRUCTURE

Under this heading there are two items to be considered in the design specification: thermal transmittance coefficients (*U*-values) of the general structure, and the specific weight of the structure.

3.9.1 Structural *U*-values

As in the case of fenestration, thermal transmittance coefficients of building fabrics are governed by the Building Regulations according to usage classification.

Except in the case of the fenestration, the *U*-values of the elements of the building structure are not itemised according to the form of construction; they are limited to particular values for surfaces as a whole or related to specified maximum permitted areas of windows and rooflights.

The applicable sections of the Building Regulations are Part F relating to dwellings and Part FF to other buildings. A group classification is laid down as follows:

Part F

Group I — Small residential: private dwelling houses, flats and maisonettes.

Part FF

Group II — Institutional: hospitals, schools, hostels, etc.

Group III — Other residential: apartments, hotels, etc.

Group IV — Offices: all types of offices, banks, drawing offices and so on.

Group V — Shops: all premises used for retail sales; restaurants, libraries, public houses, etc.

Group VI — Factories: all places covered by Section 175 of the Factories Act 1961.

Group VII — Places of assembly: all places (public or private) used for social, recreational or business purposes not covered by the preceding groups.

Group VIII — Storage: places used for storage of goods and equipment, including the parking of vehicles.

The transmittance coefficients for walls, floors and roofs, according to the Building Regulations are shown in Tables 3.7 and 3.8.

Table 3.9 gives the maximum permitted areas of windows and rooflight openings expressed as percentages of the total areas of the walls and roofs to which the *U*-values of Table 3.8 apply.

The application of these Regulations is mandatory, but in a combined sense, i.e. the areas of window and rooflight openings must be complied with or, alternatively, they may be varied providing that the resulting total rate of heat loss through a building surface does not exceed what it would be with single-glazing used as part of the surface.

This means that, with the regulation *U*-values for glazing listed in Tables 3.7 and 3.8, the architect has the option of selecting his window areas in the proportions of 5.7/2.8 if he uses double-glazing, and 5.7/2.0 with triple-glazing.

The Building Regulations include additional specifications which must be complied with, namely:

(a) The area of the window or rooflight is to be measured on the inner faces of each.
(b) The areas of the relevant walls or roofs are to be measured on the inner faces of each between finished surfaces of flanking walls, floors and ceilings.

(c) In buildings of Group V (shops, etc.) ground-floor windows and ground-floor walling are to be excluded from the total areas of windows and walls.

Table 3.7 *U*-values to Part F3, Dwellings

Window openings	Single-glazing 5.7 W/m²/°C Double-glazing 2.8 W/m²/°C
Other openings	*U*-value equal to that of the wall in which it is situated
Party walls and walls adjoining an unventilated space	0.5 W/m²/°C
Walls, floors and roofs	
Element of building	*Maximum U-value of any part of element (W/m²/°C)*
External wall	1.0
Wall between a dwelling and a ventilated space	1.0
Wall between a dwelling and a partially ventilated space	1.7
Wall between a dwelling and any part of an adjoining building to which Part F is not applicable	1.7
Wall or partition between a room and a roof space, including that space and the roof over that space	1.0
External wall adjacent to a roof space over a dwelling, including that space and any ceiling below that space	1.0
Floor between a dwelling and the external air	1.0
Floor between a dwelling and a ventilated space	1.0
Roof, including any ceiling to the roof or any roof space and any ceiling below that space	0.6

3.9.2 Specific weights of structures

The radiant components from sources of heat emission (sunlight, illumination, occupants, etc.) must first be absorbed by the interior surfaces of the structure and the contents of a building before they become measurable as part of the imposed heat gain. The absorbed radiation causes an increase in temperature at the inner surface of a building material above the air temperature adjacent to the surface, and above the temperature of the material mass behind the surface.

These temperature differences generate heat flow into the surrounding air by convection, and into the material by conduction.

The convected heat becomes an immediate heat gain to the cooling system, but the heat conducted inwards from the surface goes through a process of storage and re-emission as the temperature of the material is raised thereby towards the surrounding air temperature, and the material becomes less capable of storing more heat.

Table 3.8 *U*-**values to Part FF4, Buildings other than dwellings**

Windows and rooflight openings	Single-glazing 5.7 $W/m^2/°C$ Double-glazing 2.8 $W/m^2/°C$ Triple-glazing 2.0 $W/m^2/°C$

Walls, floors and roofs

Element of building	*Maximum U-value of every part of element (in W/m^2 °C) having regard to the purpose group of the building or part of a building*	
	Groups II, III, IV, V or VII or (if not for storage) VIII	*Groups VI or (if for storage) VIII*
External wall (other than any such wall enclosing a ventilated space or a partially heated space) Internal wall exposed to a ventilated space Floor having its under-surface exposed to the external air or to a ventilated space Roof (other than a roof over a ventilated space or a partially heated space) including: (a) any ceiling to the roof; or (b) any roof space and any ceiling below that space	0.6	0.7

Table 3.9 Maximum permitted areas of window and rooflight openings

Building group	*II or III*	*IV, V or VII*	*VI or VIII*
% window openings	25	35	15
% rooflight openings	20	20	20

The proportion of the radiant heat that is stored in the structure will depend upon the ratio of the resistances of the surface air film and the structural material. Since the resistances of usual building materials are considerably lower than the air resistance, most of the radiant heat will be stored.

This storage and re-emission process results in a delay between the time of the occurrence of the initial radiant effect and the emergence of the resulting heat load; the extent of the delay, or time-lag, being a function of the mass weight of the constructional materials used. It follows that the time-lag will be shorter for a lightweight construction than for one more massive.

The time-lag between the immediately imposed radiant heat and its emission from storage results in a reduction in the peak magnitude of the load imposed on the cooling plant due to change in the cyclic phase of the load: heat removed must, in due course, be equal to the heat stored, but the removal phase occurs over a period which is extended beyond and out of phase with the instantaneous load.

A factor in addition to the mass weight of the structure which will affect the phasing of the actual cooling load is the period of plant operation: with intermittent operation, some of the stored heat will remain in storage during the shutdown period and this must be removed as a pulldown load when the cooling process is recommenced.

Fig. 3.9 Cooling load pattern for solar heat gain on a west exposure with plant operating for 16 hours

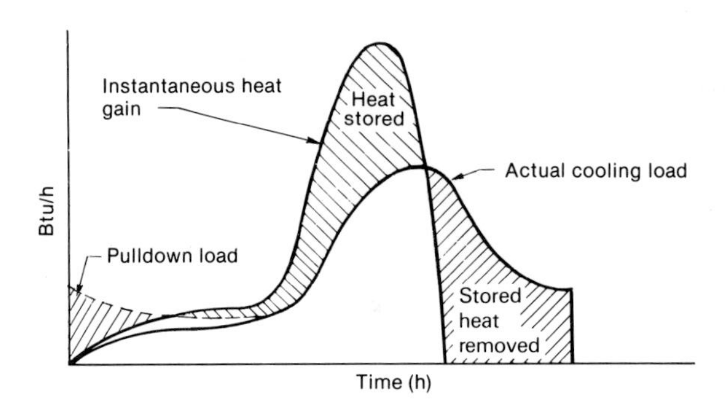

The sketch in Fig. 3.9, taken from the Carrier *Handbook*, gives a diagrammatic illustration of a typical storage and cooling-load process for a plant operating period of 16 hours.

The *specific weight* of the structure is expressed in terms of unit floor area of the building (kg/m^2 or lb/ft^2) and takes into account the particular elements of the structure bounding a reference area or a module of the building. It can be most suitably illustrated by example, thus:

EXAMPLE 3.1 Calculate the specific weight of structure of the building arrangement shown in Fig. AI.1 of Appendix I. The floors are not carpeted.

Solution From p. 136 of Appendix I, the constructional details may be tabulated, thus:

Surface	*Weight (kg/m^2)*	*Area (m^2)*
Perimeter wall	430	2.98
Internal wall	98	8.84
Floors	552	18.60
Ceiling	28	18.60

The adjoining areas of the building are air conditioned with the exception of the service core. Therefore, the proportions of the boundary surfaces to be considered are the whole weights of the perimeter and inner walls and half each of the floor and ceiling slab weights; the weight of the glazing is neglected. The reference area is one module, 3.05 m $\times$ 6.1 m = 18.6 m^2.

From the foregoing the specific weight of structure is calculated, as shown in Table 3.10.

The specific weight is used in the selection of factors to be applied to the instantaneous rates of heat gain due to radiation from sunlight, lighting and occupants. These are termed storage, or cooling-load, factors according to the authority concerned, and the values vary from one authority to another.

Using the specific weight calculated for the specimen module having double-glazing, internal venetian blinds 45° drawn, no carpeting, southwest aspect and cooling plant operating for 12 hrs, the storage load factor for 50° N latitude at 16.00 hours in August can be selected from the CIBS, ASHRAE and Carrier handbooks as shown on page 45.

Table 3.10 Typical calculation of specific weight of building structure

Surface	m^2	$\times$ kg/m^2	=	kg
Perimeter wall	2.98	$\times$ 430	=	1 281
Internal wall	8.84	$\times$ 98	=	866
½ floor slab	18.60	$\times \frac{552}{2}$	=	5 134
½ ceiling slab	18.60	$\times \frac{552}{2}$	=	5 134
Ceiling	18.60	$\times$ 28	=	521
				12 936

$$\text{Specific weight} = \frac{12\ 936}{18.6} = 695\ \text{kg/m}^2\ (142\ \text{lb/ft}^2)$$

Authority	*Solar*	*Lighting*	*Occupants*
CIBS, lightweight construction	Included in instantaneous heat gain values	Not quoted	Not quoted
ASHRAE, all room constructions	0.81	0.80	0.82
Carrier, 142 lb/ft²	0.69	0.94	0.95

It is interesting to note that the resultants of the ASHRAE and Carrier factors are approximately equal, i.e. $0.81 \times 0.80 \times 0.82 = 0.53$ and $0.69 \times 0.94 \times 0.95 = 0.61$.

If, at the design stage, it is known that floors will be carpeted then, according to ASHRAE and Carrier, the factors should be adjusted to allow for the insulating effect of the carpet; CIBS makes no mention of this.

In the Carrier case, each of the factors is adjusted by halving the weight of the floor slab, calculating a new specific weight and using this to select other storage factors.

ASHRAE apply a correction only to the storage factor for lighting.

Applying these corrections to the calculation in Table 3.10 produces the following adjustments:

Carrier adjusted specific weight = 557 kg/m² (114 lb/ft²)

Storage factors	*Solar*	*Lighting*	*Occupants*
ASHRAE	0.81	0.85	0.82
Carrier	0.70	0.94	0.95

In the design specification the specific weight, as calculated by the Carrier method, should be stated, with or without carpets, as may be the case.

3.10 NOISE LEVELS

Acceptable sound levels within buildings are specified by Noise Rating (NR) or Noise Criteria (NC) curves which are curves of equal levels of acceptable noise related to a scale of frequencies from 63 to 8000 Hz, or cycles per second; NR curves are used in Europe and NC curves in the United States and elsewhere. The NR curves are somewhat more exacting in the higher frequencies than are the NC equivalents, but the differences are marginal and, therefore for all practical purposes, either form is applicable.

Figure 3.10 is a chart of NR curves reproduced from Section A1 of the CIBS *Guide*. Each curve is classified by a number corresponding to the speech interference level which, as it suggests, is the level of background noise at each frequency which will not interfere with normal conversation.

At the left-hand side of the chart, a scale is shown of equivalent sound pressure levels in decibels (dB) above a reference datum of 2×10^{-5} N/m². This scale gives single-figure values of acceptable noise levels over the full frequency spectrum as would be measured using the 'A' scale of a sound-level meter; the 'A' scale of the meter being one that is weighted to measure sounds as they appear to the human ear.

This, the dBA scale, is a useful indication of a prevailing noise level but, being an aggregate of the levels in all frequencies, it is incapable of displaying peaks of noise which may be outside acceptable tolerances; for this purpose a sound-level analyser

Fig. 3.10 Chart of noise rating (NR) curves

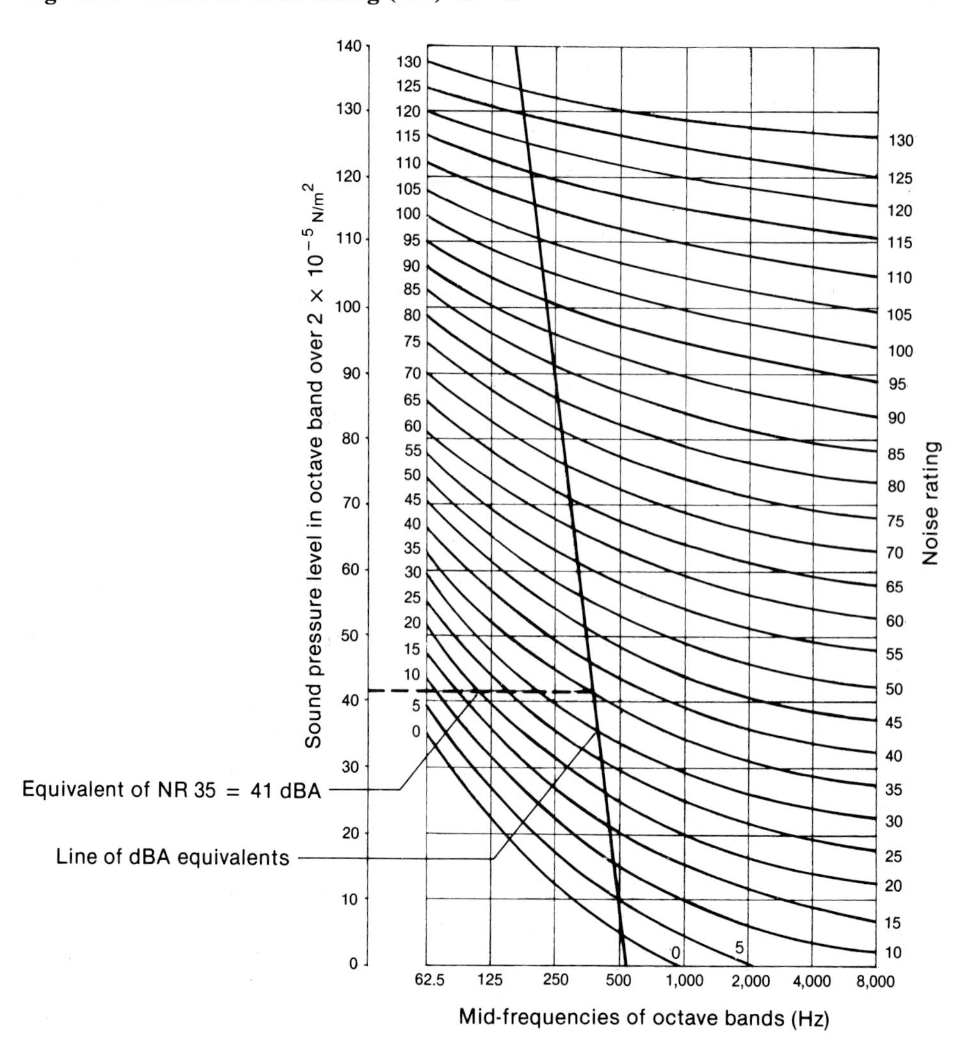

meter is required for measurement of the levels at each frequency and, thereby, to establish whether tolerances are being exceeded.

The human ear is generally insensitive to variations in noise levels of 3 dB or below. Therefore, the tolerances to be specified are plus or minus 2 dB. Within these tolerances there is a relationship between dBA scale readings and NR values which is usable at the design stage when precise details of the relevant sources of noise may not be available. The relationship is shown in Fig. 3.10 by the superimposed line of 'dBA equivalents'. A reading from the intersection of this line with any NR curve will give the dBA equivalent ± 2 dB. For example, the equivalent of NR 35 is 41 dBA ± 2 dB; this is as indicated on the chart.

Table 3.11, taken from the CIBS *Guide*, Section A1, shows the recommended NR criteria for most building usages likely to be encountered. These, it must be stressed, relate to the aggregates of all sources of noise. It follows that noise from systems and plant must be lower than the ratings specified.

Noise levels from separate sources in dB are added or subtracted logarithmically. This is a relatively lengthy process, but one that is necessary at the design stage in

Table 3.11 Recommended noise ratings

Situation	*NR criterion*
Concert halls, opera halls, studios for sound reproduction, live theatres (>500 seats)	20
Bedrooms in private homes, live theatres (<500 seats), cathedrals and large churches, television studios, large conference and lecture rooms (>50 people)	25
Living rooms in private homes, board rooms, top management offices, conference and lecture rooms (20–50) people), multi-purpose halls, churches (medium and small), libraries, bedrooms in hotels, etc., banqueting rooms, operating theatres, cinemas, hospital private rooms, large courtrooms	30
Public rooms in hotels, etc., ballrooms, hospital open wards, middle management and small offices, small conference and lecture rooms (<20 people), school classrooms, small courtrooms, museums, libraries, banking halls, small restaurants, cocktail bars, quality shops	35
Toilets and washrooms, large open offices, drawing offices, reception areas (offices), halls, corridors, lobbies in hotels, hospitals, etc., laboratories, recreation rooms, post offices, large restaurants, bars and night clubs, department stores, shops, gymnasia	40
Kitchens in hotels, hospitals, etc., laundry rooms, computer rooms, accounting-machine rooms, cafeteria, canteens, supermarkets, swimming-pools, covered garages in hotels, offices, etc., bowling alleys	45

NR 50 and above
NR 50 will generally be regarded as very noisy by sedentary workers, but most of the classifications listed under NR 45 could just accept NR 50. Higher noise levels than NR 50 will be justified in certain manufacturing areas; such cases must be judged on their own merits.

order that acceptable levels of plant or system noise can be established. To assist in this process Figs. 3.11 and 3.12 are given, these being, respectively, charts for the addition and subtraction of decibel values.

The charts are used in conjunction with Table 3.11 and Fig. 3.10 to arrive at an approximation of the required equipment noise level. Also for their use, it is necessary to know the background noise level in a particular building; this should be obtained from the site or within a building of similar nature in the vicinity. The procedure is illustrated by example 3.2 on p. 49.

Fig. 3.11 Chart for addition of decibels

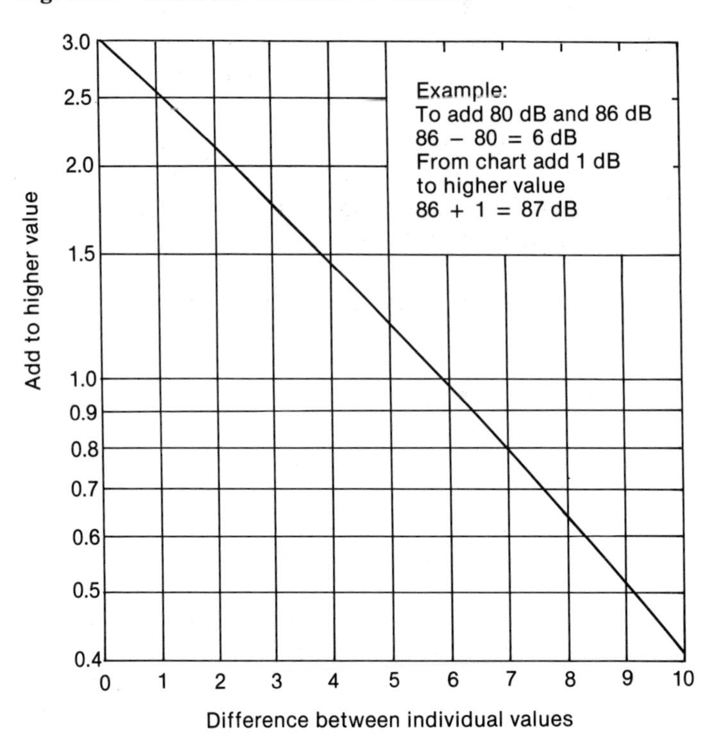

Fig. 3.12 Chart for the subtraction of decibels

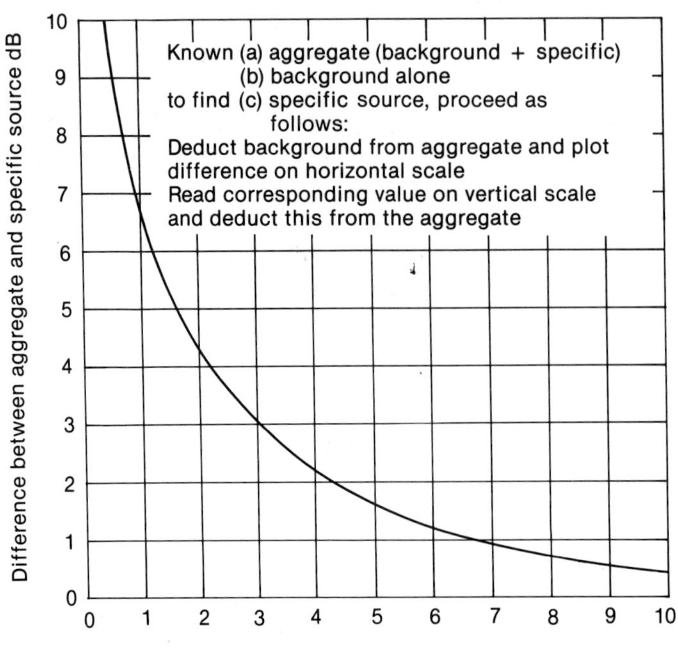

EXAMPLE 3.2 In an office building having a background noise level of 34 dBA, calculate the equipment maximum noise level to achieve the recommended noise rating.

Solution

Noise criterion from Table 3.11	NR 35
Decibel equivalent from Fig. 3.10	= 41 dBA
Measured background noise level	34 dBA
dBA equivalent minus background level	= 7 dBA

From Fig. 3.12, for the 7 dBA difference between the aggregate and background noise levels, the aggregate minus specific (plant) noise level is 1dB. Therefore, the plant or system noise level must not exceed 41 − 1 = 40 dBA.

Referring now to Fig. 3.11:

Difference between plant and background noise levels (40 − 34 dBA)	= 6 dBA
From Fig. 3.11, the addition to the higher value of the two	= 1 dBA
40 dBA plant noise + 1 dB	= 41 dBA

From Fig. 3.10 this aggregate of plant and background noise levels can be confirmed as the equivalent of NR 35.

However, it must again be stressed, that this adjustment of the dBA level may not deal with excessive noise levels in particular frequencies. To establish these an analysis must be made over the octave band and, if necessary, attenuation applied to remove peak levels. In this respect, if the aggregate noise level is not to be increased, it will be necessary for the plant or system level to be at least 5 dB lower than the aggregate at the frequency where the intrusive peak occurs.

The foregoing relates to the limitation of equipment noise levels within the building. A further aspect that will require attention concerns the effect of plant noise on the surrounding neighbourhood.

Noise nuisance of this nature is a subject of the Control of Pollution Act 1974 which, under section 58 of the Act, gives local authorities the power to serve notice of summary proceedings imposing the following requirements:

'(a) requiring the abatement of the nuisance or prohibiting or restricting its occurrence or recurrence;

'(b) requiring the execution of such works, and the taking of such other steps, as may be necessary for the purpose of the notice or as may be specified in the notice.'

The Act gives no definition of a noise nuisance; the procedure being that, resulting from detection by the local authority or complaint from a resident, an official will measure the ambient noise level and, if this is deemed to be a nuisance, will serve notice on the owner or occupier of the premises from which the noise is emitted for it to be abated to a level acceptable to the local authority.

There is also no information given in the Act concerning the method of measuring the noise. Therefore, as a guide, BS 4142:1967 should be referred to which recommends that measurement should be made on the dBA scale at a height of 1.2 m from a surface and 3.6 m away from any walls, buildings or other reflecting structures.

If plant noise is not to be judged as being the cause of a nuisance, it should be attenuated (by distance, silencers, enclosure or screening) to a level at least 5 dBA below a background level measured, or estimated, in accordance with BS 4142.

From Fig. 3.12 it can be seen that a difference of 5 dB between two sources of noise will result in an increase of less than 2 dB when they are combined. This will scarcely be detectable subjectively and, therefore, it should not be evident to a possible complainant.

3.11 CONCLUSION

Collating the various data discussed in the foregoing sections, a typical design specification for a five-storey office building in the City of London, having the modular characteristics of the example in Appendix I (p. 135), would appear as shown in Table 3.12.

With the establishment of the air-conditioning design specification, a framework exists from which the cooling and heating load calculations can be made. These are the subjects of Chapters 4, 5 and 6 and, thence in Chapter 7, a typical example is worked through.

Table 3.12 Typical design specification

Item	*Value*	*References*
Temperatures:		
Outdoor, summer	28 °C DB/18.5 °C WB (82 °F DB/65 °F WB)	Section 3.1. By calculation, CIBS *Guide*, Section A or Fowler, Vol. 1
winter	−5.5 °C DB/−6.0 °C WB (22 °F DB/21 °F WB)	
Indoor, summer	22 °C DB/45% RH (72 °F DB/45% RH)	Section 3.2, Fig. 3.2
winter	20 °C DB/45% RH (68 °F DB/45% RH)	
Air movement:		
summer	0.21 m/sec (42 ft/min)	Section 3.2, Fig. 3.3
winter	0.15 m/sec (30 ft/min)	
Population:	9.3 m^2 (100 ft^2) floor area per person	Section 3.3, Table 3.4
Illumination:	500 lux. Recessed fittings. 27.5 W/m^2 total wattage	Section 3.4, Fig. 3.4
Ventilation:		
Offices, supply	Some smoking. 1.3 litres/sec/m^2 (0.25 cfm/ft^2) floor area	Section 3.5, Fig. 3.5(b)
extract	0.56 litres/sec/m^2 (0.11 cfm/ft^2)	Section 3.5.2
Enclosed toilets	10.0 air changes/hr extract. 8.0 air changes/hr supply	Section 3.6.1
Toilet lobbies	3.0 air changes/hr supply	Section 3.6.1
Kitchens	Heat gain 500 W/m^2 18.0 air changes/hr supply. 22.5 air changes/hr extract	Section 3.6.2, Fig. 3.6
Underground car-park	3.0 air changes/hr extract. 3.0 air changes/hr supply	Section 3.6.3
Infiltration rate:	Maximum 1.5 litres/sec/m^2 (0.3 cfm/ft^2) window opening area at a pressure difference of 75 Pa (0.3 ins wg) across the windows	Section 3.7
Fenestration:		
U-value	3.3 $W/m^2/°C$ (0.58 BTU/hr/ft^2/°F) for window and frame	Section 3.8.1, Table 3.6
Shading coeff.	0.53	Section 3.8.2, Appendix II
Building structure:		
U-values	0.6 $W/m^2/°C$ (0.10 Btu/hr/ft^2/°F) for walls, floors and roof	Section 3.9.1
Specific weight	695 kg/m^2 (142 lb/ft^2) floor area	Section 3.9.2
Noise levels:	NR 35. Equivalent to dBA 41	Section 3.10, Table 3.11 and Fig. 3.10

4 Calculation of cooling loads

There are three forms of cooling-load calculations to be examined, namely face peak loads, inner zone loads and the building instantaneous load.

Face peak loads consist of the heat gains that are imposed on the perimeter areas flanking each of the faces of a building. These heat gains derive from a combination of largely variable constituents: solar, external conduction loads, fresh-air load, if relevant; and relatively constant loads: population, illumination, equipment, internal conduction loads from uncooled spaces.

The sum of the gains in the reference areas of a building (modules, rooms, etc.) determines the terminal cooling capacity required in each to maintain the specified indoor design conditions of temperature and humidity.

Inner zone loads are those which occur within the interior of a building away from perimeter effects. They comprise heat gains which are relatively constant from population, illumination, equipment and internal conduction.

The *instantaneous* load is the maximum aggregate of the face peak loads and the inner zone loads plus the resultant of the heat gains and losses which will occur in the central plant and distribution systems, i.e. fan and pump gains, pipe and duct gains or losses, etc. This load determines the overall cooling capacity that is required.

It will be noted that the fresh-air load is included, where relevant, as part of the direct heat gains to the perimeter areas. This is a design feature which should be applied in certain cases: if the latent heat of the fresh air is removed at the central plant serving induction and fan-coil systems and the sensible heat is made part of the unit load, then a condensate drainage system will not be necessary; with Versatemp-type systems, removal of both latent and sensible heat from the fresh air at the units will simplify the central plant and allow insulation of the distribution pipework and ductwork to be omitted.

Inner zone areas are usually served by all-air systems (variable-air-volume, terminal reheat, etc.) In these cases the fresh-air load will be dealt with by the central plant.

The constituent loads of the face peak, inner zone and instantaneous heat gains derive from: solar radiation and conduction; population, illumination, equipment and fresh air; the fans and pumps of the conditioning plant; and the ducts and pipes of the distribution systems.

These are now discussed in that order, commencing with the peripheral loads which, in the presence of sunlight, will comprise the transmission of heat into a building by radiation and conduction through the structural carcase.

4.1 SOLAR RADIATION LOADS

The intensity of solar radiation at the atmospheric fringe (the tropopause) has been relatively accurately established by satellite as 1353 W/m^2 (429.5 $Btu/hr/ft^2$) normal to the sun's rays. This is referred to as the solar constant.

During its passage through the atmosphere the solar intensity is reduced through absorption by the water vapour in the atmosphere, and by reflection and diffusion due to cloud cover and haze. The intensity at the earth's surface is also dependent upon the length of the radiation path through the atmosphere. This is a function of solar altitude (variable by latitude and time of the year) and solar distance, the latter varying over the year because of the elliptical form of the earth's orbit around the sun and from place to place, according to height above sea-level.

In July the distance of the earth from the sun is so much greater than in January that January intensities exceed those in July by about 7%. This variation of 1% per month may be discounted in northern latitudes, where maximum cooling-load conditions occur from June to September but, in the southern latitudes the summer period is from December to March. Hence, allowance must be made for the increases that occur over the latter period.

Solar irradiation of the earth's surface appears in two forms – *direct* and *diffuse*. Diffuse radiation is the result of the scattering and reflection of the direct radiation that occurs through the atmosphere and at the earth's surface. It is omnidirectional and will be effective in conditions of shade and cloud, whereas direct radiation occurs only with sunlight.

Through fenestration these solar radiations will be transmitted as heat gains according to the following formulae:

$$Q_D = A_{ig} I_D S_f S_c \qquad [4.1]$$

where

Q_D	= heat transmitted by direct solar radiation	W
A_{ig}	= area of sunlit glass or area of sunlit glass and window-frame, if uninsulated	m^2
I_D	= peak solar heat gain factor	W/m^2
S_f	= storage load factor	
S_c	= shading coefficient	

$$Q_d = A_{sg} I_d S_f S_c \qquad [4.2]$$

where

Q_d	= heat transmitted by diffuse radiation	W
A_{sg}	= area of shaded glass and frame if uninsulated	m^2
I_d	= peak diffuse heat gain factor	W/m^2

Published values of peak solar heat gains include both direct and diffuse radiation constants except for north-facing aspects (south in the Southern hemisphere) which are for diffuse radiation only. Therefore, the expression to be used for the combined radiation effects is:

$$Q_{Dd} = A_{ig} I_{Dd} S_f S_c \qquad [4.3]$$

where

Q_{Dd}	= aggregate heat transmitted by solar radiation	W
I_{Dd}	= peak solar heat gain factor, direct and diffuse	W/m^2

When glazed areas are partially shaded, equation [4.3] is used for the sunlit portion and equation [4.2] for the portion in shade.

Figures 4.1(a) and 4.1(b) show charts of peak solar radiation through vertical window glass in 50° north and south latitudes; inset on the figures are the peak values for horizontal glass. Figure 4.1(a) is for the months of June in the Northern hemisphere and December in the Southern hemisphere; Fig. 4.1(b) relates to July and May for northern latitudes and January and November for southern latitudes.

In Appendix III (p. 148) peak solar radiation charts for other latitudes and months are shown (Figs. AIII.1–AIII.24).

Notes concerning Figs 4.1(a), 4.1(b) and the similar charts in Appendix III are as follows:

1. *Atmospheric haze* due to airborne contaminants will reduce the incident direct solar radiation. Therefore in city and industrial locations the charted values should be reduced by 10%.
2. *Dewpoint temperature* is a measure of the moisture content of the atmosphere which, in turn, regulates the capacity of the atmosphere to absorb solar radiation. For dewpoint temperatures other than 13 °C (56 °F) adjust the chart values, thus:
   Add 0.4% for each °C *below* 13 °C dewpoint (0.7% for each °F below 56 °F dewpoint);
   Subtract 0.4% for each °C *above* 13 °C dewpoint (0.7% for each °F above 56 °F dewpoint).
3. *Altitude* above sea-level: add to the charted values 0.7% per 300 m (1000 ft). Make no further correction for dewpoint temperature variation.
4. *Southern latitudes* in December and January, add 7% to the chart values.
5. *North exposures* in northern latitudes (south in southern latitudes) consist of diffuse radiation only.
6. *Inclined glazing* on pitched roofs, use the adjustment factors in Table 4.1, reproduced from the CIBS *Guide*, Section A:

Table 4.1 Intensity of direct solar radiation on a sloping roof with a clear sky

Inclination of roof to horizontal (degrees)	Position of sun with respect to roof surface					
	On same side of ridge			On opposite side of ridge		
	Per cent intensity on horizontal roof		Per cent intensity on vertical wall	Per cent intensity on horizontal roof		Per cent intensity on vertical wall
5	99.6	plus	8.7	99.6	minus	8.7
10	98.5	plus	17.4	98.5	minus	17.4
15	96.6	plus	25.9	96.6	minus	25.9
20	94.0	plus	34.2	94.0	minus	34.2
25	90.6	plus	42.3	90.6	minus	42.3
30	86.6	plus	50.0	86.6	minus	50.0
40	76.6	plus	64.3	76.5	minus	64.3
50	64.3	plus	76.6	64.3	minus	76.6
60	50.0	plus	86.6	50.0	minus	86.6
70	34.2	plus	94.0	34.2	minus	94.0

Fig. 4.1 Peak solar radiation through common glass; 50°N and S latitudes

(a)

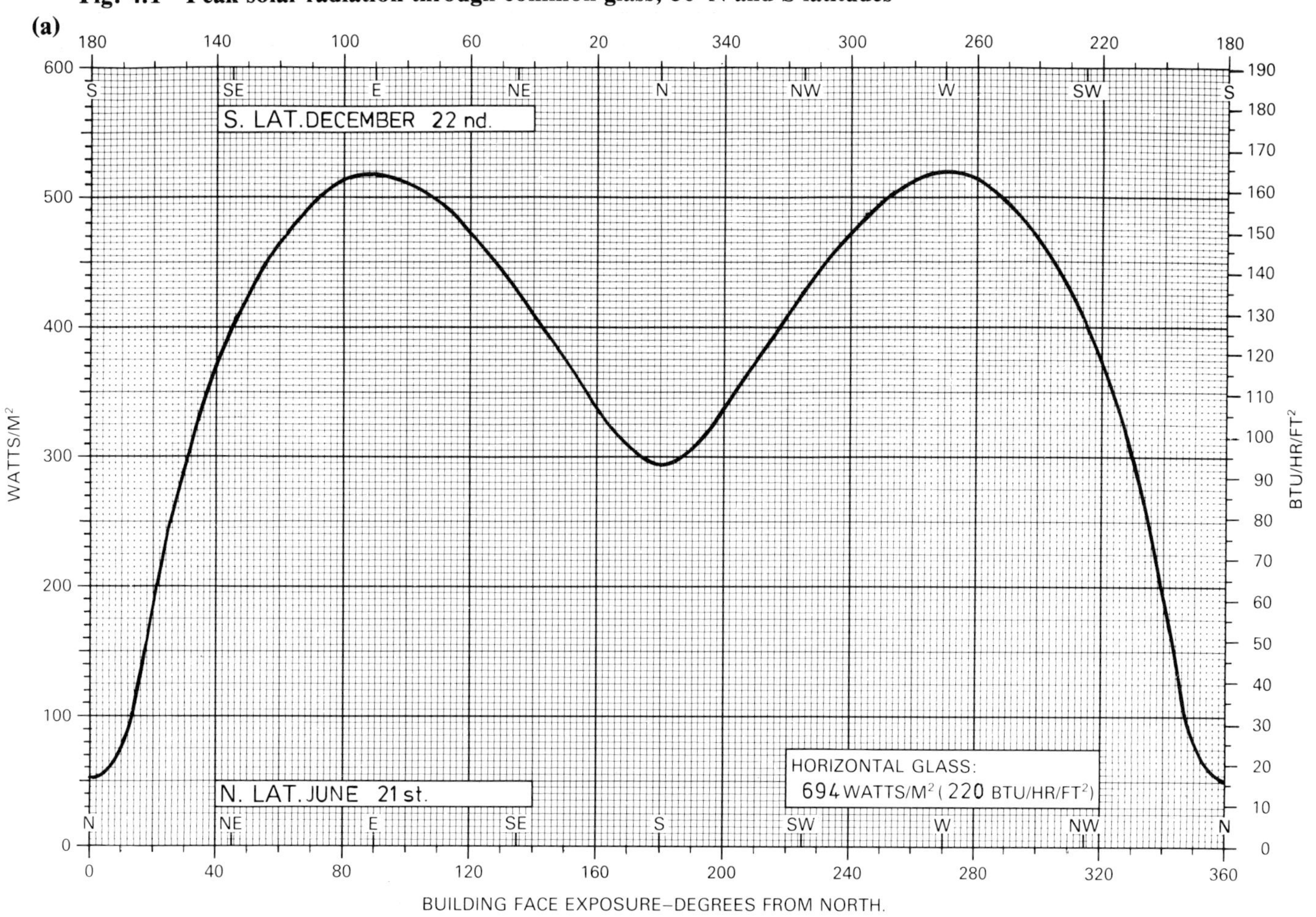

(b)

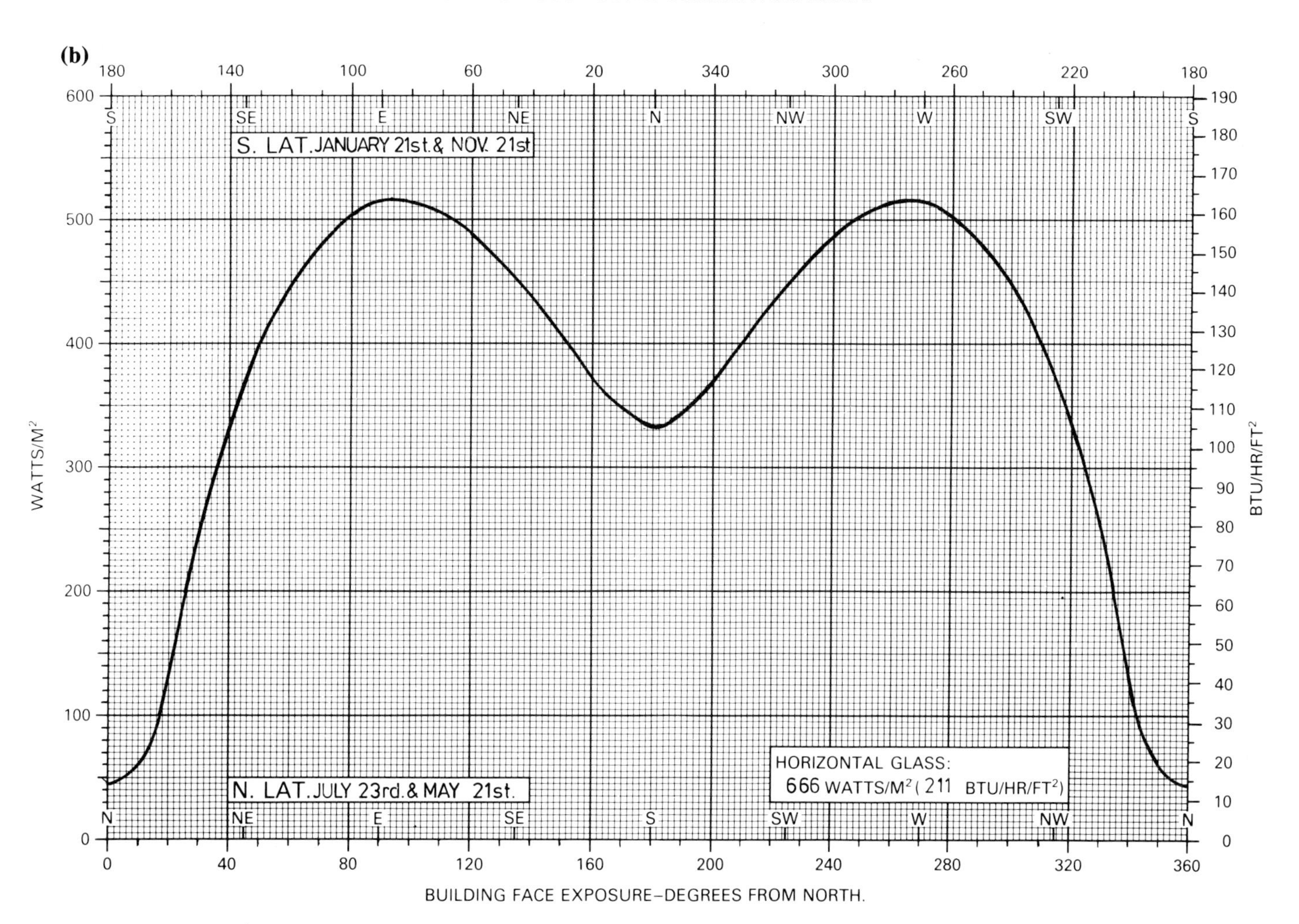

Fig. 4.2 Storage load factors for solar radiation through glass; N and S latitudes; 12-hour plant cooling, interior shades, specific weight 500 kg/m²

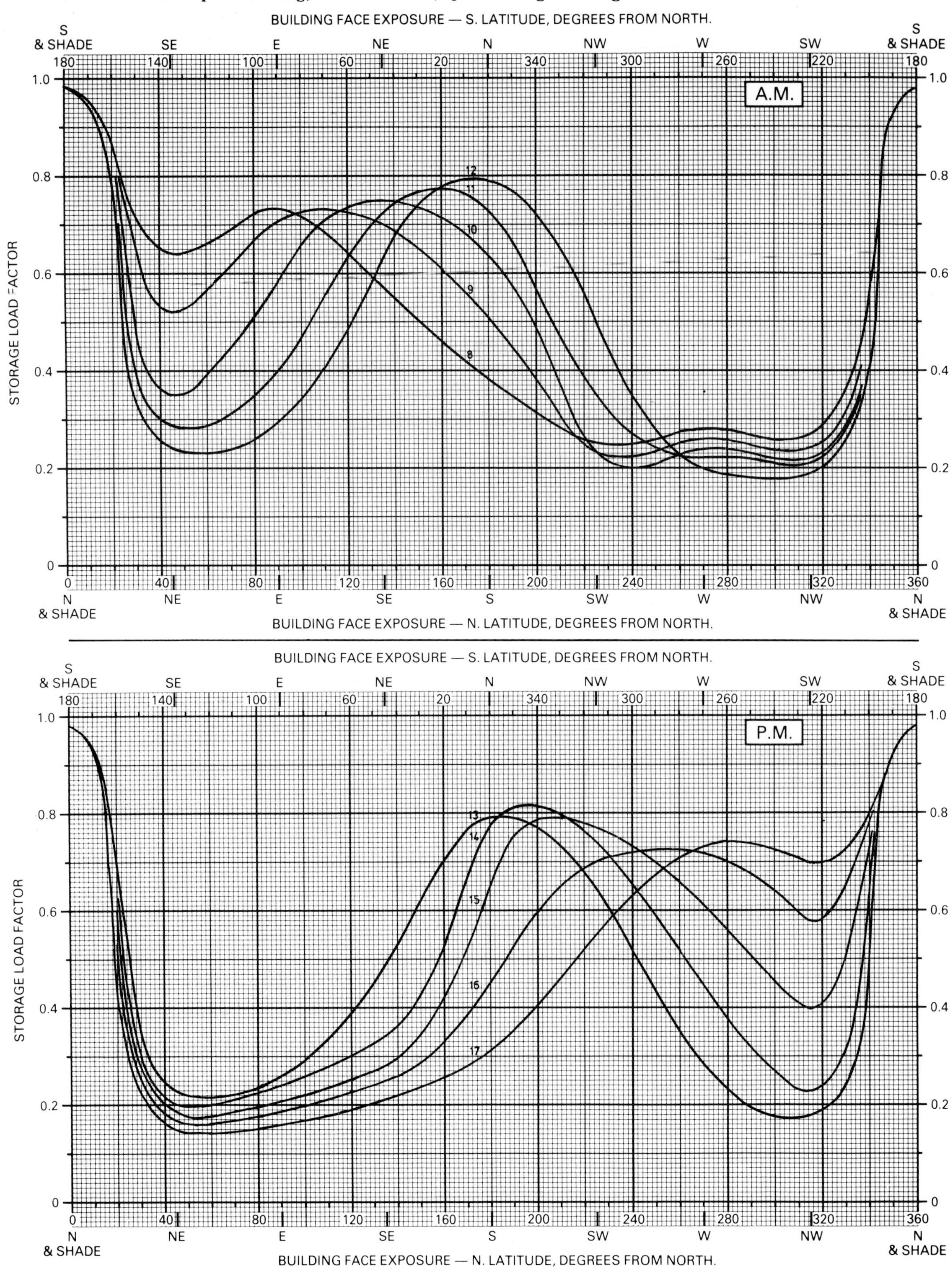

EXAMPLE 4.1 Calculate the direct solar radiation values through the ridge glazing, shown in the sketch, facing 240° from north for the month of July in latitude 50°N.

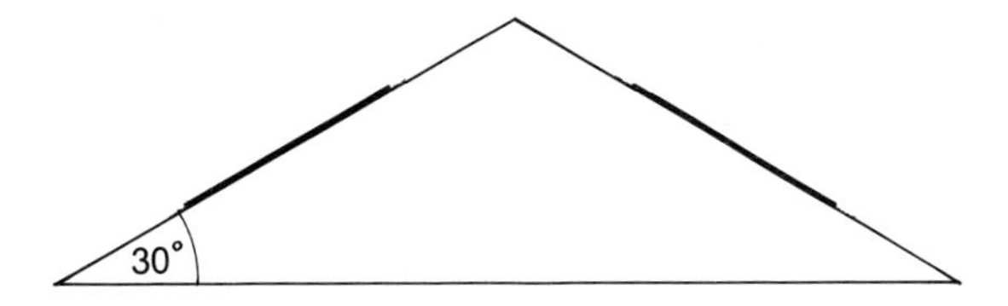

Solution

(a) Glazing facing sun

From Fig. 4.1(b): direct radiation value (inset) on horizontal glass = 666 W/m^2 (211 Btu/hr/ft^2); direct radiation on vertical glass = 487 W/m^2 (155 Btu/hr/ft^2). From Table 4.1 at 30° ridge inclination the direct radiation:

$$I_D = (0.866 \times 666) + (0.5 \times 487) = 820 \text{ W/m}^2$$
$$= ((0.866 \times 211) + (0.5 \times 155) = 260 \text{ Btu/hr/ft}^2))$$

(b) Glazing facing away from sun:

$$I_D = (0.866 \times 666) - (0.5 \times 487) = 333 \text{ W/m}^2$$
$$= ((0.866 \times 211) - (0.5 \times 155) = 105 \text{ Btu/hr/ft}^2))$$

Figure 4.2 shows typical plots of morning and afternoon values of storage load factors for solar radiation through *vertical glass*, again for north and south latitudes. These examples relate to the conditions for a building having a specific weight of 500 kg/m^2 (100 lb/ft^2), interior window shades and the cooling plant running for 12 hrs.

The horizontal abscissae of the charts in Figs 4.1 and 4.2, etc. are scales of compass bearings from the north point with the principal bearing points denoted; this to enable readings to be made against the precise orientation of particular building face aspects.

Figure 4.3 is a typical chart of storage load factors for *horizontal glass*, with internal shading. In this case the horizontal abscissa is a time-scale since the factors are related to solar altitude (and hence time) rather than orientation.

Appendix IV (p. 161) consists of charts of storage load factors for vertical and horizontal glass related to other specific weights of structure, and other glazing configurations and periods of cooling plant operation.

The use of these charts is demonstrated by the following example.

EXAMPLE 4.2 Single-glazed window facing 240° from north with interior shades.
Shading coefficient 0.54.
Glass area 1.5 m^2 (16.1 ft^2), 25% in shade due to window opening reveals. Frame insulated.
Latitude 50°N.
Time 15.00 hours in July.
Specific weight of building 500 kg/m^2 (100 lb/ft^2) of floor area.
Cooling plant operating for 12 hours.
Calculate the heat gain through the window due to solar radiation.

Fig. 4.3 Storage load factors for horizontal glass with internal shading

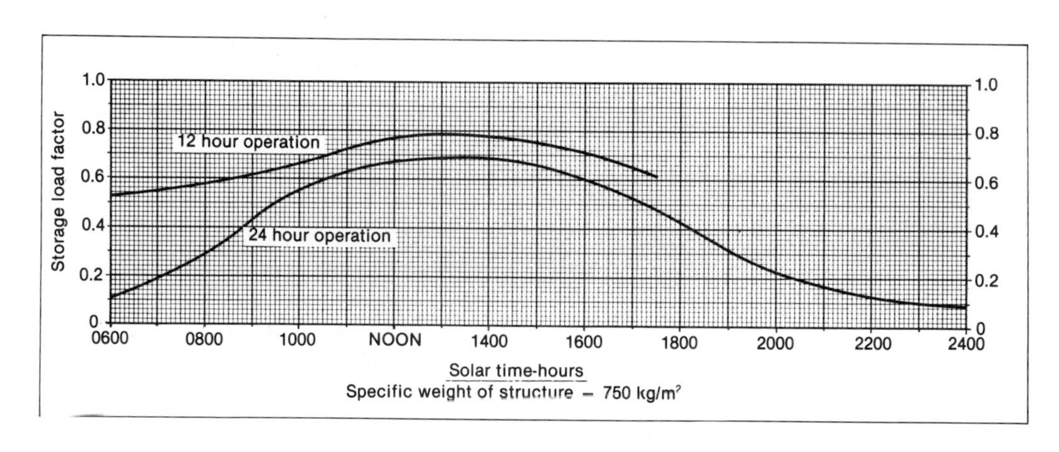

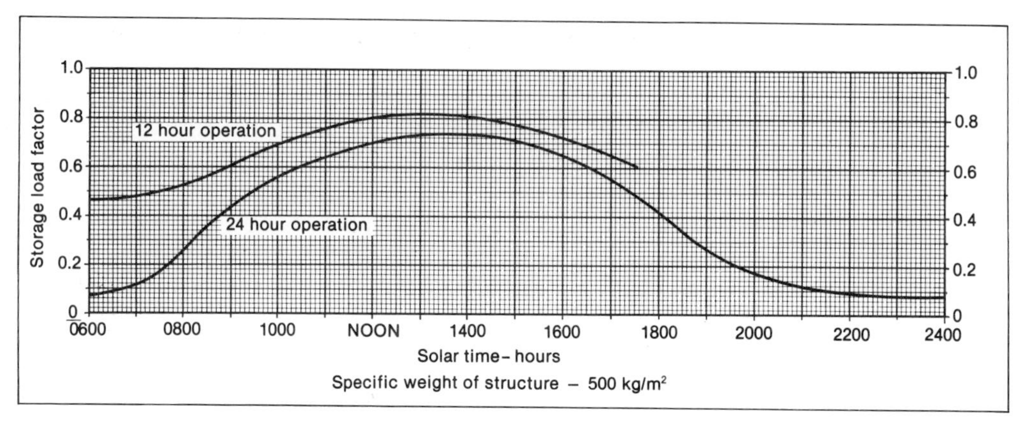

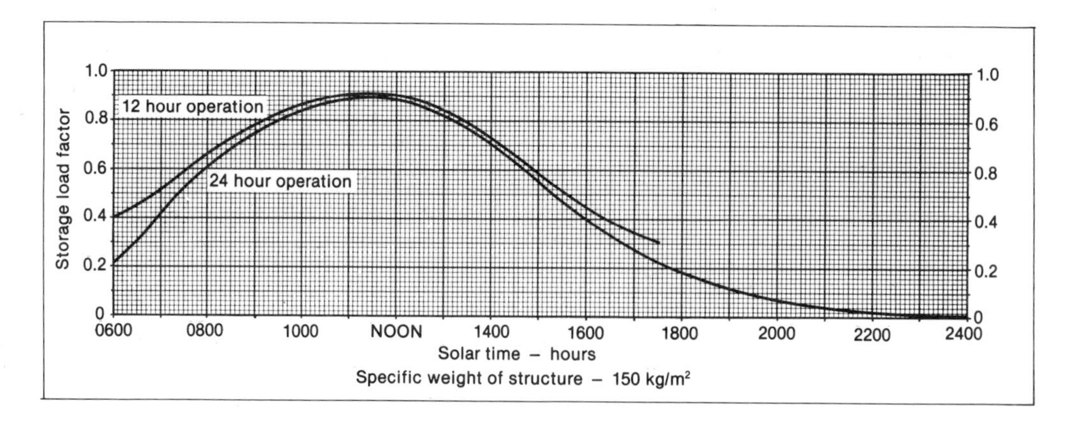

Solution From p. 53 the equation for diffuse radiation through the shaded glass is:

$$Q_d = A_{sg}\, I_d\, S_f\, S_c$$

In Fig. 4.1(b) the value of I_d is read at the north (shaded) line as 44 W/m² (14 Btu/hr/ft²), and from Fig. 4.2 the storage load factor is 0.73. Hence:

$$Q_d = 1.5 \times 0.25 \times 44 \times 0.73 \times 0.54 = 6.5 \text{ W}$$
$$(16.1 \times 0.25 \times 14 \times 0.73 \times 0.54) = 22 \text{ Btu/hr})$$

For the sunlit area equation [4.3] is used:

$$Q_{Dd} = A_{ig}\, I_{Dd}\, S_f\, S_c$$

Referring again to Fig. 4.1(b) the value of I_{Dd} at 240° from north is 487 W/m² (155 Btu/hr/ft²).

$$Q_{Dd} = 1.5 \times 0.75 \times 487 \times 0.73 \times 0.54 \quad = 216 \text{ W}$$
$$(16.1 \times 0.75 \times 155 \times 0.73 \times 0.54 = 738 \text{ Btu/hr})$$

The aggregate heat gain over the whole window glass area due to diffuse and direct radiation is:

$$6.5 + 216 = 222.5 \text{ W}$$
$$(22 + 738) = 760 \text{ Btu/hr})$$

4.2 CONDUCTION LOADS

4.2.1 Conduction through glass

The foregoing calculations for heat gains due to solar radiation do not include the heat transmission through fenestration by conduction. This is a straightforward process using equation [3.3] (p. 35), i.e.

$$Q_c = A_f \, U_f \, (t_o - t_i)$$

The window area, A_f, is the total area including the frame.

EXAMPLE 4.3 The window of Example 4.2 has an aluminium frame with a thermal break, occupying 20% of the total window area. Outdoor and indoor air temperatures are, respectively, 28 °C (82.4 °F) and 22 °C(71.6 °F).

Calculate the heat gain due to conduction.

Solution From Table 3.6 (p. 36) the *U*-value for the single-glazed window is 5.8 W/m²/°C (1.02 Btu/hr/ft²/°F), and the total area is $1.5 \div 0.8 = 1.875 \text{ m}^2$ (20.2 ft^2).

$$Q_c = 1.875 \times 5.8\,(28 - 22) \quad = 65 \text{ W}$$
$$(20.2 \times 1.02\,(82.4 - 71.6) = 222 \text{ Btu/hr})$$

4.2.2 Correction of outdoor air temperatures

The value of 28 °C in Example 4.3 above is the optimum outdoor dry-bulb temperature used in computing cooling loads for London in the UK (82.4 °F is the precise conversion of 28 °C used to produce an accurate Btu/hr equivalent of the answer in watts; in practice 82 °F is adopted for the design temperature in conventional or imperial units). In the hypothetical design year for London, this optimum temperature can be said to occur at 16.00 hours on 23 July at latitude 50°N (the latitude for London is 51° 28′N, but little inaccuracy will result from using the rounded value).

However, at other times of the day and year in the UK, and in other latitudes, it will be necessary to know the outdoor design temperatures to be used in place of the optimum. Therefore, it is appropriate to consider this at this stage.

Figure 4.4 is a nomogram from which daily variations of dry-bulb temperature can be extracted. Its use requires a knowledge of the summer outdoor design dry-bulb temperature and the daily temperature range for the locality concerned: these are obtained from the relevant meteorological data as explained in Section 3.1 (p. 18).

Figure 3.1 (p. 20) gives meteorological tables for London, New York and Johannesburg and on Fig. 4.4 an example, based upon the London Meteorological Office data, demonstrates the application of the nomogram: To obtain the outdoor dry-bulb temperature at 08.00 hours on the design day, the upper left-hand scale is entered at 08.00 hours and a line drawn horizontally to the relevant latitude curve of 50°N. From this intersection a line is drawn vertically downwards to meet an oblique line from the daily range scale (London daily range for July = 71 °F−55 °F) at 9 °C, or 16 °F in rounded figures. A horizontal line from this intersection to the lower right-hand scale shows the temperature reduction from the optimum that will apply at 08.00 hours, i.e. 6 °C (11 °F).

Fig. 4.4 Daily variation of outdoor temperature

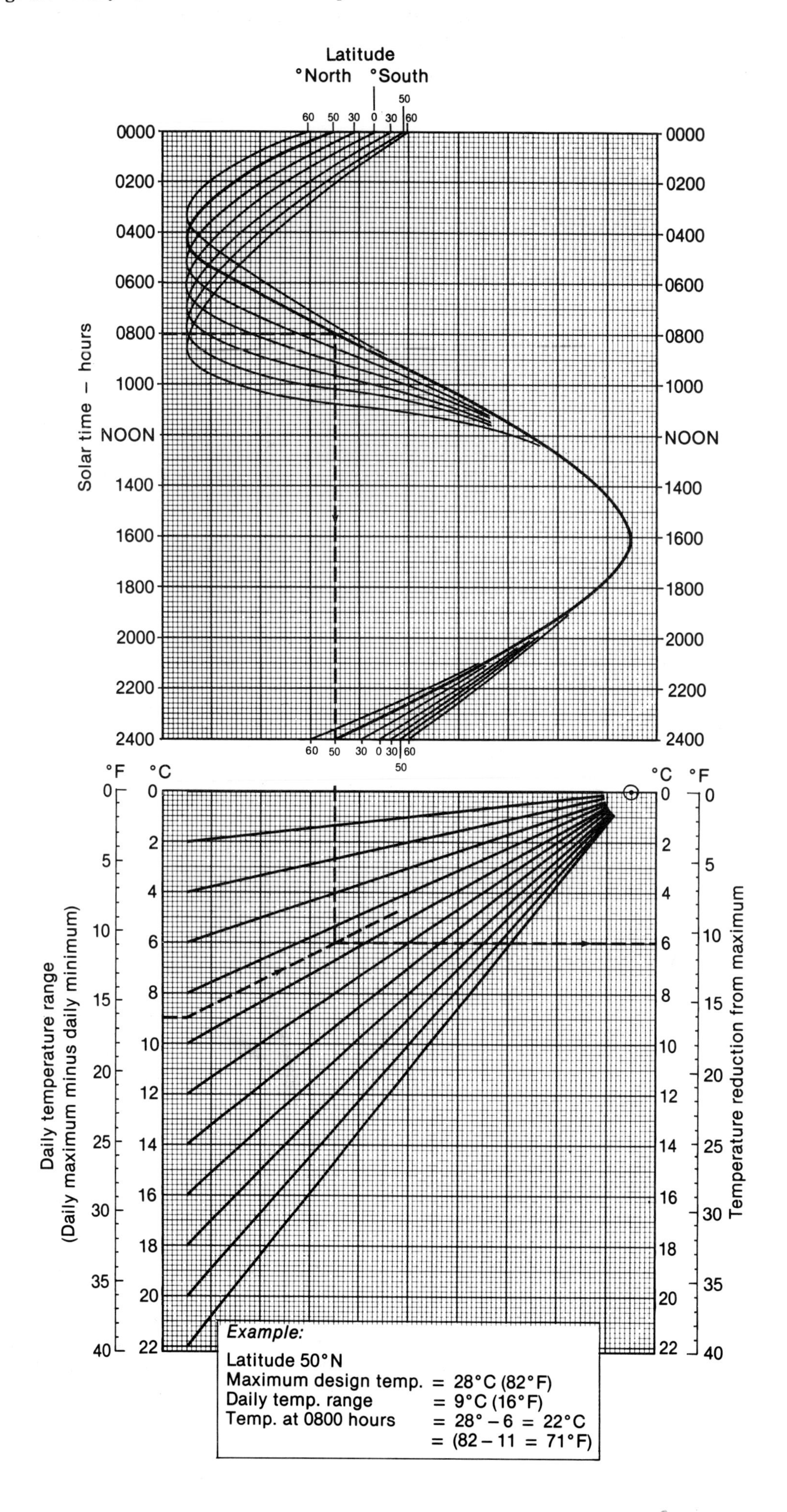

Hence, at 08.00 hours on the July design day for London, UK, the outdoor dry-bulb temperature will be:

28 °C − 6 °C = 22 °C
(82 °F − 11 °F = 71 °F)

Over a summer design day without rain the moisture content of the outdoor air will remain approximately constant; a state which is used for the estimation of the design wet-bulb temperature at times other than at the optimum.

The optimum outdoor design conditions for London, UK, are 28 °C DB/18.5 °C WB sling (82 °F DB/65 °F WB), and from the psychrometric tables of the CIBS *Guide*, Section C, the moisture contents at these conditions can be interpolated as 0.009 321 kg/kg of dry air (0.009321 lb/lb of dry air).

Referring again to the CIBS psychrometric tables, the calculation of the wet-bulb temperature to be associated with the dry-bulb temperature is made as follows:

Moisture content at 28 °C DB/18.5 °C WB = 0.009 321 kg/kg
(82 °F DB/65 °F WB = 0.009 321 lb/lb)
Wet-bulb temp. at 22 °C DB/0.009321 kg/kg = 16.3 °C
(71 °F DB/0.009321 lb/lb = 61.1 °F)

Figure 4.4 and the procedures described can be applied to produce the outdoor design temperatures for conditions at other times, months and latitudes by application of the relevant optimum design and daily range temperatures.

4.2.3 Conduction through sunlit walls and roofs

For the calculation of heat gains through opaque fabrics resulting from solar irradiation, the standard transmission equation is modified to read:

$$Q_c = A_o \, U_o \, (t_{eo} - t_i) \qquad [4.4]$$

where

Q_c	= heat transmitted by conduction	W
A_o	= area of opaque fabric	m^2
U_o	= transmittance coefficient of the fabric	$W/m^2/°C$
t_{eo}	= sol-air temperature	°C
t_i	= indoor air temperature	°C

Sol-air temperature is a concept used to evaluate the effect of solar radiation on opaque building surfaces. It is defined as the hypothetical temperature of the outdoor air which, in the absence of solar radiation, would give the same rate of heat transfer as would occur with an actual condition of outdoor temperature and incident solar radiation. In other words, the solar irradiation is deemed to have the effect of raising the outdoor air temperature to a level at which the rate of heat transfer is the equivalent of the transmission due to the prevailing outdoor temperature plus the solar radiation.

In Section A2 of the CIBS *Guide* sol-air temperatures are tabulated for southeast England over the months of March to October. These are used in the CIBS appropriate formulae for the conduction heat gains through sunlit walls and roofs. The procedure is shown in Appendix I (p. 135).

ASHRAE publish similar tables in Chapter 26 of the *Fundamentals Handbook*. In this case, the sol-air temperatures are given for the month of July in 40°N latitude with correction procedures for other months and latitudes. ASHRAE have used these sol-air temperatures to produce values of *Cooling-load Temperature Differences* (CLTD) for the calculation of heat gains through sunlit walls and roofs. The values are for July in latitude 40°N and other specified conditions of surface colour, indoor and outdoor base temperatures, external surface resistance, etc. with, again, correction procedures described for all other conditions. The application of these CLTD factors also appears in Appendix I.

Carrier, in their *Handbook*, do not specifically refer to sol-air temperature. Instead they go straight to equivalent temperature differences (Δt_e) which incorporate the effects of solar radiation. Values of these are tabulated in Chapter 5 of the *Handbook* for July in latitude 40°N and for specified conditions of surface colour, outdoor and indoor temperatures, daily temperature range, period of cooling plant operation, solar time and weight of wall and roof construction. It should be noted that the last refers to the relevant weights of walls and roofs as distinct from the specific weights of building constructions described in Section 3.9.2. Correction procedures are given for the adjustment of the tabulated temperature differentials to suit other applicable conditions.

For application of the factors of equivalent temperature difference, equation [4.4] is transposed to read:

$$Q_c = A_o \, U_o \, \Delta t_e \qquad [4.5]$$

where

Δt_e = equivalent temperature difference °C

Figure 4.5 shows solar time plots of equivalent temperature differences for sunlit and shaded *walls* versus horizontal scales of compass bearings from north, for Northern and Southern hemispheres: lower scales for north latitudes and upper scales for south latitudes. The charts in Fig. 4.5 relate to the following bases:

Month of July in 50°N and S latitudes
Outdoor temperature 28 °C (82 °F)
Indoor temperature 22 °C (72 °F)
Daily temperature range 9 °C (16 °F)
Dark-coloured surfaces
Weight of wall construction 500 kg/m^2 (100 lb/ft^2)

For clarity separate charts are presented for morning (06.00 to 11.00 hours) and afternoon (12.00 to 17.00 hours) readings.

Appendix V (p. 182) shows similar charts for 100, 300 and 700 kg/m^2 (20, 60 and 140 lb/ft^2).

Figure 4.6 comprises three charts for equivalent temperature differences for sunlit, water sprayed and shaded *roofs*. In these cases the horizontal abscissae are solar time-scales with the temperature differential curves given for various weights of roof construction.

The following example illustrates the use of Figs. 4.5 and 4.6.

EXAMPLE 4.4

(a) A wall having a density of 500 kg/m^2 and a transmittance coefficient of 0.6 W/m^2/°C (0.1 Btu/hr/ft^2/°F) faces 240° from north).
(b) A roof construction weighing 200 kg/m^2 has a transmittance coefficient of 0.6 W/m^2/°C.

Calculate the rate of heat transmission through each at 16.00 hours.

Fig. 4.5 Equivalent temperature differences for sunlit and shaded walls, N and S latitudes

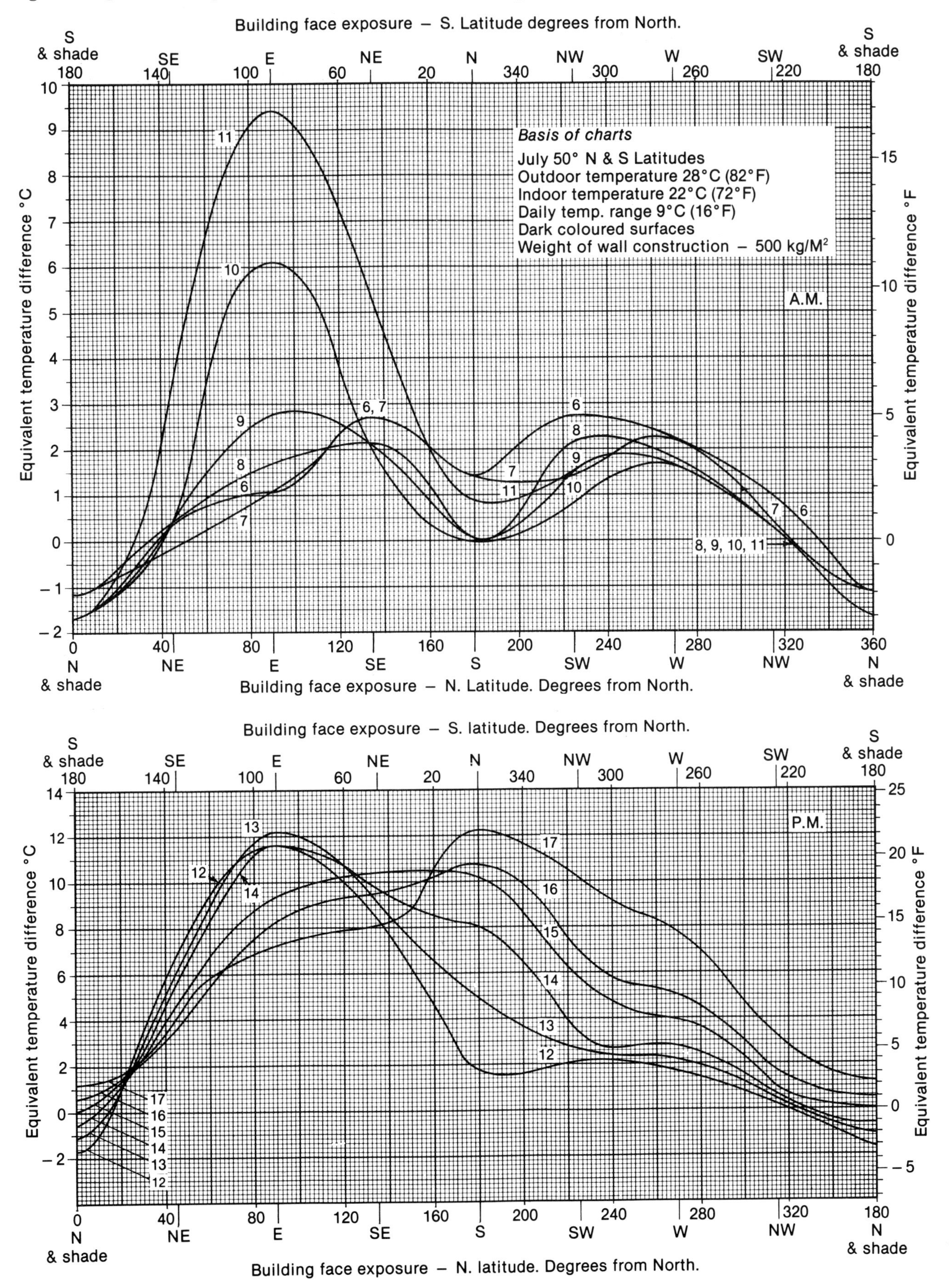

Fig. 4.6 Equivalent temperature differences for sunlit and shaded roofs

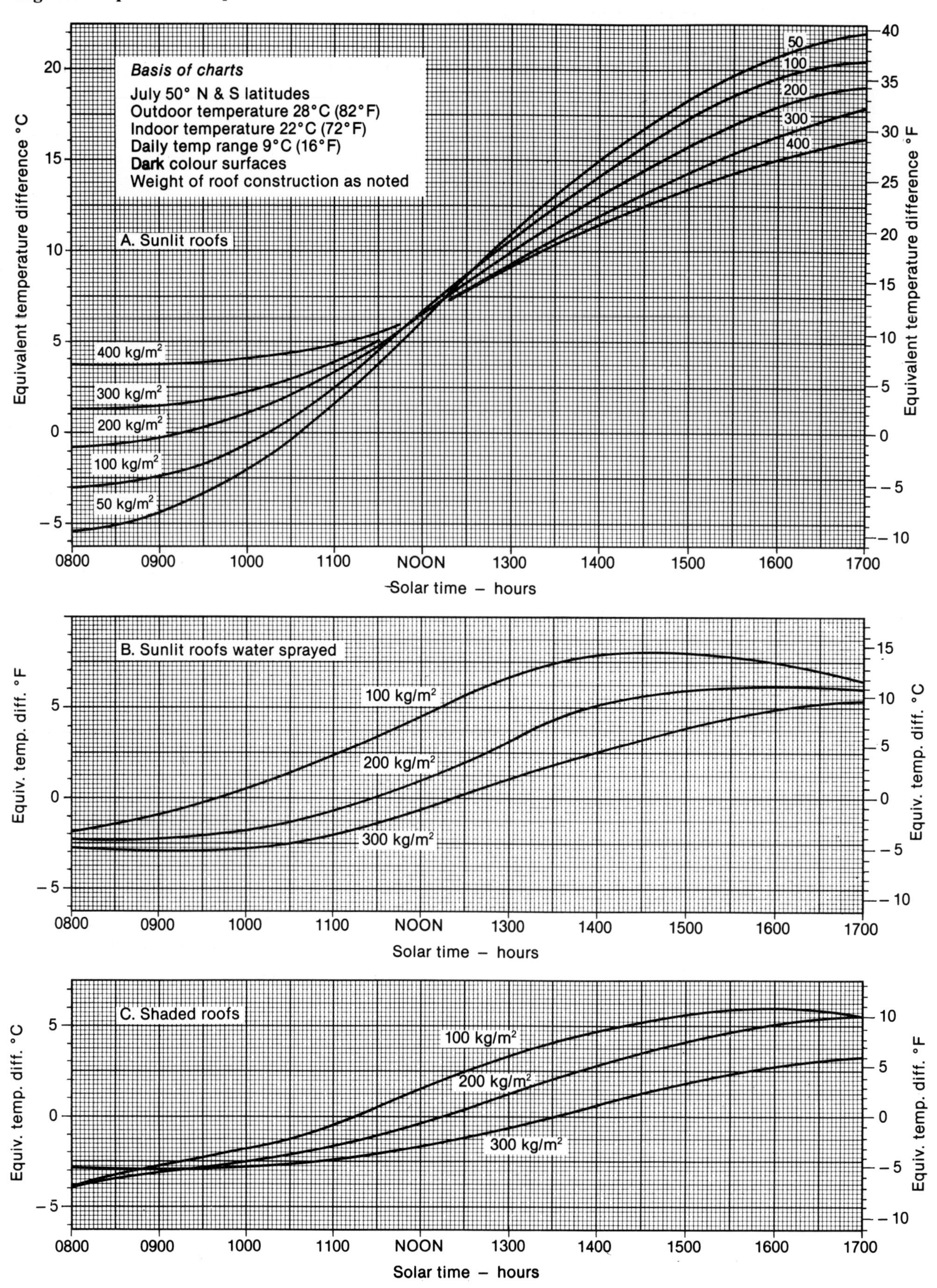

Solution
From equation [4.5]: $Q_c = A_o\, U_o\, \Delta t_e$
From Fig. 4.5: Δt_e wall = 5.8 °C (10.5 °F)
From Fig. 4.6: Δt_e roof = 18.0 °C (32.5 °F)

Hence, for the wall transmission rate:

$$Q_c = 1 \times 0.6 \times 5.8 = 3.48 \text{ W/m}^2$$
$$(1 \times 0.1 \times 10.5) = 1.05 \text{ Btu/hr/ft}^2)$$

and for the roof construction:

$$Q_c = 1 \times 0.6 \times 18 = 10.8 \text{ W/m}^2$$
$$(1 \times 0.1 \times 32.5 = 3.25 \text{ Btu/hr/ft}^2)$$

To apply corrections to Figs. 4.5 and 4.6 (and similar charts in Appendix V, p. 182) the procedures given under headings (a) to (d) below are used.

(a) Correction for alternative outdoor, indoor and daily range temperatures

Procedure

1. From the basic equivalent temperature difference charts for the relevant structural weight (Figs. 4.5, 4.6 or Appendix V) select the Δt_e values for the orientation and time of day required.
2. Find the difference between the new outdoor and indoor design temperatures and the new daily temperature range (= daily maximum temperature minus daily minimum temperature).
3. On Fig. 4.7, enter the new outdoor/indoor temperature difference at scale A. Proceed vertically to the new daily range temperature at scale B. Read the correction to the basic Δt_e at scale C.
4. Add the corrections to the basic values of Δt_e found in (1) above.

EXAMPLE 4.5 In Example 4.4 the equivalent temperature differences for the representative wall and roof were read from Figs. 4.5 and 4.6 as 5.8 °C (10.5 °F) and 18.0 °C (32.5 °F) respectively.

The base temperature differentials of Figs. 4.5 and 4.6, etc. are:
outdoor minus indoor = 6 °C nominal (10 °F)
daily range = 9 °C nominal (16 °F)

If, for another locality the base differentials are 8.3 °C (15 °F) outdoor/indoor and 11.1 °C (20 °F) daily range, find the new equivalent temperature differences that would apply for the wall and roof.

Solution From Fig. 4.7 the correction to the equivalent temperature differences is traced out as being +1.7 °C (+3 °F). This is added to the values found in Example 4.4 to produce the equivalents of the new temperature differentials, thus:

Δt_e wall = 5.8 °C + 1.7 °C = 7.5 °C
(10.5 °F + 3.0 °F = 13.5 °F)
Δt_e roof = 18.0 °C + 1.7 °C = 19.7 °C
(32.5 °F + 3.0 °F = 35.5 °F)

(b) Shaded walls

Procedure

For northern latitudes select the Δt_e values at the north point for a given time of day.

Fig. 4.7 Corrections to equivalent temperature differences

Basis of chart

Outdoor/Indoor temp. difference = + 5.6°C (+ 10°F)
Daily temperature range = 8.9°C (16°F)
Correction from scale C = 0
For other design conditions enter scale A and proceed through scale B to scale C

Example:

Outdoor/Indoor temp. difference = + 8.3°C (+ 15°F)
Daily temperature range = 11.1°C (20°F)
Correction from scale C = 1.7°C (+ 3°F)
To be added to equivalent temperature difference values of Fig. 4.5, etc.

B Daily temperature range (= Daily maximum minus daily minimum)
5°C (9°F)
10°C (18°F)
15°C (27°F)
20°C (36°F)
25°C (45°F)

C Corrections to equivalent temperature differences

A Outdoor design minus indoor design temperature

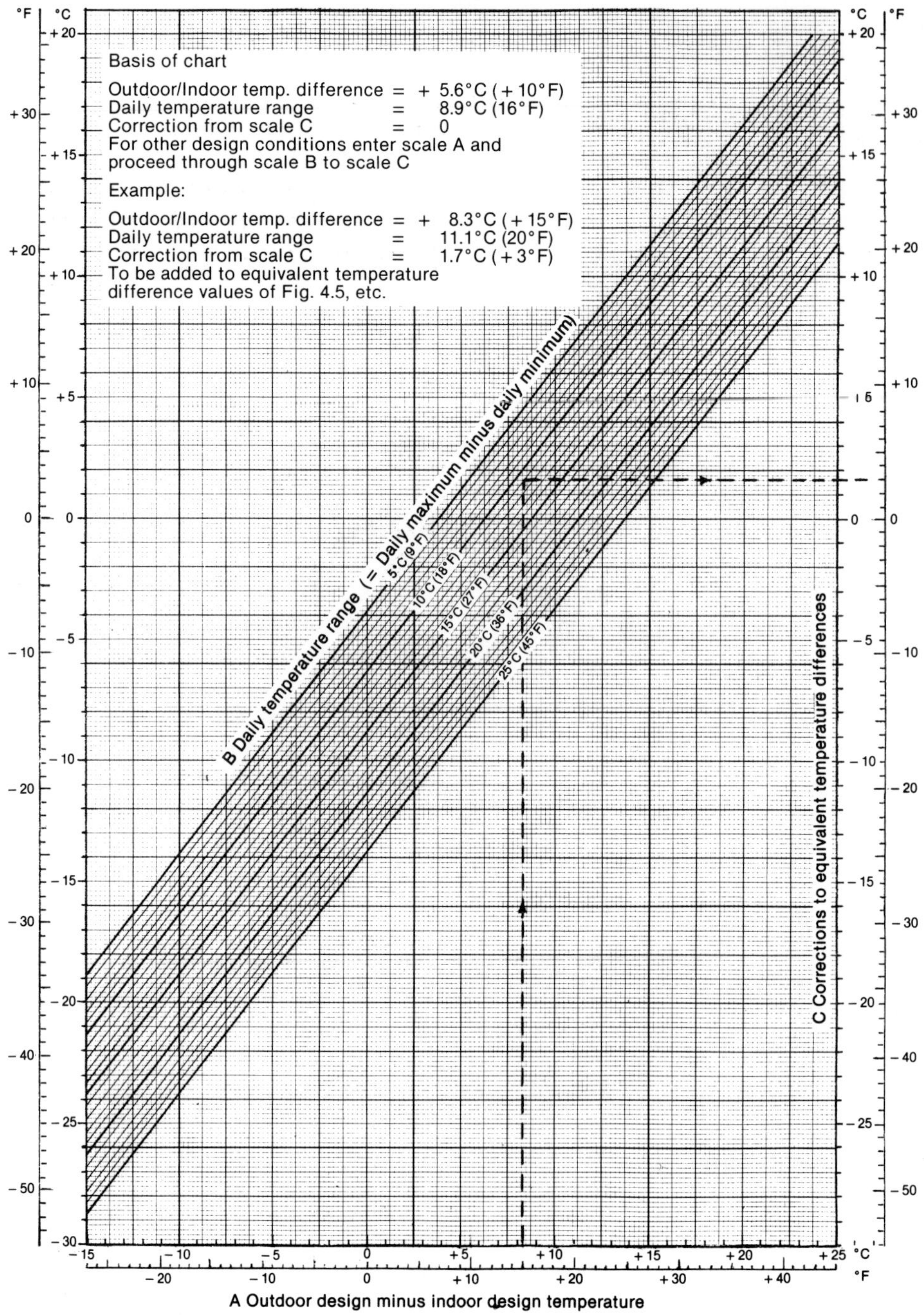

For southern latitudes select the Δt_e values at the south point for a given time of day.

(c) Correction for other months and latitudes

Procedure

From Chapter 5 of the Carrier *Handbook* the following formula is applied:

$$\Delta t_e = \Delta t_{es} + \frac{R_s}{R_m} (\Delta t_{em} - \Delta t_{es}) \quad [4.6]$$

where

Δt_e = equivalent temperature difference for month and time of day required °C

Δt_{es} = equivalent temperature difference for wall or roof in shade at the required time of day corrected, if necessary, for new design conditions °C

Δt_{em} = equivalent temperature difference for wall or roof exposed to the sun for the required time of day corrected, if necessary, for new design conditions °C

R_s = peak solar heat gain through glass for wall aspect (or horizontal value for roofs) for the month and latitude required W/m²

R_m = peak solar heat gain through glass for wall aspect (or horizontal value for roofs) for July at 50°N latitude W/m²

Example 4.6 illustrates the procedure.

EXAMPLE 4.6 One wall of a building in New York faces southeast. The wall is dark coloured and of density 500 kg/m² (100 lb/ft²). Calculate the equivalent temperature difference for the wall at 11.00 hours in August when the indoor temperature is 24 °C (75 °F).

Solution 1. Correction for outdoor/indoor temperature difference and daily temperature range. From the meteorological table for New York (Fig. 3.1, p. 20) the summer outdoor design temperature for August is 34.5 °C (94 °F) and the daily temperature range is 7.8 °C (80 °F − 66 °F = 14 °F).

From Fig. 4.5:
Δt_{es} (in shade at 11.00 hours) = −1.7 °C (−3 °F)
Also from Fig. 4.5:
Δt_{em} (southeast at 11.00 hours) = 5.3 °C (9.5 °F)
The outdoor/indoor temp. difference:
(34.5 °C − 24 °C) = 10.5 °C (18.8 °F)

From Fig. 4.7 the correction to the equivalent temperature differences for outdoor/indoor temperature difference 10.5 °C and daily range 7.8 °C = +5.2 °C(+9.3 °F).

Hence:
Δt_{es} corrected = −1.7 °C + 5.2 °C = 3.5 °C
(−3 °F + 9.3 °F = 6.3 °F)
Δt_{em} corrected = 5.3 °C + 5.2 °C = 10.5 °C
(9.5 °F + 9.3 °F = 18.8 °F)

2. Corrections for temperature differences, month and latitude. From Fig. AIII.7 (p. 152), the peak solar radiation value at southeast in August at latitude 40 °N,
R_s = 460 W/m²
(145 Btu/hr/ft²)

From Fig. 4.1(b) the peak solar radiation value at southeast in July at latitude 50°N,
R_m = 450 W/m²
(143 Btu/hr/ft²)

From equation [4.6]:

$$\Delta t_e = \Delta t_{es} + \frac{R_s}{R_m}(\Delta t_{em} - \Delta t_{es})$$

$$= 3.5 + \frac{460}{450}(10.5 - 3.5) = 10.6\ °C$$

$$\left(6.3 + \frac{460}{450}(18.8 - 6.3) = 19.0\ °F\right)$$

By using the appropriate outdoor/indoor and daily range temperature differences in conjunction with Figs. 4.5, 4.6 and 4.7 (or the alternative charts in Appendix V) the equivalent temperature differences can be found for any world locality.

(d) Correction for surfaces other than dark colour
The charts in Figs. 4.5 and 4.6 (and those in Appendix V (p. 182) for other constructional weights) refer to dark-coloured roof and wall surfaces. In Chapter 5 of their *Handbook of Air-conditioning System Design*, Carrier provide formulae for light- and medium-colour surfaces. The colour definitions are:
Light colour – white, cream, etc.
Medium colour – light green, light blue, grey, etc.
Dark colour – dark blue, dark red, dark brown, etc.

Procedure

1. For light-colour walls and roofs:
   $\Delta t_e = 0.55\ \Delta t_{em} + 0.45\ \Delta t_{es}$ [4.7]

2. For medium-colour walls and roofs:
   $\Delta t_e = 0.78\ \Delta t_{em} + 0.22\ \Delta t_{es}$ [4.8]

EXAMPLE 4.7 Had the wall of Example 4.6 been of light colour what would have been the equivalent temperature difference?

Solution

1. Correction for light colour

The values in Example 4.6 of Δt_{em} and Δt_{es} corrected for outdoor/indoor and daily range temperature differences were 10.5 °C (18.8 °F) and 3.5 °C (6.3 °F) respectively.

For a light-colour wall:
$\Delta t_e = 0.55\ \Delta t_{em} + 0.45\ \Delta t_{es}$
Δt_{em} corrected $= 0.55 \times 10.5 = 5.7$ °C (10.3 °F)
Δt_{es} corrected $= 0.45 \times 3.5 = 1.6$ °C (2.8 °F)
$\Delta t_e = 5.7 + 1.6 = 7.3$ °C (13.1 °F)

2. Correction for months and latitude

$$\Delta t_e = \Delta t_{es} + \frac{R_s}{R_m}(\Delta t_{em} - \Delta t_{es})$$

From Example 4.6 $R_s = 460\ W/m^2$ and $R_m = 450\ W/m^2$. Therefore, corrected for temperature differentials, colour and month and latitude,

$$\Delta t_e = 1.6 + \frac{460}{450}(5.7 - 1.6) = 5.8\ °C$$

$$\left(2.8 + \frac{460}{450}(10.3 - 2.8) = 10.4\ °F\right)$$

4.3 POPULATION LOADS

For healthy existence the human body has involuntary regulatory systems to maintain a deep-tissue temperature within critical limits of 37 °C (99 °F). The regulatory systems operate at the body surfaces by blood circulation through the skin capillaries, by muscular relaxation and tension, in the case of overheating, and by muscular tension and shivering when over-cooling occurs.

By these processes, and through body wastes, heat that is generated internally due to the oxidation of food intake, and imposed or removed externally by the environment, is dissipated at the body surfaces and, thereby, in healthy individuals, preserves the skin temperature within measurable limits of 36 °C (96 °F).

The extent of the heat generation and its subsequent dissipation is known as the *metabolic rate*. It is dissipated from the body in sensible and latent heat forms: (a) by radiation to surrounding surfaces; (b) by convection to the surrounding air; (c) by moisture evaporation from the skin and respiration to the surrounding air.

The metabolic rate is a function of age, sex, activity and the temperature difference between the body surfaces and its surroundings. In relation to these variables metabolic rates have been established and are published by many authorities but, as is indicated in Table 1.3 (p. 10), with divergent views of their resulting levels.

The comparisons made in Table 1.3 are between the CIBS, ASHRAE and Carrier each of which differs considerably from the others. Therefore, the values of these authorities have been averaged and, in Fig. 4.8, plotted as constant lines of sensible and latent heat emission in Watts and Btu/hr against scales of room air dry-bulb temperature in °C and °F.

Notes are appended to Fig. 4.8 to which the following comments apply:

(a) *Total heat emissions*. The emission items 1 to 8 refer to the numbered lines of sensible and latent heat in the chart. The sum of these at a given room temperature will be equal to the total heat emission values listed. For example at 22 °C room air temperature the sensible and latent heat emissions for condition 3 are, respectively, 79.5 W (271 Btu/hr) and 52.5 W (179 Btu/hr). The sum of these is 132 W (450 Btu/hr) as listed.

(b) *Activity*. The activities listed relate to the rates of total heat emission and to the working conditions most likely to be encountered in air-conditioning practice.

(c) *Typical applications*. These are offered as likely equivalents of the total heat emissions and activities.

For the emissions in restaurants the total emission rate includes 17.5 W (60 Btu/hr) for the food being consumed. This consists of equal rates for sensible and latent heat (8.75 W or 30 Btu/hr each).

(d) *Adjustments*. The plotted values are for equally mixed communities of adult males and females. For other conditions adjust as follows:
all male – increase values by 7½%;
all female – decrease values by 7½%;
all children – decrease values by 20%.

(e) *Storage load factors*. The sensible heat emissions from people are mainly radiant. Therefore, in computing the resultant heat gains to an occupied space, storage load factors are applicable. For this purpose the charts in Figs 4.9(a), 4.9(b) and 4.9(c) are used.

Fig. 4.8 Sensible and latent heat emissions from humans

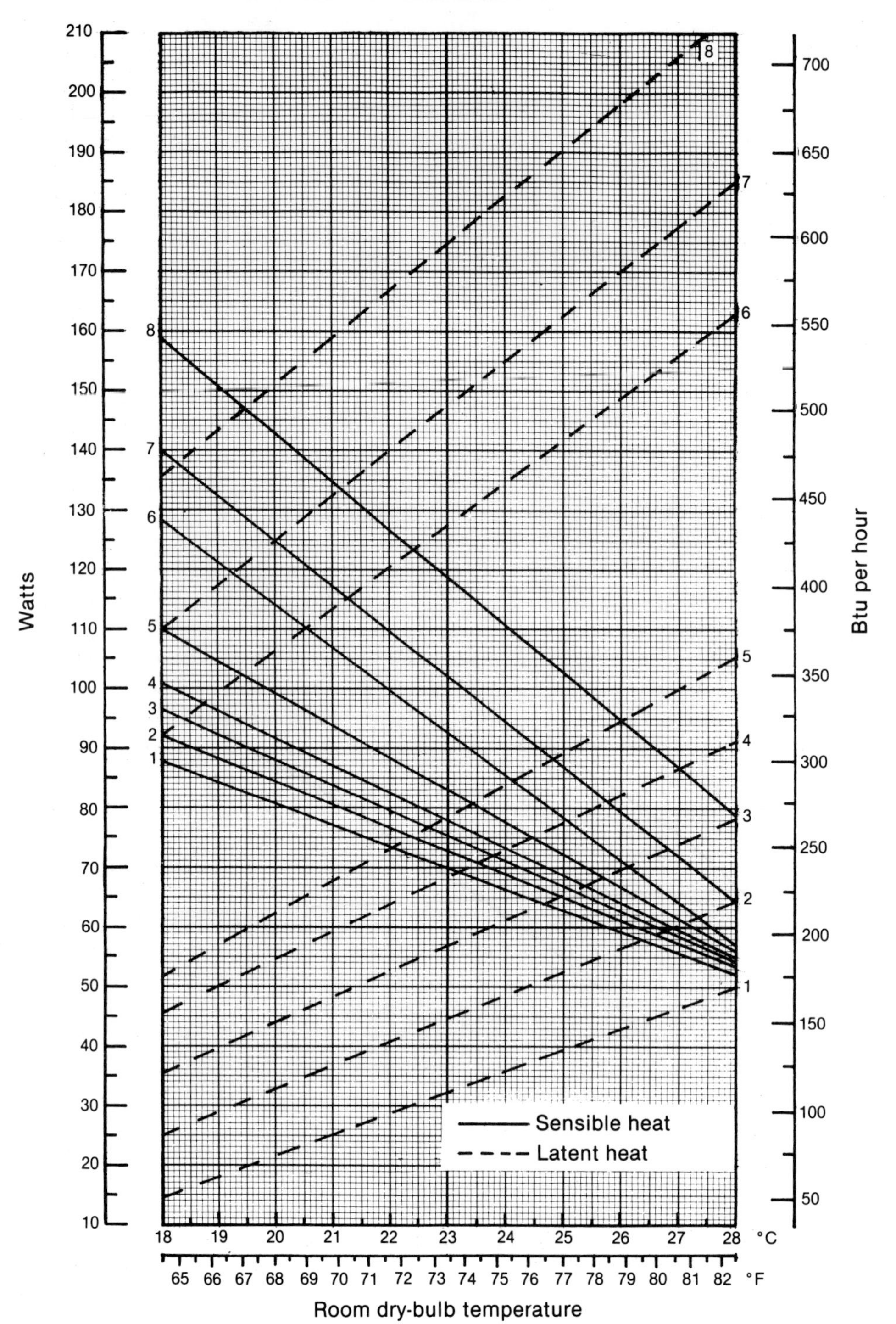

Total heat emission Watts	Btu/hr.	Activity			Typical application	Adjustments
1 – 102	350	Seated,	at rest.	—	Cinemas.	All values are for mixed
2 – 117	400	Seated,	light work.	—	School.	male & female assemblies.
3 – 132	450	Seated,	light work.	—	Offices.	For all male assemblies
4 – 146	500	Walking,	seated.	—	Shops.	increase values by 7½%.
5 – 161	550	Seated,	eating.	—	Restaurants*	For all female assemblies
6 – 220	750	Standing,	light work.	—	Factories.	decrease values by 7½%.
7 – 249	850	Standing,	moderate work.	—	Dancing.	For all children assemblies
8 – 293	1000	Standing,	heavy work.	—	Factories.	decrease by 20%.

*Includes sensible and latent heat of food consumed.

4.4 ILLUMINATION AND EQUIPMENT LOADS

4.4.1 Electrical loads

These loads consist of heat gains from the installed illumination and equipment in use, the latter comprising typewriters and computers; food and drink preparation and dispensers; refrigerators, drinking-water coolers, etc. The heat gains resulting from these sources will represent some 20 to 25% of the overall sensible heat gains in a typical office building and, in a main-frame computer room the proportion can be as high as 80%. Therefore, as much accuracy as possible should be exercised in calculating these gains.

Generally, the process equipment, dispensers, etc. will be fully contained within the conditioned areas so that the whole of the input energy will become a component of the direct gains to the space.

In the case of the illumination, however, it is customary in modern office buildings for fluorescent lighting fittings to be recessed into suspended ceilings and, with good practice, for these to be ventilated into the air-conditioning extract or supply air systems, or both. This gives combined benefits in reducing the space direct heat gain and in prolonging the life of the fluorescent tubes.

In view of the relatively high heat gains resulting from equipment and illumination, it is advisable for data to be obtained from manufacturers, nameplates, etc., giving precise details of the electrical inputs and, in the case of the luminaire configurations, the proportions of the energy equivalents which will be radiated upwards and downwards.

If such information is not readily available, representative details of equipment ratings can be selected from the CIBS *Guide*, Section A7, *ASHRAE Fundamentals Handbook,* Chapter 26 and from Chapter 7 of the Carrier *Handbook.*

For illumination, Fig. 3.4 (p. 27) shows the approximate heat equivalents of typical lighting fittings related to lighting intensities in lux (lumens per square metre). These are guidance figures, usable for estimating purposes, since the actual heat equivalent to lux relationship will depend upon the type of fitting used, mounting height, surface characteristics, etc.

The wattage figures from Fig. 3.4 are for tungsten (filament) and fluorescent (gas-discharge) fittings. In the case of the tungsten fittings the values selected from the chart give the actual heat equivalents in watts per square metre to be used in the cooling-load calculations. These are applied as a direct component of the heat gains unless they are recessed (as downlighters, for example) into suspended ceilings. With this arrangement the proportion factors in Table 4.2 will apply.

Fluorescent fittings are operated with a choke, or starter, which limits the voltage rise and serves to ignite the lamp. For this purpose a small auxiliary glow-lamp with thermal contact is connected in parallel with the main lamp and this results in an increase in the input watts for a given output rating. This loss appears in the starting gear directly as heat, resulting in an increase in the input wattage to the fitting, an increase which will depend upon the type of starter that is used. However, it is customary to use an average factor of 1.25 for this effect; the energy equivalent of an 80 W fluorescent tube then becoming 100 W.

For the percentage of the heat equivalents from illumination that will become a direct gain to the space, or will be returned to the central plant, Table 4.2 can be used.

In addition to the reduction factors that result from the configuration of the lighting fittings, a diversity factor may be applied to the illumination and equipment gains as is illustrated by typical examples (a) and (b) on page 72.

(a) To the illumination where the lights are separately switched:

Accommodation	Diversity factor
Offices, separate rooms	0.85
Offices, open plan	0.75
Hotel rooms and apartments	0.50

(b) To equipment that is separately operated:

Accommodation	Diversity factor
Typing pools using electric typewriters and business machines	0.25
Visual display instruction rooms	0.80
Computer rooms	0.90

Table 4.2 Proportions of direct and indirect heat gains from lighting fittings

Luminaire arrangement	Heat to space (%)	Heat to plant (%)
Fully exposed	100	Nil
Recessed in unventilated ceiling void	100	Nil
Recessed in ceiling, unventilated fittings, extract from ceiling void	70	30
Recessed in ceiling, ventilated fittings, extract from ceiling void	60	40
Recessed in ceiling, ventilated fittings with connected extract	45	55
Recessed in ceiling, ventilated fittings with connected extract and supply	35	65

The heat emission from electrical equipment and lighting fittings is mainly radiant which must be absorbed by the structure and surroundings, and be re-emitted as convected heat, before becoming a component of the space heat gains. Therefore, storage load factors are applicable.

The storage load factors relating to equipment and illumination will depend upon the specific weight of the structure, the overall period for which the equipment or lighting is in use, the period of operation of the associated cooling plant and the configuration of the lighting fittings.

Figures 4.9(a), 4.9(b) and 4.9(c) show plots of storage load factors, respectively for 12-, 16- and 24-hour periods of cooling-plant operation. They also relate to exposed fluorescent lights, specific weights of 150, 500 and 750 kg/m^2 (30, 100 and 150 lb/ft^2) and overall periods of usage of equipment or lighting of 5, 10 and 15 hours.

Referring to Fig. 4.9(a) it will be seen that, exposed fluorescent lights on for a total of 10 hours with a specific weight of 500 kg/m^2 and cooling plant operating for 12 hours, will have a storage load factor of 0.95 seven hours after the lights were switched on.

Notes concerning the charts

(a) Figures 4.9(a), 4.9(b) and 4.9(c) are also used for storage load factors relating to building occupants, as referred to in Section 4.3.

Figure 4.9(a) Storage load factors for lighting, equipment & occupants

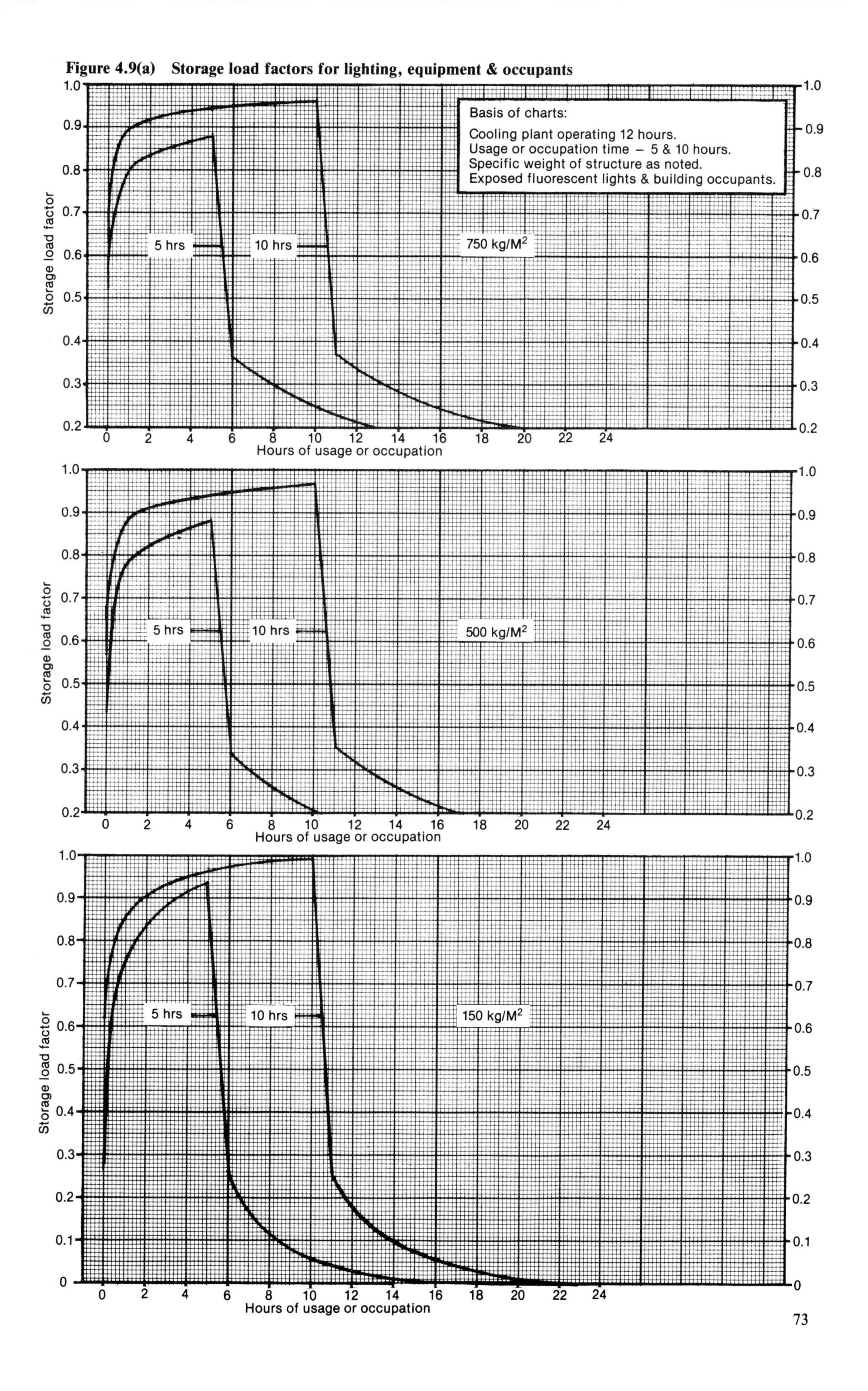

Figure 4.9(b) Storage load factors for lighting, equipment & occupants

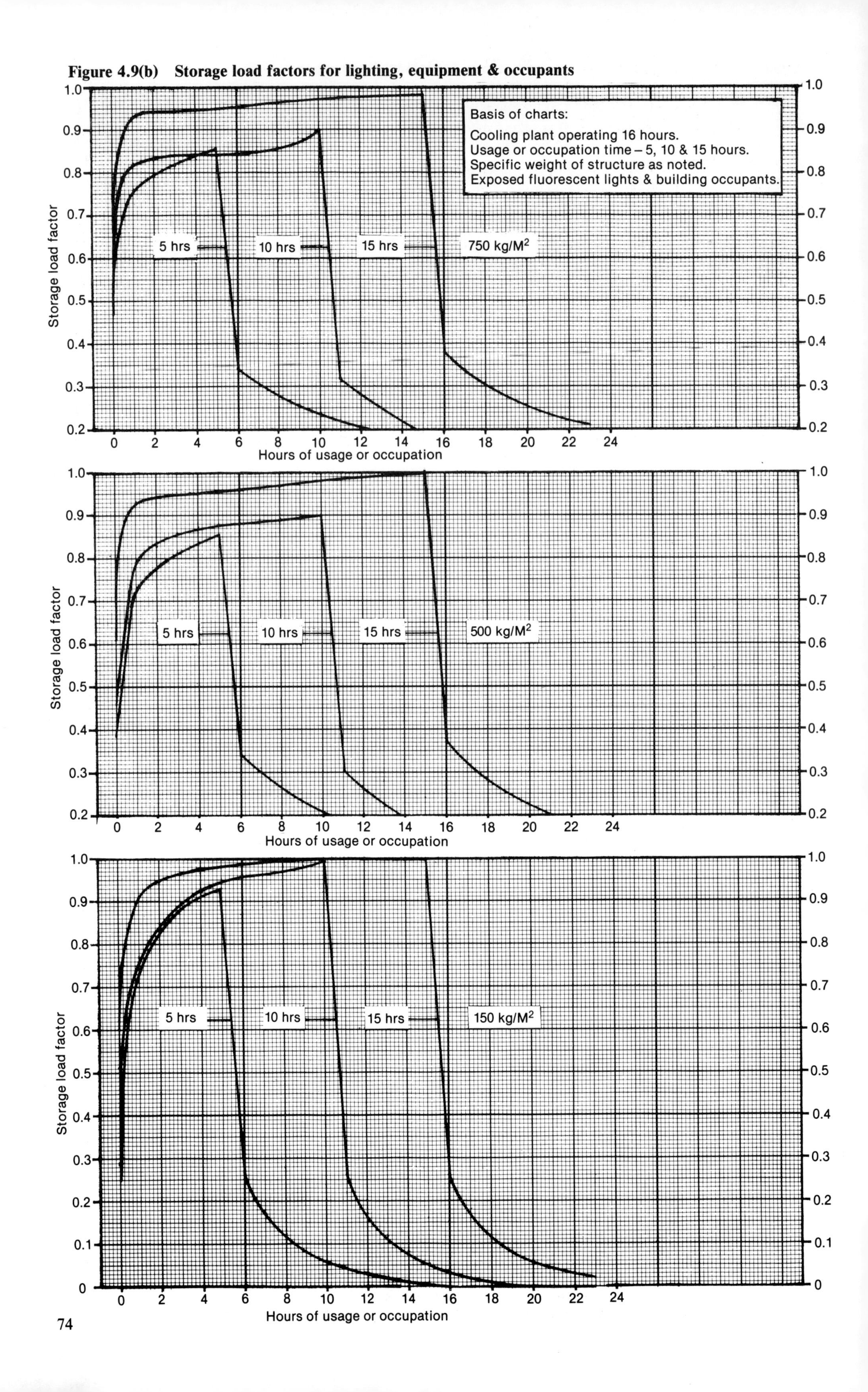

Figure 4.9(c) Storage load factors for lighting, equipment & occupants

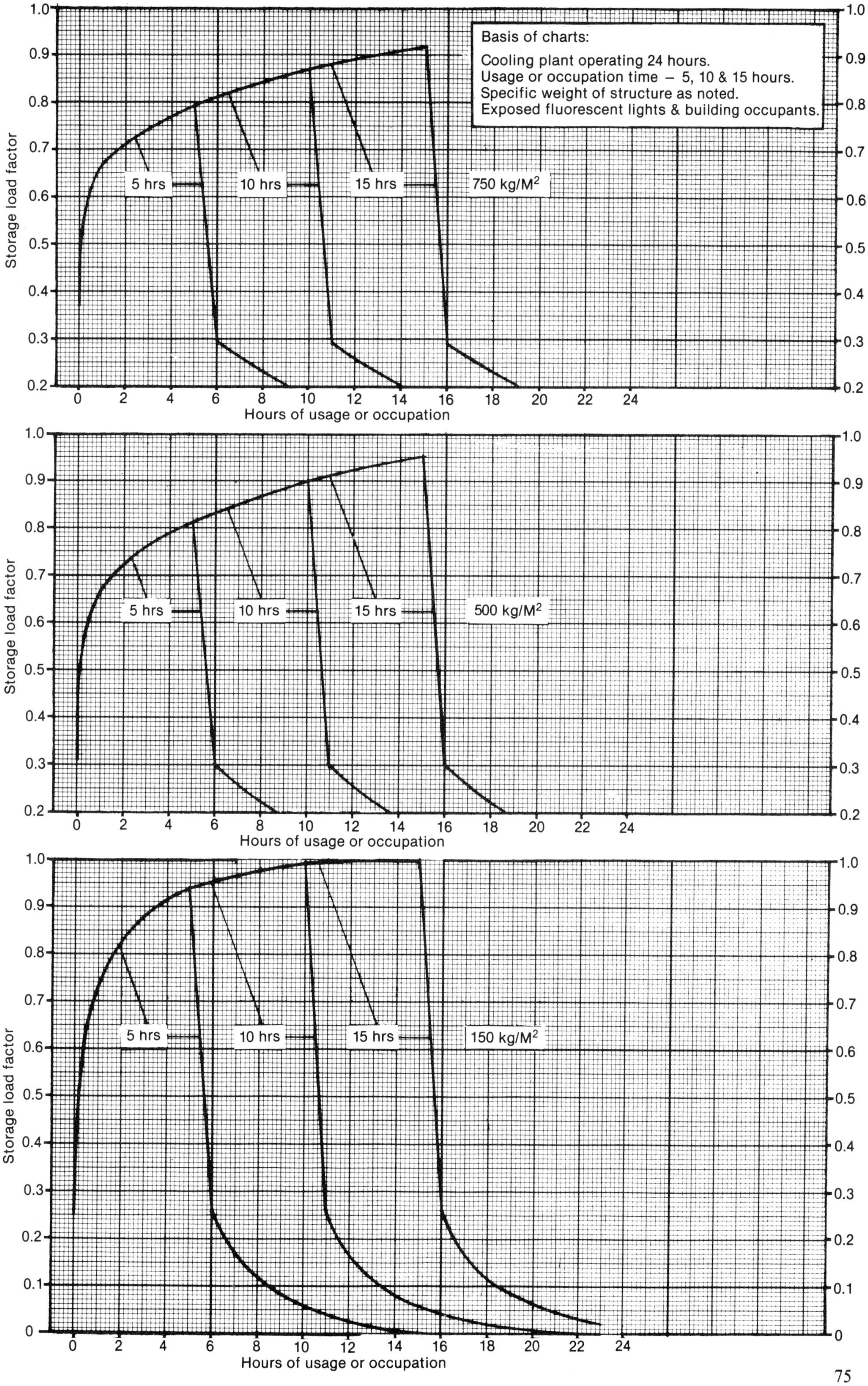

Basis of charts:

Cooling plant operating 24 hours.
Usage or occupation time – 5, 10 & 15 hours.
Specific weight of structure as noted.
Exposed fluorescent lights & building occupants.

Storage load factor
1.0 0.9 0.8 0.7 0.6 0.5 0.4 0.3 0.2
5 hrs
10 hrs
15 hrs
750 kg/M²
0 2 4 6 8 10 12 14 16 18 20 22 24
Hours of usage or occupation

Storage load factor
1.0 0.9 0.8 0.7 0.6 0.5 0.4 0.3 0.2
5 hrs
10 hrs
15 hrs
500 kg/M²
0 2 4 6 8 10 12 14 16 18 20 22 24
Hours of usage or occupation

Storage load factor
1.0 0.9 0.8 0.7 0.6 0.5 0.4 0.3 0.2 0.1 0
5 hrs
10 hrs
15 hrs
150 kg/M²
0 2 4 6 8 10 12 14 16 18 20 22 24
Hours of usage or occupation

(b) Appendix VI (p. 187) consists of a series of similar charts for lighting and equipment only with alternative arrangements of lighting fittings, thus:

Figures AVI.4, AVI.5 and AVI.6 (12-, 16- and 24-hour cooling)	Fluorescent lights recessed into unventilated ceiling voids, or exposed tungsten lights.
Figures AVI.7, AVI.8 and AVI.9 (12-, 16- and 24-hour cooling)	Fluorescent and tungsten lights recessed into ventilated ceiling voids.

EXAMPLE 4.8 An open-plan office is fitted with fluorescent open diffusing lighting fittings recessed into the suspended ceilings with unventilated voids above. The illumination level is 500 lux; the specific weight of structure is 500 kg/m^2; the lights are on from 08.00 hrs to 18.00 hrs; and the cooling plant operates for 12 hours per day.

Calculate the heat gains from the illumination in each 20 m^2 module at 15.00 hours.

Solution From Fig. 3.4 (p. 27), the heat equivalent of 500 lux with open-type fluorescent fittings is 27.5 W/m^2. The starting-gear factor is 1.25 and, from Table 4.2, the proportion of the heat gain to the module will be 70%; also being open-plan, a diversity factor of 0.75 will apply. From Fig. AVI.4 the storage load factor after the lights have been on for 7 hours (08.00 to 15.00) is 0.94.

Therefore, the heat gain is:
$20\ \text{m}^2 \times 27.5\ \text{W/m}^2 \times 1.25 \times 0.70 \times 0.75 \times 0.94 = 339\ \text{W}$

4.4.2 Other equipment loads

Some equipment that may be used in buildings to be air conditioned such as hospitals, laboratories, shops, etc. will emit latent heat as well as sensible heat: gas burners, sterilisers, hairdryers, cookers, coffee-urns and so on. The sensible heat will be largely radiant and, therefore, subject to the design procedure discussed above. The latent heat will constitute a moisture gain to the space which must be accounted for by the method to be described later.

For details of these emissions the suppliers should be consulted or data used as presented in the handbooks of the CIBS, ASHRAE and Carrier.

4.5 VENTILATION AND INFILTRATION LOADS

The methods for computing fresh-air ventilation rates are explained in Section 3.5 (p. 28), and infiltration rates in Section 3.7 (p. 32). To assess the resulting sensible, latent and total heat gains (or losses) the following expressions are used.

Sensible heat:

Watts: $Q_s = 1.23\, V \Delta t$ [4.9]
(Btu/hr: $Q_s = 1.08\, V \Delta t$)

Latent heat:

Watts: $Q_l = 3012\, V \Delta g$ [4.10]
(Btu/hr: $Q_l = 4830\, V \Delta g$)

Total heat (enthalpy):

Watts: $Q_t = 1.21\, V \Delta h$ [4.11]
(Btu/hr: $Q_t = 4.5\, V \Delta h$)

where

Q_s	= sensible heat exchange	W(Btu/hr)
Q_l	= latent heat exchange	W(Btu/hr)
Q_t	= total heat exchange	W(Btu/hr)
V	= relevant air volume	litres/sec(cfm)
Δt	= temperature difference	°C (°F)
Δg	= moisture content difference	kg/kg(lb/lb)
Δh	= enthalpy difference	kJ/kg(Btu/lb)

For calculations involving ventilation and infiltration loads, Δt, Δg and Δh, refer to the differences in the respective values between the outdoor and indoor air, i.e. $\Delta t = t_o - t_i$, $\Delta g = g_o - g_i$ and $\Delta h = h_o - h_i$

t_o	= outdoor air temperature	°C(°F)
t_i	= indoor air temperature	°C(°F)
g_o	= outdoor air moisture content	kg/kg(lb/lb)
g_i	= indoor air moisture content	kg/kg(lb/lb)
h_o	= outdoor air enthalpy	kJ/kg(Btu/lb)
h_i	= indoor air enthalpy	kJ/kg(Btu/lb)

EXAMPLE 4.9 In an office building where some smoking is anticipated, calculate the heat gains per module resulting from the fresh-air ventilation when the following design conditions apply:

Module floor area, 18.6 m^2 (200 ft^2)
Floor area per person, 9.3 m^2 (100 ft^2)
Outdoor air at 25 °C/60% RH (77 °F/60% RH)
Indoor air at 20 °C/50% RH (68 °F/50% RH)

Solution From Fig. 3.5(b) (p. 29), the fresh-air rate is 1.3 litres/sec/m^2 (0.25 cfm/ft^2). Hence:

V = 18.6 × 1.3 = 24.18 litres/sec
(51.2 cfm)
t_o = 25 °C (77 °F)
t_i = 20 °C (68 °F)

From CIBS psychrometric tables:

g_o at 25 °C/60% RH = 0.011 94 kg/kg
(77 °F(60% RH = 0.011 94 lb/lb)
g_i at 20 °C/50% RH = 0.007 28 kg/kg
(68 °F/50% RH = 0.007 28 lb/lb)
h_o = 55.56 kJ/kg
(24.10 Btu/lb)
h_i = 38.62 kJ/kg
(16.70 Btu/lb)

Using equations [4.9], [4.10] and [4.11]:

Q_s	= 1.23 × 24.18 (25 − 20)	= 149 W
	((1.08 × 51.2 (77 − 68)	= 498 Btu/hr))
Q_l	= 3012 × 24.18 (0.011 94 − 0.007 28)	= 339 W
	((4830 × 51.2 (0.011 94 − 0.007 28)	= 1152 Btu/hr))
Q_t	= 1.21 × 24.18 (55.56 − 38.62)	= 496 W
	((4.5 × 51.2 (24.1 − 16.7)	= 1705 Btu/hr))

If the results are transposed it will be found that small discrepancies exist, e.g. 149 W × 3.415 = 508 Btu/hr. Also, $Q_t = Q_s + Q_l$. Here 149 + 339 = 488 W compared with the result from equation [4.11] of 496 W. These errors are due to differences in conversions and in tabulated values, but they are sufficiently small to be neglected.

When the air volume rates of infiltration are established the above procedures are applicable in similar manner.

The equations can also be transposed to find other required values for example:

$$\Delta t = \frac{Q_s}{1.23V} \quad \text{or} \quad t_o = t_i + \frac{Q_s}{1.23V}, \text{ etc.}$$

4.6 FAN AND PUMP HEAT GAINS

4.6.1 Fan gains and temperature rise

(a) For a fan with the driving motor and drive outside the airstream the heat gain expression is:

$$Q_s = \frac{VP}{\eta}$$

where

Q_s = sensible heat gain W(Btu/hr)
V = fan air volume litres/sec (cfm)
P = fan static pressure kPa (in. w.g)
η = fan static efficiency %

If an average efficiency of 70% is used then:

$$Q_s = \frac{VP}{0.7} = 1.43\,VP \qquad [4.12]$$

$$\left(\frac{VP \times 2540}{6256 \times 0.7} = 0.57\,VP\right)$$

By transposition of equation [4.9]:

$$\Delta t = \frac{Q_s}{1.23\,V}$$

$$\left(\frac{Q_s}{1.08\,V}\right)$$

Therefore:

$$\Delta t = \frac{1.43\,VP}{1.23\,V} = 1.16P \qquad [4.13]$$

$$\left(\frac{0.57\,VP}{1.08\,V} = 0.53P\right)$$

(b) For a fan with a driving motor and drive within the airstream the overall efficiency will be in the order of 60%. Therefore the equivalent expressions become:

$$Q_s = 1.67\,VP \qquad [4.14]$$
$$(0.66\,VP)$$
$$\Delta t = 1.35P \qquad [4.15]$$
$$(0.61P)$$

EXAMPLE 4.10 Calculate the temperature rise through a centrifugal fan with external motor and drive, and an axial-flow fan with internal motor and drive when each operates at a static pressure of 0.75 kPa (3 ins w.g)

Solution Centrifugal fan:

Δt = 1.16 × 0.75 = 0.87 °C
(0.53 × 3.0 = 1.59 °F)

Axial-flow fan:

Δt = 1.35 × 0.75 = 1.01 °C
(0.61 × 3.0 = 1.83 °F)

4.6.2 Pump gains and temperature rise

The driving motor and drive of a pump are almost always external to the water circuit. An average efficiency of the type of water circulating pump used in air-conditioning practice is 65%. Therefore, the heat gain

$$Q_s = \frac{VP}{\eta} = \frac{VP}{0.65} \qquad = 1.54\,VP \qquad [4.16]$$

$$\left(\frac{VP \times 10 \times 2540}{33\,000 \times 0.65} = 1.18\,VP\right)$$

and the temperature rise

$$\Delta t = \frac{1.54\,VP}{3600\,V} = 0.0004P \qquad [4.17]$$

$$\left(\frac{1.18\,VP}{600\,V} = 0.002P\right)$$

where

Q_s	= sensible heat gain	W(Btu/hr)
V	= water flow rate	litres/sec (gpm)
P	= pump pressure head	kPa (ft)
η	= pump efficiency	%

EXAMPLE 4.11 Calculate the temperature rise in the water circulated by a pump working against a pressure head of 120 kPa (40 ft).

Solution Applying equation [4.17]:

$$\Delta t = 0.0004 \times 120 = 0.05\ °C$$
$$(0.002 \times 40 = 0.08\ °F)$$

The slight differences in the °C/°F equivalents of the solutions to Examples 4.10 and 4.11 are due to the rounding off of the various derived factors.

4.7 DUCT AND PIPE HEAT TRANSFER

Data for heat transfer (heat gains and losses) from air ducts and water pipes are not well documented and the associated calculations are tedious, requiring systems to be sized and laid out for their application.

Therefore, at the design stage during the calculation of the overall heat gains and losses, it is sufficient for these loads to be expressed as percentages of the aggregates of the other load components. The percentages used should be as accurate as possible, and for this purpose the methods given in Sections 4.7.1 and 4.7.2 are usable.

4.7.1 Duct heat transfer

It is customary for duct insulation thicknesses of 25, 38 and 50 mm (1, 1½ and 2 in) to be used for ducts carrying heated or cooled air. For the latter the insulation should include an outer wrapped vapour barrier of aluminium foil or neoprene.

With these thicknesses the percentages of the aggregate loads to be added are:

25 mm 1% for each 2.8 °C (5 °F) difference between the ducted air and the surrounding air temperatures.
38 mm 1% for each 4.2 °C (7.5 °F) of similar temperature difference.
50 mm 1% for each 5.6 °C (10 °F) of similar temperature difference.

4.7.2 Pipe heat transfer

In this case the insulation thickness is related to the nominal pipe size and again, for cold-water pipes, an external vapour barrier should be used.

The following is a schedule of insulation thickness according to pipe diameter, each given in millimetres:

Pipe size	15–20	25–100	125	150 and above
Insulation thickness	25	32	38	50

The addition in each case is 2.5% for each 5.6 °C (10 °F) difference between the piped water and the surrounding air temperatures.

From this it will be seen that, with a surrounding air temperature of 21 °C (70 °F) and water temperatures of 15.6 °C (60 °F) and 71 °C (160 °F), the percentage heat transfers, respectively, would be:

$$21 - 15.6 = 5.4\ °C \quad - \quad 2.5\%\ \text{heat gain}$$

$$71 - 21 = 50\ °C \quad - \quad 2.5 \times \frac{50}{5.6} = 22.3\%\ \text{heat loss}$$

4.8 SHADING EFFECTS OF WINDOW RECESSES AND ADJACENT BUILDINGS

The extent of shading areas due to vertical and horizontal projections is dependent upon the compound angles of the sun's rays on the face of a building that result from the solar altitude, α and the wall solar azimuth γ. The wall solar azimuth is the angle subtended by the solar azimuth and a horizontal line perpendicular to any particular wall. Figure 4.10 depicts these relationships and, in Appendix VII (p. 197), tables of altitudes and azimuths for north and south latitudes 0 to 55° are reproduced from the CIBS *Guide* Section A6.

Fig. 4.10 Illustration of solar angles

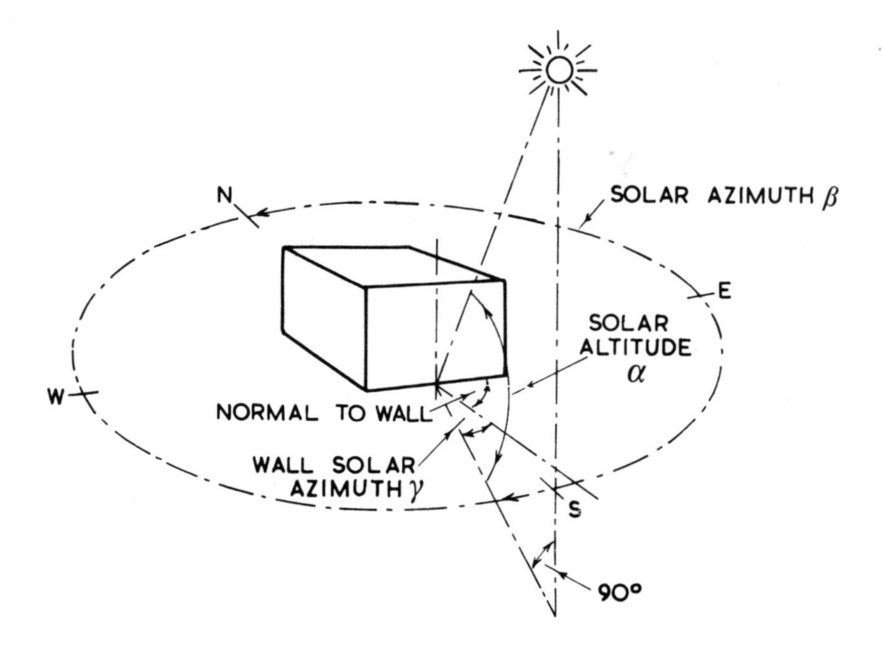

4.8.1 Window shading

Figure 4.11 shows the solar angles of altitude and wall azimuth related to a recessed window and the resulting shading effects.

The width, X, of the vertical component of the shadow, is calculated from the expression:

$$X = L \tan \gamma \qquad [4.18]$$

and the height, Y, of the horizontal component, from

$$Y = \frac{L \tan \alpha}{\cos \gamma} \qquad [4.19]$$

where

L = depth of recess

The expression for the sunlit area, A_s, is:

$$A_s = (W - X)(H - Y) \qquad [4.20]$$

where

W = width of window opening
H = height of window opening

Figure 4.12 permits the values of X and Y to be obtained directly, on a straight-line basis.

Fig. 4.11 Window shade patterns produced by solar altitude and wall solar azimuth

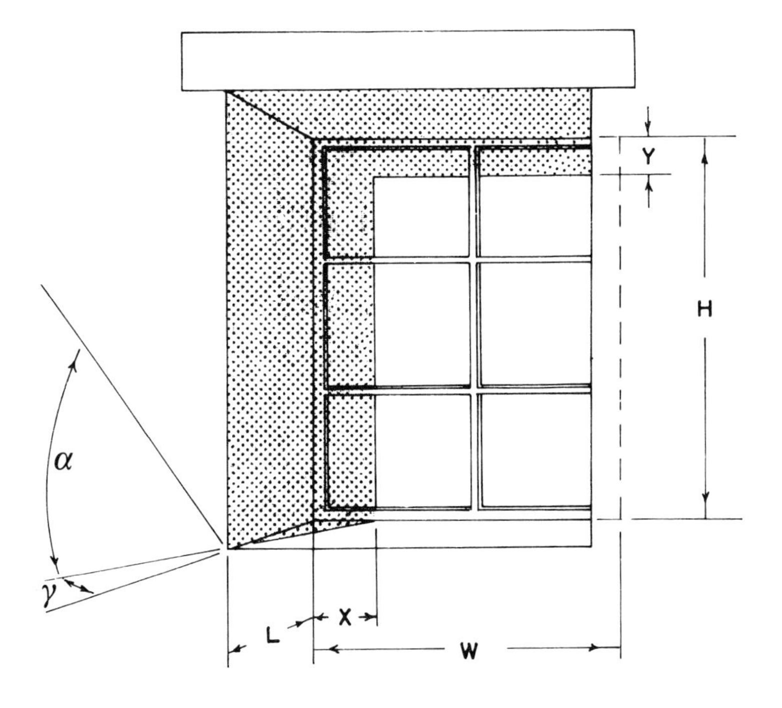

Fig. 4.12 Nomogram for determining vertical and horizontal shade components

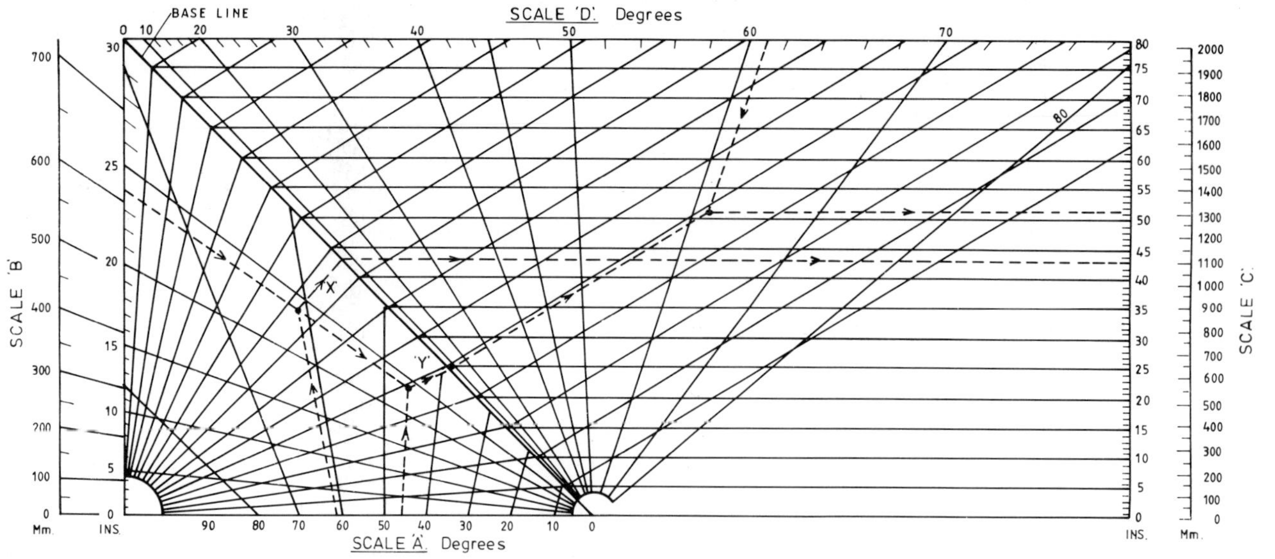

EXAMPLE 4.12 Determine the vertical and horizontal shading components of the window shown in Fig. 4.11 when the depth of recess is 610 mm (24 in), the solar altitude angle is 46° and the wall solar azimuth angle is 61°.

If the width of the window is 1219 mm (48 in) and the height is 1829 mm (72 in), find the sunlit area.

Solution To find *X*: On Fig. 4.12 enter 61° on scale A and 610 mm on scale B. Extend a line from each to intersect. From the intersection produce a line radially to the base line and thence horizontally to scale C. Read the value of *X* as 1092 mm (43 in).

To find *Y*: Select 46° on scale A and 610 mm on scale B. Extend a line from each to intersect. From the intersection extend a line radially to the base line.

From the base line proceed diagonally to intersect with a line drawn from 61° on scale D and thence horizontally to scale C. Read the value of *Y* as 1308 mm (51.5 in).

Sunlit area:

$$\begin{aligned} A &= (W-X)(H-Y) \\ &= (1219-1092)(1829-1308) \\ &= 0.066 \text{ m}^2 \ (0.71 \text{ ft}^2) \end{aligned}$$

4.8.2 Building shading

Equations [4.18] and [4.19] are also used to establish the shadow pattern projected on to one building by another. To illustrate the procedure Fig. 4.13 is referred to wherein the shadow of building A appears on building B as a result of a wall solar azimuth, γ, of 30° and a solar altitude angle, α, of 40°. Using the relevant building layout dimensions shown in the figure, the calculations are made thus:

$$\begin{aligned} X &= L \tan \gamma &&= 12 \text{ m} \tan 30° &&= 6.93 \text{ m} \\ X' &= L' \tan \gamma &&= 24 \text{ m} \tan 30° &&= 13.86 \text{ m} \end{aligned}$$

$$Y = \frac{L \tan \alpha}{\cos \gamma} = \frac{12 \text{ m} \tan 40°}{\cos 30°} = 11.63 \text{ m}$$

$$Y' = \frac{L' \tan \alpha}{\cos \gamma} = \frac{24 \text{ m} \tan 40°}{\cos 30°} = 23.25 \text{ m}$$

The outline dimensions of the shadow pattern are then computed by association of the derived values of X, X', Y and Y' with the building layout dimensions, as shown in Fig. 4.13.

Fig. 4.13 Illustration of building shadow patterns

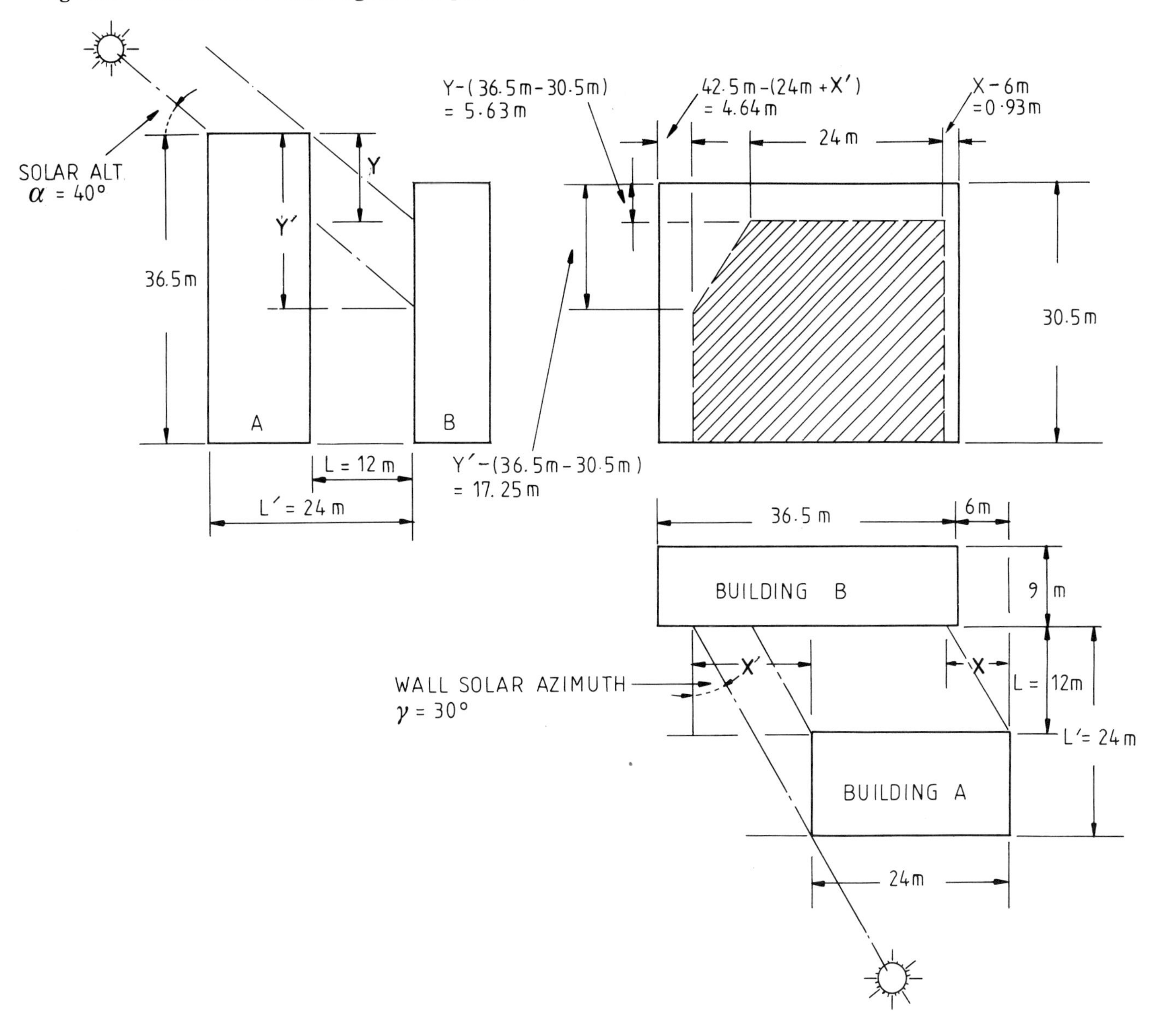

5 Calculation of heating loads

Compared with cooling-load calculations the calculation of heating loads is relatively straightforward, comprising the sensible heat losses through the building construction, the sensible and latent heat losses in the ventilation and infiltration air volumes, and the latent heat gains from the population in the building, together with other applicable latent gains such as food in restaurants.

It has been customary for sensible heat gains from solar radiation, illumination, etc. to be discounted when making heating load calculations unless they derive from sources which are in continuous operation; for example, computers and lighting in computer rooms. However, with the current emphasis on design economy and energy conservation, it is becoming common practice for the heating-load calculations to comprise an energy balance between the losses and gains to enable the capacities of the plant and distribution systems to be matched with the actual load requirements.

For the calculation of the annual running costs of heating and air-conditioning installations, a year-round energy balance is essential. This is a lengthy task when performed manually which becomes comparatively simple by the use of a suitable computer program.

5.1 CONSTRUCTIONAL HEAT LOSSES

Prior to the introduction in the UK, and elsewhere, of government regulations limiting the heat losses from buildings, it was necessary to make a detailed study of the various constructional elements of a building and their associated *U*-values before embarking on the design. In the UK this process has been simplified by Parts F and FF of the 1974 and 1978 Building Regulations as explained in Section 3.9.1 (p. 41).

According to these regulations the *U*-values are specified for window and rooflight openings, and for walls, floors and roofs. The values are given in Tables 3.7 and 3.8 (pp. 42, 43) and they are used in the standard heat transmission equation:

$$Q = AU\,\Delta t \qquad [5.1]$$

where

Q	= heat transmitted	W (Btu/hr)
A	= area of building element	m^2 (ft^2)
U	= transmittance coefficient	$W/m^2/°C$ ($Btu/hr/ft^2/°F$)
Δt	= temperature difference across the building element	°C (°F)
	= $t_i - t_o$ for external elements	
	= $t_i - t_{i'}$ for internal elements	
t_i	= controlled indoor air temperature	°C (°F)
t_o	= outdoor air temperature	°C (°F)
$t_{i'}$	= non-controlled indoor air temperature	°C (°F)

5.1.1 Temperature differences

(a) Outdoor design dry-bulb temperatures, t_o, used in the above expression are derived from the procedure described in Section 3.1 (p. 18).
(b) Indoor design dry-bulb temperatures, t_i, are extracted from Fig. 3.2 (p. 24) using the derived value of outdoor temperature.
(c) Here, $t_{i'}$ is used to denote temperatures that will apply in areas adjacent to air-conditioned spaces wherein the temperature is not controlled to a given level, i.e. corridors, kitchens, plant rooms, etc. If it is not possible for such temperatures to be measured then the following expressions should be used:

1. Adjacent spaces without heating:

$$t_{i'} = \frac{t_o + t_i}{2} \qquad [5.2]$$

2. Adjacent spaces with random heat (kitchens, boiler rooms, plant rooms, etc.):

$$t_{i'} = \frac{t_o + t_i}{2} + 3\ °\text{C to } 14\ °\text{C} \qquad [5.3]$$

$$\left[\left(\frac{t_o + t_i}{2}\right) + 5.5\ °\text{F to } 25\ °\text{F}\right]$$

5.1.2 Transmittance coefficients (U-values)

Although the maximum values of transmittance coefficients are regulated in the UK and elsewhere, it is advisable that they should be calculated for actual constructions relative to the applicable design conditions. These conditions should be for the winter case: summer values will be lower, but to such a marginal extent that the difference may be neglected. The equation to be used is:

$$U = \frac{1}{R_{si} + R_1 + R_2 + R_3 \ \ldots \ + R_a + R_{so}} \qquad [5.4]$$

where

U	= transmittance coefficient	W/m²/°C (Btu/hr/ft²/°F)
R_{si}	= inside surface resistance	m²/°C/W (ft²/hr/°F/Btu)
R_1, R_2, R_3	= thermal resistances of structural elements	m²/°C/W (ft²/hr/°F/Btu)
R_a	= airspace resistance	m²/°C/W (ft²/hr/°F/Btu)
R_{so}	= outside surface resistance	m²/°C/W (ft²/hr/°F/Btu)

The thermal resistance of unit area of the homogeneous materials forming the elements of a composite construction is:

$$R = \frac{l}{k} \qquad [5.5]$$

where

R	= thermal resistance	m²/°C/W (ft²/hr/°F/Btu)
l	= thickness of element	m (in)
k	= thermal conductivity	W/m/°C (Btu/in/ft²/hr/°F)

From the CIBS *Guide*, Section A3, the following relevant data are reproduced on pp. 86–8.

Table 5.1 Inside surface resistances
Table 5.2 Outside surface resistances
Table 5.3 Thermal resistances of unventilated airspaces
Table 5.4 Thermal resistances of ventilated (i.e. unsealed) airspaces
Table 5.5 Thermal conductivities of various standard constructional elements

Table 5.1 Inside surface resistance, R_{si}

Building element	*Heat flow*	*Surface resistance (m²/°C/W)* High-emissivity factor ($\frac{6}{5}E$ = 0.97)	Low-emissivity factor ($\frac{6}{5}E$ = 0.05)
Walls	Horizontal	0.12	0.30
Ceilings or roofs, flat or pitched, floors	Upward	0.10	0.22
Ceilings and floors	Downward	0.14	0.55

Table 5.2 Outside surface resistance (R_{so}) for stated exposure

Building element	*Emissivity of surface*	*Surface resistance for stated exposure (m²/°C/W)* Sheltered	Normal	Severe
Wall	High	0.08	0.06	0.03
	Low	0.11	0.07	0.03
Roof	High	0.07	0.04	0.02
	Low	0.09	0.05	0.02

Table 5.3 Standard thermal resistances for unventilated airspaces

Type of air space Thickness (mm)	Surface emissivity	*Thermal resistance (m²/°C/W) for heat flow in stated direction* Horizontal	Upward	Downward
5	High	0.10	0.10	0.10
	Low	0.18	0.18	0.18
25 or more	High	0.18	0.17	0.22
	Low	0.35	0.35	1.06
High-emissivity plane and corrugated sheets in contact		0.09	0.09	0.11
Low-emissivity multiple foil insulation with airspace on one side.		0.62	0.62	1.76

EXAMPLE 5.1 Calculate the U-value of a wall construction comprising inner and outer leaves of 114 mm brickwork with a 50 mm airspace between, and an inner finish of 12 mm dense plaster.

Solution From:

Table 5.1 $R_{si} = 0.12$
Table 5.2 $R_{so} = 0.06$
Table 5.3 $R_{a} = 0.18$
Table 5.5 $k = 0.84$ (brickwork outer leaf)

Table 5.4 Standard thermal resistance of ventilated airspaces

Type of airspace (thickness 25 mm minimum)	*Thermal resistances ($m^2/°C/W$)*
Airspace between asbestos cement or black metal cladding with unsealed joints, and high-emissivity lining	0.16
Airspace between asbestos cement or black metal cladding with unsealed joints, and low-emissivity surface facing airspace	0.30
Loft space between flat ceiling and unsealed asbestos cement sheets or black metal cladding pitched roof	0.14
Loft space between flat ceiling and pitched roof with aluminium cladding instead of black metal or low-emissivity upper surface on ceiling	0.25
Loft space between flat ceiling and pitched roof lined with felt or building paper	0.18
Airspace between tiles and roofing felt or building paper	0.12
Airspace behind tiles on tile-hung wall*	0.12
Airspace in cavity wall construction	0.18

* For tile-hung wall or roof, the value includes the resistance of the tile.

Notes:
Emissivity factor, E = $H\varepsilon_1 \varepsilon_2$
Where H = shape factor
ε_1 and ε_2 = emissivity of surface
In Table 5.2 High emissivity (dull surfaces) = 0.9
Low emissivity (bright surfaces) = 0.05
In Table 5.1 Surface temp. = 20 °C
Surface airspeed = 0.1 m/sec

$$R_1 = \frac{0.114}{0.84} = 0.136$$

Table 5.5 k = 0.62 (brickwork inner leaf)

$$R_2 = \frac{0.114}{0.62} = 0.184$$

Table 5.5 k = 0.50 (dense plaster)

$$R_3 = \frac{0.012}{0.50} = 0.024$$

$$U = \frac{1}{0.12 + 0.136 + 0.184 + 0.024 + 0.18 + 0.06}$$

$$= \frac{1}{0.704} = 1.42\ \text{W/m}^2/°\text{C}$$

Table 5.5 Thermal conductivities of various standard constructional elements

Material	*Density (kg/m^2)*	*Thermal Conductivity ($W/m/°C$)*	*Specific Heat Capacity ($J/kg/°C$)*
Walls (external and internal)			
Asbestos cement sheet	700	0.36	1050
Asbestos cement decking	1500	0.36	1050
Brickwork (outer leaf)	1700	0.84	800
Brickwork (inner leaf)	1700	0.62	800
Cast concrete (dense)	2100	1.40	840
Cast concrete (lightweight)	1200	0.38	1000
Concrete block (heavyweight)	2300	1.63	1000
Concrete block (medium weight)	1400	0.51	1000
Concrete block (lightweight)	600	0.19	1000
Fibreboard	300	0.06	1000
Plasterboard	950	0.16	840
Tile hanging	1900	0.84	800
Surface finishes			
External rendering	1300	0.50	1000
Plaster (dense)	1300	0.50	1000
Plaster (lightweight)	600	0.16	1000
Roofs			
Aerated concrete slab	500	0.16	840
Asphalt	1700	0.50	1000
Felt/bitumen layers	1700	0.50	1000
Screed	1200	0.41	840
Stone chippings	1800	0.96	1000
Tile	1900	0.84	800
Wood-wool slab	500	0.10	1000
Floors			
Cast concrete	2000	1.13	1000
Metal tray	7800	50.00	480
Screed	1200	0.41	840
Timber flooring	650	0.14	1200
Wood blocks	650	0.14	1200
Insulation			
Expanded polystyrene (EPS) slab	25	0.035	1400
Glass fibre quilt	12	0.040	840
Glass fibre slab	25	0.035	1000
Mineral fibre slab	30	0.035	1000
Phenolic foam	30	0.040	1400
Polyurethane board	30	0.025	1400
Urea formaldehyde (UF) foam	10	0.040	1400

This exceeds the maximum regulation value of 0.6. Therefore, insulation must be added. If the airspace is filled with expanded polystyrene, then R_a is replaced by R_4 which, from Table 5.5, is equal to 0.05/0.035 = 1.43 and the improved value becomes:

$$U = \frac{1}{0.12+0.136+0.184+0.024+1.43+0.06}$$

$$= \frac{1}{1.954} = 0.51 \text{ W/m}^2 \text{ °C}$$

To convert the SI *U*-value to imperial, or conventional units, the divisor is 5.678. Hence:

$$\frac{0.51}{5.678} = 0.09 \text{ Btu/hr/fr}^2\text{/°F}$$

EXAMPLE 5.2 If the *U*-value calculated above relates to a wall area of 3 m^2 (32.3 ft^2) calculate the heat loss when the outdoor temperature is −5.5 °C (22 °F) and the indoor temperature is 20 °C (68 °F).

Solution From equation [5.1]:

$$Q = 3 \times 0.51 \times 25.5 = 39 \text{ W}$$
$$(32.3 \times 0.09 \times 46 = 134 \text{ Btu/hr})$$

5.1.3 *U*-values for floors in contact with the earth or suspended above a ventilated cavity

Heat losses through basement floor and edge slabs in contact with the earth are greatest at the perimeter due to the fact that the earth temperature to a depth of approximately 3 m will vary with the outdoor air temperature. In the centre the earth temperature remains more or less constant. Hence, for the calculation of heat losses through basement floors, equation [5.1] is used in conjunction with the *U*-values in Table 5.6 reproduced from Section A3 of the *CIBS Guide*.

The losses occur mainly at the perimeter, and they can be considerable. Therefore, where basements are to be used for occupation, storage, equipment operation, etc. it is recommended that edge insulation should be applied either between the floor slab and the basement walls or in the floor slab for a distance of 1 m from the adjoining walls.

If insulation is used in this manner then the *U*-values of Table 5.6 can be modified in accordance with the percentage reductions reproduced in Table 5.7 from the *CIBS Guide*, Section A3.

The *U*-values of Table 5.6, with and without insulation, are usable for floor slabs of any thickness including surface finishes such as terrazzo, thermoplastic tiles, etc.

Fully exposed floors, such as occur in stilted buildings, must be insulated sufficiently to prevent discomfort to occupants at foot-level. A maximum *U*-value of 0.35 $W/m^2/°C$ (0.06 $Btu/hr/ft^2/°F$) is recommended for this purpose.

5.2 INFILTRATION AND VENTILATION HEAT LOSSES

The constructional heat losses discussed in Section 5.1 are of a direct nature, i.e. they form a component of the heating load which is dealt with by terminal air-conditioners or airflows. Infiltration is a similarly direct component, but the fresh-air ventilation usually comprises a heating load at the central plant: an exception to this is with perimeter Versatemp and fan-coil systems wherein the fresh air is delivered separately to the conditioned areas at temperatures of 10° to 13 °C (50° to 55 °F).

Table 5.6 ***U*-values for solid and suspended floors**

		U-value (W/m²/°C)		
Length (m)	*Breadth (m)*	*Four edges exposed*	*Two perpendicular edges exposed*	*Suspended floor‡*
Very long	*100*	*0.06**	*0.03†*	0.07
Very long	60	0.09*	0.05†	0.11
Very long	40	0.12*	0.07†	0.15
Very long	20	0.22*	0.12†	0.26
Very long	10	0.38*	0.22†	0.43
Very long	6	0.55*	0.33†	0.60
Very long	4	0.74*	0.45†	0.76
Very long	2	1.19*	0.74†	1.04
100	100	0.10	0.05	0.11
100	60	0.12	0.07	0.14
100	40	0.15	0.09	0.18
100	20	0.24	0.14	0.28
60	60	0.15	0.08	0.16
60	40	0.17	0.10	0.20
60	20	0.26	0.15	0.30
60	10	0.41	0.24	0.46
40	40	0.21	0.12	0.22
40	20	0.28	0.16	0.31
40	10	0.43	0.25	0.47
40	6	0.59	0.35	0.63
20	20	0.36	0.21	0.37
20	10	0.48	0.28	0.51
20	6	0.64	0.38	0.65
20	4	0.82	0.49	0.79
10	10	0.62	0.36	0.59
10	6	0.74	0.44	0.71
10	4	0.90	0.54	0.83
10	2	1.31	0.82	1.08
6	6	0.91	0.54	0.79
6	4	1.03	0.62	0.89
6	2	1.40	0.87	1.11
4	4	1.22	0.73	0.96
4	2	1.52	0.95	1.15
2	2	1.96	1.22	1.27

* These values can be used for a floor with two parallel edges exposed, taking the breadth as the distance between the exposed edges.

† These values can be used for a floor with one exposed edge, taking the breadth as the distance between the exposed edge and the edge opposite it.

‡ These values have been computed for $R_g = 0.2\,m^2/°C/W$. For other values of R_g a corrected *U*-value can be obtained from:

$$U' = \left(\frac{1}{U} - 0.2 + R_g\right)^{-1}$$

Table 5.7 Corrections to U-values of solid floors with edge insulation

Floor dimensions (m)	Percent reduction in U-value for insulation extending to indicated depth (m)		
	0.25	*0.5*	*1.0*
Very long × 100	2	6	10
Very long × 60	2	6	11
Very long × 40	3	7	11
Very long × 20	3	8	11
Very long × 10	4	9	14
Very long × 6	4	9	15
Very long × 4	5	12	20
Very long × 2	6	15	25
100 × 100	3	11	16
60 × 60	4	11	17
40 × 40	4	12	18
20 × 20	5	13	19
10 × 10	6	14	22
6 × 6	6	15	25
4 × 4	7	18	28
2 × 2	10	20	35

Note:
These corrections are based on thermal insulation having a minimum thermal resistance of 0.25 m²/°C/W

In winter both the infiltration and ventilation airflows will be deficient in both sensible and latent heat and the heating loads involved in making good these deficiencies are calculated from equations [4.9] and [4.10], namely:

Sensible heat $Q_s = 1.23\ V\Delta t$ W
$(1.08\ V\Delta t$ Btu/hr)

Latent heat $Q_l = 3012\ V\Delta g$ W
$(4830\ V\Delta g$ Btu/hr)

EXAMPLE 5.3 24 litres/sec (51 cfm) of outdoor fresh air is delivered to a building module at 10 °C DB/4.5 °C WB (50 °F DB/40 °C WB). The module air temperature is maintained at 20 °C DB/35% RH (68 °F DB/35% RH). Calculate the sensible and latent heat required to raise the fresh air to room conditions.

Solution

(a) Sensible heat

$Q_s = 1.23 \times 24\ (20-10) = 295$ W
$((1.08 \times 51\ (68-50) = 991$ Btu/hr))

(b) Latent heat

From the CIBS psychrometric tables the moisture contents of air at 10 °C DB/4.5 °C WB and 20 °C DB/35% RH are, respectively, 0.002 91 kg/kg (0.002 91 lb/lb) and 0.005 084 kg/kg (0.005 084 lb/lb).

$Q_l = 3012 \times 24\ (0.005\ 084 - 0.002\ 91) = 157$ W
$(4830 \times 51\ (0.005\ 084 - 0.002\ 91) = 536$ Btu/hr)

5.3 LATENT HEAT GAIN FROM POPULATION AND PROCESSES

In common with the sensible heat gain from solar radiation, illumination, etc. it has been customary to neglect the sensible heat emissions from building populations, food, etc. However, the latent heat gain is taken into account since it will partially offset the latent heat to be added to the ventilation air and the deficiency due to infiltration. Figure 4.8 (p. 70) is used for this purpose in conjunction with the total air circulation (fresh air plus recirculated air).

EXAMPLE 5.4 In the module of example 5.3 two occupants are seated at light work. Assuming an infiltration rate of 6 litres/sec (13 cfm), calculate the amount of moisture that must be added to the input air volume of 24 litres/sec (51 cfm) in order to achieve the design condition of 20 °C DB/35% RH (68 °F DB/35% RH) against outdoor temperatures of −5.5 °C DB/−6.0 °C WB (22 °F DB/21 °F WB).

Solution Latent heat deficiency in fresh air, from example 5.3 = −157 W (−536 Btu/hr).

Latent heat gain from occupants, from Fig. 4.8 (p. 70) = 44 W (150 Btu/hr) per person = +88 W (+300 Btu/hr).

Latent heat deficiency in infiltration: moisture content at 20 °C DB/35% RH = 0.002 910 kg/kg; at −5.5 °C DB/−6 °C WB = 0.002 095 kg/kg.

$$Q_l = 3012 \times 6\,(0.002\,910 - 0.002\,095) = -15\text{ W}$$
$$(4830 \times 13\,(0.002\,910 - 0.002\,095) = -51\text{ Btu/hr})$$

Net latent heat make-up required (−157 + 88 − 15) = 84 W (287 Btu/hr)

Air density at CIBS standard of 20 °C/50% RH = 0.001 204 kg/litre (0.075 lb/cu. ft)

Mass weight of input air volume is:

$$24 \times 0.001\,204 \times 3600 = 104\text{ kg/hr}$$
$$(51 \times 0.075 \times 60 = 229.5\text{ lb/hr})$$

Latent heat of water vapour at 20 °C/50% RH = 2454 kJ/kg.

$$\frac{2454}{3.6} = 681\text{ W/kg of dry air}$$
$$(1054\text{ Btu/lb of dry air})$$

Therefore, moisture equivalent of 84 W (287 Btu/hr) latent heat is:

$$\frac{84}{104 \times 681} = 0.001\,186\text{ kg/kg}$$

$$\left(\frac{287}{229.5 \times 1054} = 0.001\,186\text{ lb/lb}\right)$$

6 Time incidence of maximum cooling loads

6.1 FACE PEAK COOLING LOADS

Little guidance is given in guides and handbooks to the time of year when cooling loads will be at their maxima on the various faces of a building. The suggestion is usually made that it should be related to the times of occurrence of the highest solar radiation values or that it should be a matter of judgment.

Neither proposal is particularly helpful since the maximum will depend upon several contributory factors: the compass aspect of a building face; the type of window shading (bare glass, internal or external shades); the outdoor air temperature; building usage (offices, hotels, apartments, hospitals, etc.); population numbers, etc.

For precise accuracy in establishing the time of incidence of peak face cooling loads, and their values, it is necessary for calculations to be made over the four months of the recognised cooling season (Northern hemisphere June to September; Southern hemisphere December to March) and for times over the design day of each month, ranging from 06.00 to 18.00 hours solar time. The operating periods will be one or two hours later, depending upon the locality.

This is a lengthy process, but one that can be foreshortened by dealing only with the variable components of the overall cooling load. In most buildings, and particularly office blocks, these will comprise window solar radiation and conduction, conduction through the walls, roof and exposed floors, and the fresh-air loads.

Calculations of each component are made bi-hourly over the period of usage of the building for the design day of each month of the cooling season, and the values totalled in order to find the time when the peak occurs. Then, for this time only, the full calculation is made to include also the other components of the load: lighting, population, internal gains, etc.

The process is further shortened if a computer program is available. In Figs 6.1(a) and (b) print-outs are shown of the first part of the procedure in Btu per hour for the intermediate and roof floors of a typical office building; the program in this case being set up for imperial units.

From comparison of the two figures, it will be seen that the program first calculated the loads of the variable components for the intermediate floors; totalled these for each time of day, and then added the totals to the roof loads to arrive at the totals for the roof floor. In each case the highest peak loads are printed out by the program and, for clarity, these have been boxed in Figs 6.1(a) and (b).

As a further tool to assist the design engineer the computer program has been set up to examine the peaks of a wide range of office buildings for the principal compass aspects in northern and southern latitudes and for the variables of specific weight of structure (150, 500 and 750 kg/m^2) and window shading (unshaded, internal shades and external shades). Figures 6.2 and 6.3 depict the results for intermediate and exposed roof floors respectively.

Fig. 6.1 Computer print-outs of typical face peak cooling load calculations

(a) Intermediate floor

S – E FACE LOADS MONTH: – JUNE	......	07.00	09.00	11.00	13.00	15.00	17.00
Sensible Heat	Glass Solar	503.50	680.40	789.26	748.44	612.36	503.50
Typical Module	Glass Cond.	– 54.00	18.00	81.00	90.00	144.00	108.00
......	Ext. Wall	13.29	6.69	44.08	84.32	97.52	75.21
......	Roof	0.00	0.00	0.00	0.00	0.00	0.00
......	Exp. Floor	0.00	0.00	0.00	0.00	0.00	0.00
......	Fresh Air	– 81.00	27.00	121.50	135.00	216.00	162.00
S.H. Typical Module Load		381.79	732.09	1035.84	1057.76	1069.88	848.70
L.H. Typ. Module	Fresh Air	85.00	85.00	85.00	85.00	85.00	85.00
FACE PEAK LOADS	Sen. Heat	381.79	732.09	1035.84	1057.76	1069.88	848.70
......	Lat. Heat	85.00	85.00	85.00	85.00	85.00	85.00
S – E Face Peak:-	JUNE	466.79	817.09	1120.84	1142.76	1154.88	933.70

S – E FACE LOADS MONTH:- JULY	......	07.00	09.00	11.00	13.00	15.00	17.00
Sensible Heat	Glass Solar	533.33	720.72	836.04	792.79	648.65	533.33
Typical Module	Glass Cond.	– 18.00	54.00	117.00	162.00	180.00	153.00
......	Ext. Wall	32.34	25.74	65.34	107.58	120.78	96.36
......	Roof	0.00	0.00	0.00	0.00	0.00	0.00
......	Exp. Floor	0.00	0.00	0.00	0.00	0.00	0.00
......	Fresh Air	– 27.00	81.00	175.50	243.00	270.00	229.50
S.H. Typical Module Load		520.67	881.46	1193.88	1305.37	1219.43	1012.19
L.H. Typ. Module	Fresh Air	102.00	102.00	102.00	102.00	102.00	102.00
FACE PEAK LOADS	Sen. Heat	520.67	881.46	1193.88	1305.37	1219.43	1012.19
......	Lat. Heat	102.00	102.00	102.00	102.00	102.00	102.00
S – E Face Peak:-	JULY	622.67	983.46	1295.88	1407.37	1321.43	1114.19

S – E FACE LOADS MONTH:- AUGUST	......	07.00	09.00	11.00	13.00	15.00	17.00
Sensible Heat	Glass Solar	585.55	791.28	917.88	870.41	712.15	585.55
Typical Module	Glass Cond.	– 27.00	36.00	99.00	144.00	162.00	135.00
......	Ext. Wall	36.80	30.20	73.68	119.40	132.60	104.50
......	Roof	0.00	0.00	0.00	0.00	0.00	0.00
......	Exp. Floor	0.00	0.00	0.00	0.00	0.00	0.00
......	Fresh air	– 40.50	54.00	148.50	216.00	243.00	202.50
S.H. Typical Module Load		554.85	911.48	1239.06	1349.81	1249.76	1027.55
L.H. Typ. Module	Fresh Air	153.00	153.00	153.00	153.00	153.00	153.00
FACE PEAK LOADS	Sen. Heat	554.85	911.48	1239.06	1349.81	1249.76	1027.55
......	Lat. Heat	153.00	153.00	153.00	153.00	153.00	153.00
S – E Face Peak:-	AUGUST	707.85	1064.48	1392.06	1502.81	1402.76	1180.55

S – E FACE LOADS MONTH:- SEPTEMBER	......	07.00	09.00	11.00	13.00	15.00	17.00
Sensible Heat	Glass Solar	607.92	821.52	952.96	903.67	739.37	607.92
Typical Module	Glass Cond.	– 126.00	– 63.00	9.00	45.00	45.00	18.00
......	Ext. Wall	– 4.19	– 10.79	34.35	81.57	94.77	65.09
......	Roof	0.00	0.00	0.00	0.00	0.00	0.00
......	Exp. Floor	0.00	0.00	0.00	0.00	0.00	0.00
......	Fresh Air	– 189.00	– 94.50	13.50	67.50	67.50	27.00
S.H. Typical Module Load		288.73	653.23	1009.81	1097.74	946.64	718.02
L.H. Typ. Module	Fresh Air	102.00	102.00	102.00	102.00	102.00	102.00
FACE PEAK LOADS	Sen. Heat	288.73	653.23	1009.81	1097.74	946.64	718.02
......	Lat. Heat	102.00	102.00	102.00	102.00	102.00	102.00
S – E Face Peak:-	SEPTEMBER	390.73	755.23	1111.81	1199.74	1048.64	820.02

MAX. LOAD : AUGUST 1300 1502.81

(b) Roof floor

S – E FACE LOADS MONTH:- JUNE	......	07.00	09.00	11.00	13.00	15.00	17.00
......	Roof	119.28	100.87	141.58	322.81	446.23	590.24
FACE PEAK LOADS	Sen. Heat	501.07	832.96	1177.42	1380.57	1516.11	1438.94
......	Lat. Heat	85.00	85.00	85.00	85.00	85.00	85.00
S – E Face Peak:-	JUNE	586.07	917.96	1262.42	1465.57	1601.11	1523.94
S – E FACE LOADS MONTH:- JULY	......	07.00	09.00	11.00	13.00	15.00	17.00
......	Roof	159.60	142.80	182.70	359.10	480.90	621.60
FACE PEAK LOADS	Sen. Heat	680.27	1024.26	1376.58	1664.47	1700.33	1633.79
......	Lat. Heat	102.00	102.00	102.00	102.00	102.00	102.00
S – E Face Peak:-	JULY	782.27	1126.26	1478.58	1766.47	1802.33	1735.79
S – E FACE LOADS MONTH:- AUGUST	......	07.00	09.00	11.00	13.00	15.00	17.00
......	Roof	124.41	112.27	149.84	312.26	429.41	560.53
FACE PEAK LOADS	Sen. Heat	679.26	1023.75	1388.90	1662.07	1679.17	1588.08
......	Lat. Heat	153.00	153.00	153.00	153.00	153.00	153.00
S – E Face Peak:-	AUGUST	832.26	1176.75	1541.90	1815.07	1832.17	1741.08
S – E FACE LOADS MONTH:- SEPTEMBER	......	07.00	09.00	11.00	13.00	15.00	17.00
......	Roof	– 62.17	– 67.69	– 33.43	109.11	219.62	337.12
FACE PEAK LOADS	Sen. Heat	226.56	585.54	976.38	1206.85	1166.26	1055.14
......	Lat. Heat	102.00	102.00	102.00	102.00	102.00	102.00
S – E Face Peak:-	SEPTEMBER	328.56	687.54	1078.38	1308.85	1268.26	1157.14

MAX. LOAD : AUGUST 1500 1832.17

EXAMPLE 6.1 One face of a building has an aspect 100° from north. The specific weight of the structure is 500 kg/m^2 (100 lb/ft^2) and the windows are fitted with internal shades. Find the time of design day and the month when the peak cooling load will occur in a latitude of 40°N.

Solution From Fig. 6.2 for a specific weight of 500 kg/m^2, a line at 100° from north on the lower compass scale to the internal shades (dashed) line shows the time of day to be 10.00 hours. The face aspect is between east and southeast. Hence, in the panel of months alongside the chart, the month at 40°N latitude is found to be August.

6.2 BUILDING INSTANTANEOUS COOLING LOADS

To establish the time when the building instantaneous load will occur, the totals of the face peak variable loads at the intermediate floors and the roof floor are added for the months in which maximum values occur. The highest aggregate value denotes the time of incidence of the instantaneous load and at this time the full-scale calculation is made to include the other load components.

The building to which the computer print-outs of Fig. 6.1(a) and (b) relate consisted of seven intermediate floors and the roof floor with wall aspects of approximately northeast, southeast, southwest and northwest.

Space does not permit the reproduction here of the whole print-out, but the totals for the four faces for the months of July and August wherein the face maximum values occurred are given in Table 6.1. The time of the instantaneous load in this case was 15.00 hours in July, as shown boxed.

Fig. 6.2 Time incidence of building face peak cooling loads. Intermediate floors

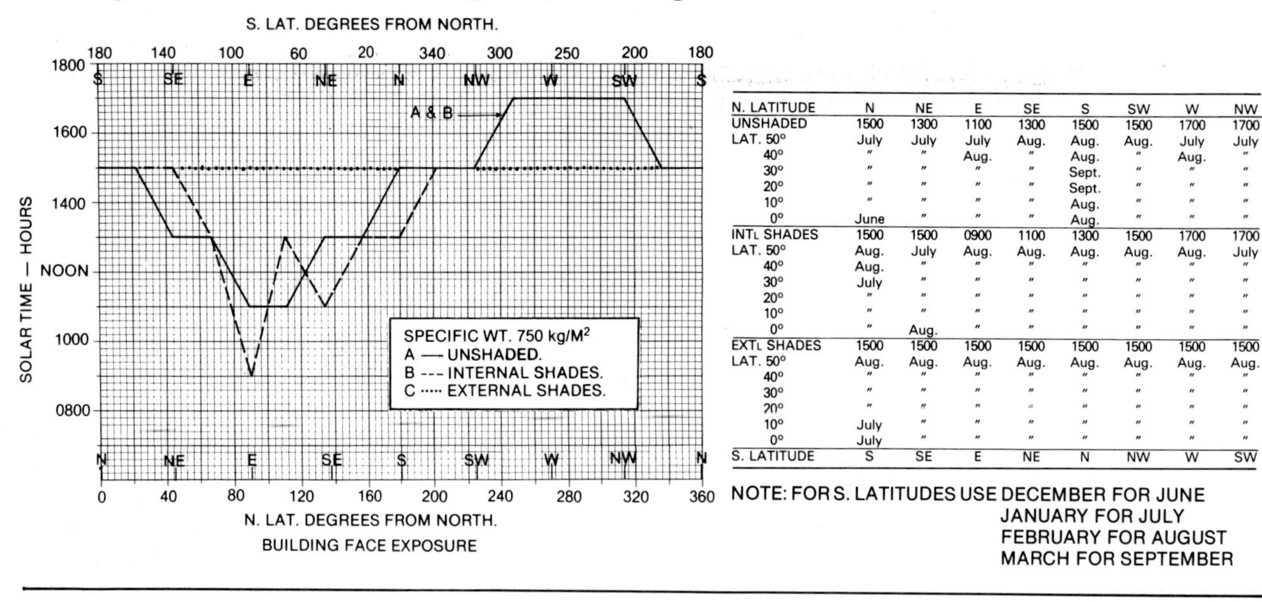

N. LATITUDE	N	NE	E	SE	S	SW	W	NW
UNSHADED	1500	1300	1100	1300	1500	1500	1700	1700
LAT. 50°	July	July	July	Aug.	Aug.	Aug.	July	July
40°	″	″	Aug.	″	Aug.	″	Aug.	″
30°	″	″	″	″	Sept.	″	″	″
20°	″	″	″	″	Sept.	″	″	″
10°	″	″	″	″	Aug.	″	″	″
0°	June	″	″	″	Aug.	″	″	″
INTL SHADES	1500	1500	0900	1100	1300	1500	1700	1700
LAT. 50°	Aug.	July	Aug.	Aug.	Aug.	Aug.	Aug.	July
40°	Aug.	″	″	″	″	″	″	″
30°	July	″	″	″	″	″	″	″
20°	″	″	″	″	″	″	″	″
10°	″	″	″	″	″	″	″	″
0°	″	Aug.	″	″	″	″	″	″
EXTL SHADES	1500	1500	1500	1500	1500	1500	1500	1500
LAT. 50°	Aug.	Aug.	Aug.	Aug.	Aug.	Aug.	Aug.	Aug.
40°	″	″	″	″	″	″	″	″
30°	″	″	″	″	″	″	″	″
20°	″	″	″	″	″	″	″	″
10°	July	″	″	″	″	″	″	″
0°	July	″	″	″	″	″	″	″
S. LATITUDE	S	SE	E	NE	N	NW	W	SW

NOTE: FOR S. LATITUDES USE DECEMBER FOR JUNE
JANUARY FOR JULY
FEBRUARY FOR AUGUST
MARCH FOR SEPTEMBER

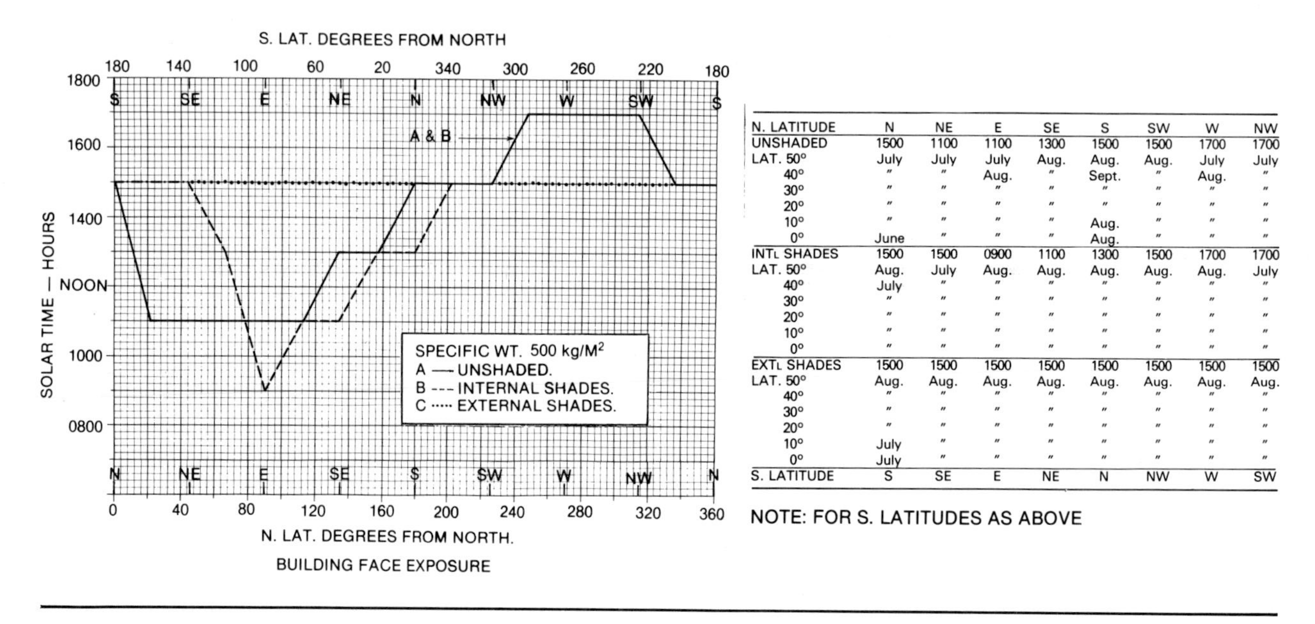

N. LATITUDE	N	NE	E	SE	S	SW	W	NW
UNSHADED	1500	1100	1100	1300	1500	1500	1700	1700
LAT. 50°	July	July	July	Aug.	Aug.	Aug.	July	July
40°	″	″	Aug.	″	Sept.	″	Aug.	″
30°	″	″	″	″	″	″	″	″
20°	″	″	″	″	″	″	″	″
10°	″	″	″	″	Aug.	″	″	″
0°	June	″	″	″	Aug.	″	″	″
INTL SHADES	1500	1500	0900	1100	1300	1500	1700	1700
LAT. 50°	Aug.	July	Aug.	Aug.	Aug.	Aug.	Aug.	July
40°	July	″	″	″	″	″	″	″
30°	″	″	″	″	″	″	″	″
20°	″	″	″	″	″	″	″	″
10°	″	″	″	″	″	″	″	″
0°	″	″	″	″	″	″	″	″
EXTL SHADES	1500	1500	1500	1500	1500	1500	1500	1500
LAT. 50°	Aug.	Aug.	Aug.	Aug.	Aug.	Aug.	Aug.	Aug.
40°	″	″	″	″	″	″	″	″
30°	″	″	″	″	″	″	″	″
20°	″	″	″	″	″	″	″	″
10°	July	″	″	″	″	″	″	″
0°	July	″	″	″	″	″	″	″
S. LATITUDE	S	SE	E	NE	N	NW	W	SW

NOTE: FOR S. LATITUDES AS ABOVE

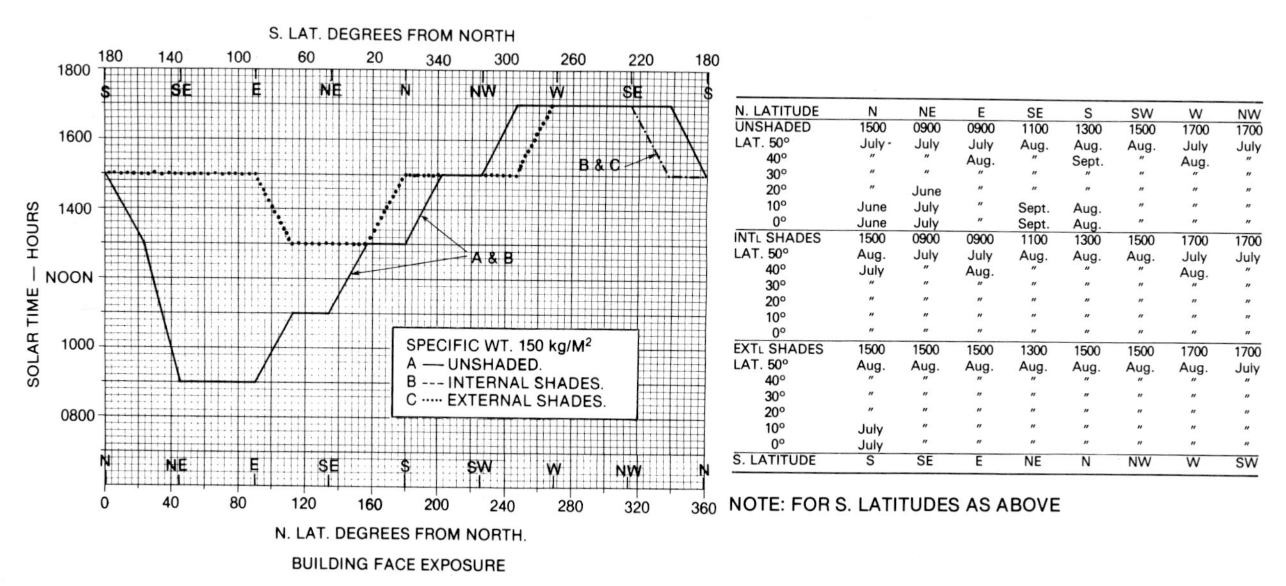

N. LATITUDE	N	NE	E	SE	S	SW	W	NW
UNSHADED	1500	0900	0900	1100	1300	1500	1700	1700
LAT. 50°	July -	July	July	Aug.	Aug.	Aug.	July	July
40°	″	″	Aug.	″	Sept.	″	Aug.	″
30°	″	″	″	″	″	″	″	″
20°	″	June	″	″	″	″	″	″
10°	June	July	″	Sept.	Aug.	″	″	″
0°	June	July	″	Sept.	Aug.	″	″	″
INTL SHADES	1500	0900	0900	1100	1300	1500	1700	1700
LAT. 50°	Aug.	July	July	Aug.	Aug.	Aug.	July	July
40°	July	″	Aug.	″	″	″	Aug.	″
30°	″	″	″	″	″	″	″	″
20°	″	″	″	″	″	″	″	″
10°	″	″	″	″	″	″	″	″
0°	″	″	″	″	″	″	″	″
EXTL SHADES	1500	1500	1500	1300	1500	1500	1700	1700
LAT. 50°	Aug.	Aug.	Aug.	Aug.	Aug.	Aug.	Aug.	July
40°	″	″	″	″	″	″	″	″
30°	″	″	″	″	″	″	″	″
20°	″	″	″	″	″	″	″	″
10°	July	″	″	″	″	″	″	″
0°	July	″	″	″	″	″	″	″
S. LATITUDE	S	SE	E	NE	N	NW	W	SW

NOTE: FOR S. LATITUDES AS ABOVE

Fig. 6.3 Time incidence of building face peak cooling loads. Exposed roof floors

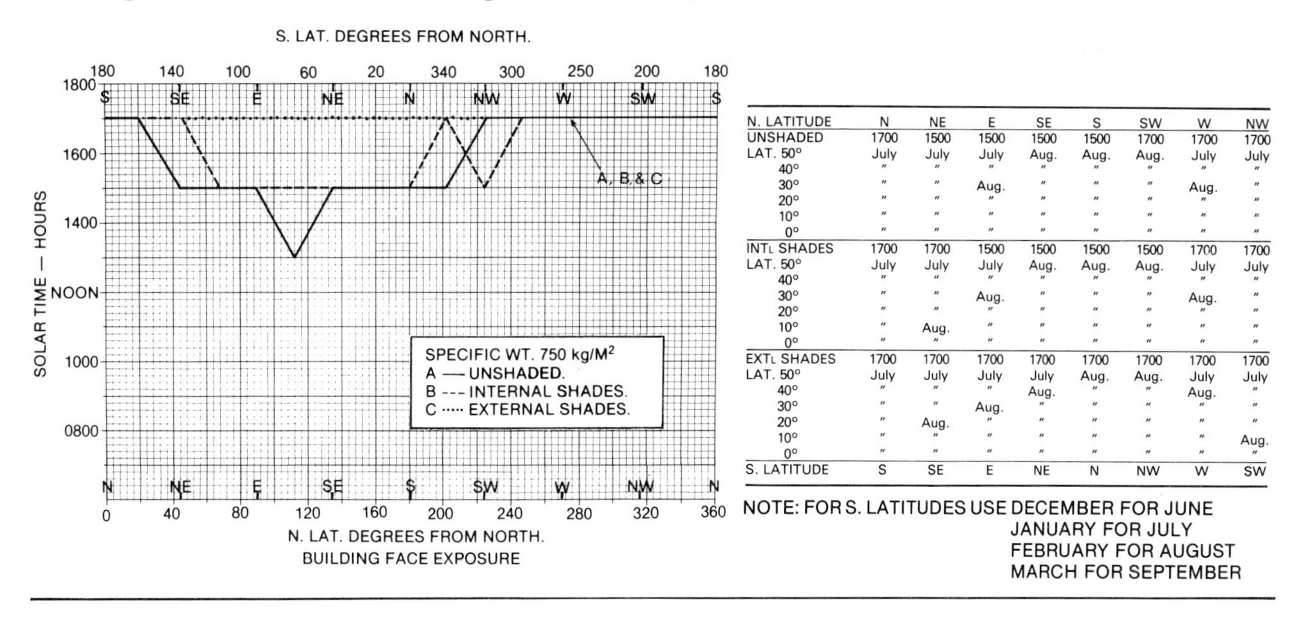

N. LATITUDE	N	NE	E	SE	S	SW	W	NW
UNSHADED	1700	1500	1500	1500	1500	1700	1700	1700
LAT. 50°	July	July	July	Aug.	Aug.	Aug.	July	July
40°	"	"	"	"	"	"	"	"
30°	"	"	Aug.	"	"	"	Aug.	"
20°	"	"	"	"	"	"	"	"
10°	"	"	"	"	"	"	"	"
0°	"	"	"	"	"	"	"	"
INTL SHADES	1700	1700	1500	1500	1500	1500	1700	1700
LAT. 50°	July	July	July	Aug.	Aug.	Aug.	July	July
40°	"	"	"	"	"	"	"	"
30°	"	"	Aug.	"	"	"	Aug.	"
20°	"	"	"	"	"	"	"	"
10°	"	Aug.	"	"	"	"	"	"
0°	"	"	"	"	"	"	"	"
EXTL SHADES	1700	1700	1700	1700	1700	1700	1700	1700
LAT. 50°	July	July	July	July	Aug.	Aug.	July	July
40°	"	"	"	Aug.	"	"	Aug.	"
30°	"	"	Aug.	"	"	"	"	"
20°	"	Aug.	"	"	"	"	"	"
10°	"	"	"	"	"	"	"	Aug.
0°	"	"	"	"	"	"	"	"
S. LATITUDE	S	SE	E	NE	N	NW	W	SW

NOTE: FOR S. LATITUDES USE DECEMBER FOR JUNE
JANUARY FOR JULY
FEBRUARY FOR AUGUST
MARCH FOR SEPTEMBER

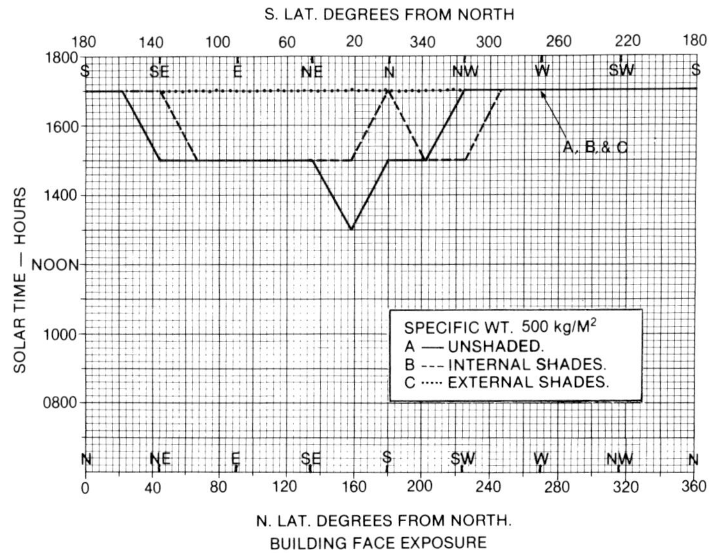

N. LATITUDE	N	NE	E	SE	S	SW	W	NW
UNSHADED	1700	1500	1500	1500	1500	1700	1700	1700
LAT. 50°	July	July	July	Aug.	Aug.	Aug.	July	July
40°	"	"	"	"	"	"	"	"
30°	"	"	Aug.	"	"	"	Aug.	"
20°	"	"	"	"	"	"	"	"
10°	"	"	"	"	"	"	"	"
0°	"	Aug.	"	"	"	"	"	"
INTL SHADES	1700	1700	1500	1500	1700	1500	1700	1700
LAT. 50°	July	July	July	Aug.	Aug.	Aug.	July	July
40°	"	"	"	"	"	"	"	"
30°	"	"	Aug.	"	"	"	Aug.	"
20°	"	"	"	"	"	"	"	"
10°	"	"	"	"	"	"	"	"
0°	"	Aug.	"	"	"	"	"	"
EXTL SHADES	1700	1700	1700	1700	1700	1700	1700	1700
LAT. 50°	July	July	July	Aug.	Aug.	Aug.	July	July
40°	"	"	"	"	"	"	"	"
30°	"	"	Aug.	"	"	"	Aug.	"
20°	"	Aug.	"	"	"	"	"	"
10°	"	"	"	"	"	"	"	Aug.
0°	"	"	"	"	"	"	"	"
S. LATITUDE	S	SE	E	NE	N	NW	W	SW

NOTE: FOR S. LATITUDES AS ABOVE

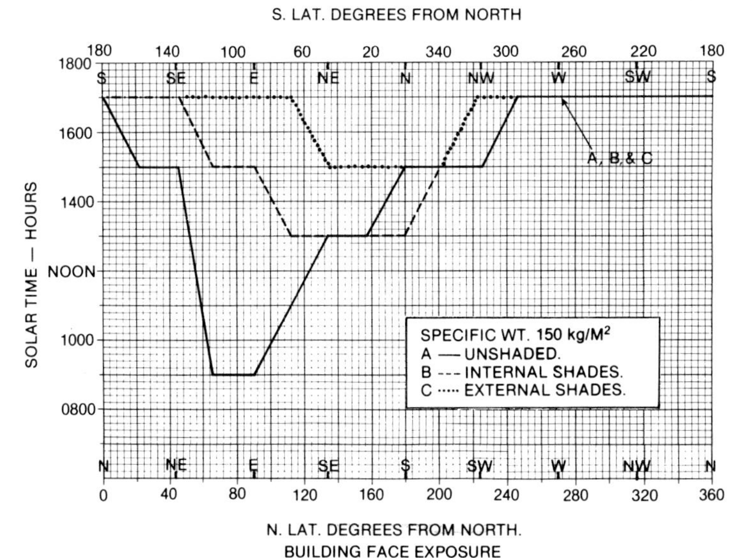

N. LATITUDE	N	NE	E	SE	S	SW	W	NW
UNSHADED	1700	1500	0900	1300	1500	1500	1700	1700
LAT. 50°	July	July	July	Aug.	Aug.	Aug.	July	July
40°	"	"	Aug.	"	"	"	"	"
30°	"	"	"	"	"	"	Aug.	"
20°	"	"	"	"	"	"	"	"
10°	"	"	"	"	"	"	"	"
0°	"	"	"	"	"	"	"	"
INTL SHADES	1700	1700	1500	1300	1300	1500	1700	1700
LAT. 50°	July	July	July	Aug.	Aug.	Aug.	July	July
40°	"	"	"	"	"	"	"	"
30°	"	"	Aug.	"	"	"	Aug.	"
20°	"	Aug.	"	"	"	"	"	"
10°	"	"	"	"	"	"	"	"
0°	"	"	"	"	"	"	"	"
EXTL SHADES	1700	1700	1700	1500	1500	1700	1700	1700
LAT. 50°	July	July	July	Aug.	Aug.	Aug.	July	July
40°	"	"	"	"	"	"	"	"
30°	"	"	Aug.	"	"	"	Aug.	"
20°	"	Aug.	"	"	"	"	"	"
10°	"	"	"	"	"	"	"	Aug.
0°	"	"	"	"	"	"	"	"
S. LATITUDE	S	SE	E	NE	N	NW	W	SW

NOTE: FOR S. LATITUDES AS ABOVE

Table 6.1 Summary of computer calculation for instantaneous load time

Month, floor	*face*	*Face peak loads (Btu/hr)*					
		07.00	*09.00*	*11.00*	*13.00*	*15.00*	*17.00*
July, intermediate	N/E	793	1 140	1 328	1 293	1 222	1 030
	S/E	622	983	1 295	1 407	1 321	1 114
	S/W	888	897	956	1 042	1 288	1 464
	N/W	581	666	752	818	917	1 041
Totals for 1 floor		2 884	3 686	4 331	4 560	4 748	4 649
Totals for 7 floors		20 188	25 802	30 317	31 920	33 236	32 543
July, roof floor	N/E	952	1 283	1 510	1 652	1 703	1 651
	S/E	782	1 126	1 478	1 766	1 802	1 735
	S/W	1 048	1 040	1 139	1 401	1 769	2 085
	N/W	740	809	935	1 178	1 398	1 662
Totals for roof floor		3 522	4 258	5 062	5 997	6 672	7 133
July totals		23 710	30 060	35 379	37 917	39 908	39 676
August, intermediate	N/E	798	1 118	1 304	1 274	1 208	1 020
	S/E	707	1 064	1 392	1 502	1 402	1 180
	S/W	891	882	944	1 031	1 271	1 440
	N/W	504	583	684	761	851	940
Totals for 1 floor		2 900	3 647	4 324	4 568	4 732	4 580
Totals for 7 floors		20 300	25 529	30 268	31 976	33 124	32 060
August, roof floor	N/E	923	1 230	1 454	1 586	1 637	1 580
	S/E	832	1 176	1 541	1 815	1 832	1 741
	S/W	1 015	994	1 094	1 344	1 701	2 001
	N/W	628	696	834	1 073	1 281	1 500
Totals for roof floor		3 398	4 096	4 923	5 818	6 451	6 822
August totals		23 698	29 625	35 191	37 794	39 575	38 882

Based upon experience, Fig. 6.4 offers a rule-of-thumb guide to the times of the incidence of instantaneous cooling loads for representative arrangements of office buildings.

It will be apparent that in building applications other than office blocks, the times of maximum loads will differ. For example, in hotel meeting rooms, department stores and shops, cinemas and theatres, etc.

In such cases the occupancy rate may dictate the maximum load incidence, i.e. at times when the greatest number of people will be present such as at banquets in the public rooms of hotels, summer peak shopping periods in stores and shops, and summer evening performances in cinemas and theatres when full houses can be expected.

6.3 COOLING-LOAD DIVERSITIES

It is unlikely that the maximum values of the cooling-load components will coincide. Therefore, whenever it is reasonable to do so, optimum values should be used together with diversification.

In the application quoted above for stores and shops, it would be unrealistic to design for the occupancy loads which would occur during summer sale periods. These

Fig. 6.4 Time incidence of building instantaneous cooling loads

Building arrangement	N	N	N	N	N	N	N	N
Window arrangement	12-hour operation				24-hour operation			
Internal shades	July 17.00	July 17.00	August 13.00	July 15.00	July 17.00	July 17.00	August 13.00	July 15.00
Bare glass	July 17.00	July 11.00	August 15.00	July 15.00	July 17.00	July 17.00	August 15.00	July 15.00
External shades	July 17.00	July 15.00	August 15.00	July 15.00	July 17.00	July 17.00	July 15.00	July 15.00
Rectangular building with glazed sides and solid ends								

Building arrangement	N	N	N	N	N	N	N	N
Window arrangement	12-hour operation				24-hour operation			
Internal shades	July 15.00	July 17.00	August 15.00	July 15.00	July 17.00	July 17.00	August 15.00	July 15.00
Bare glass	July 15.00	July 15.00	August 15.00	July 15.00	July 17.00	July 17.00	August 15.00	July 15.00
External shades	July 15.00	July 15.00	July 15.00	July 15.00	July 17.00	July 17.00	July 15.00	July 15.00
Rectangular building with glazing all round								

Building arrangement	N	N		N	N
Window arrangement	12 hr operation			24 hr operation	
Internal shades	July 15.00	July 15.00		July 15.00	July 15.00
Bare glass	August 15.00	July 15.00		July 17.00	July 15.00
External shades	July 15.00	July 15.00		July 15.00	July 15.00
Square building with glazing all round					

NOTE: FOR S. LATITUDES USE JANUARY FOR JULY AND FEBRUARY FOR AUGUST

are exceptional occasions which, if catered for, would result in oversized plant being infrequently run at full capacity.

Similar diversities can be applied for other applications but they are dependent upon building size and, therefore to some extent, upon judgment of the situation concerned: in individual rooms of an office building no diversity would be applicable, but, in the building as a whole, contracts engineers, sales representatives, etc. will be absent and their office lighting and equipment may not be in use. Also, the cooling season will coincide with the holiday period, and sickness will add to the diversification. Carrier in Chapter 3 of their *Handbook* recommend the diversity factors given in Table 6.2 for use in calculating the instantaneous cooling load.

Table 6.2 Diversity factors for cooling-load components

Application	Diversity factor	
	People	*Lights and machines*
Office buildings	0.75 to 0.90	0.70 to 0.85
Apartments and hotels	0.40 to 0.60	0.30 to 0.50
Department stores	0.80 to 0.90	0.90 to 1.00
Industrial	0.85 to 0.95	0.80 to 0.90

Additional scope for diversification of the instantaneous cooling load exists in vaulted spaces such as hotel public rooms, theatres, churches or in any space where the floor-to-ceiling height exceeds 3 m.

Because heat rises by convection, a considerable proportion of the heat generated from lighting and occupants will stratify at the upper levels and solar gains through exposed roofs will largely remain there.

If the conditioned air supply is introduced at or below the 3 m level, and air is exhausted above, then the cooling load will be considerably reduced. In such cases, the cooling load should be calculated above and below the 3 m line and a diversity factor of 0.4 to 0.5 applied to the high-level load.

6.4 PEAK HEATING LOADS

When building heat losses are calculated without regard for incident heat gains, then the maximum heating load will occur at the design time of the heating season.

Alternatively, if heat gains from internal sources are to be taken into account, then the diversities recommended above should be included.

This concludes the discussion of the detailed load calculations. In Chapter 7 a worked example puts them to practical use.

7 Worked building example

For the building in Fig. 7.1, and for the working conditions listed below, calculate:

(a) the peak cooling loads for the modules on elevations A and C;
(b) the instantaneous load for the whole building.

7.1 BUILDING

Location	– London, UK Latitude 50°N nominal. Sheltered position.
Usage	– General offices comprising five floors above ground plus roof floor. Speculative development, office planning not known. Office hours: 09.00 to 17.30 hours summer time (UK summer time = solar time plus one hour). Population loading, one person per 9.3 m^2 (100 ft^2) floor area. Some smoking anticipated. Illuminance level, 500 lux. Recessed ventilated fluorescent lighting fittings on from 08.00 to 18.00 hours. Cooling plant operates from 06.00 to 18.00 hours.
Face aspects	– From north A, 30° From north B, 120° From north C, 210° From north D, 300°

7.2 CONSTRUCTION

Windows	– Double-glazed units of 6 mm clear glass with 12 mm air gap. Aluminium frame with thermal insulation barrier. Frame area 12.5% of window-opening area. Internal white venetian blinds, 45° drawn.
External walls	– Inner and outer leaves of 114 mm brickwork with 50 mm gap between filled with expanded polystyrene. Inner finish 12 mm dense plaster. Outer surface dark coloured. Overal density 430 kg/m^2.
Internal walls	– 114 mm lightweight concrete blockwork finished each side with 12 mm dense plaster. Overall density 98 kg/m^2.
Floors	– 150 mm screeded concrete, carpeted. Density 552 kg/m^2.
Roof	– 150 mm aerated concrete with 25 mm expanded polystyrene insulating slabs and 19 mm asphalt cover; ventilated airspace above 25 mm plasterboard suspended ceiling. Overall density 600 kg/m^2.

Fig. 7.1 Typical building layout for worked example

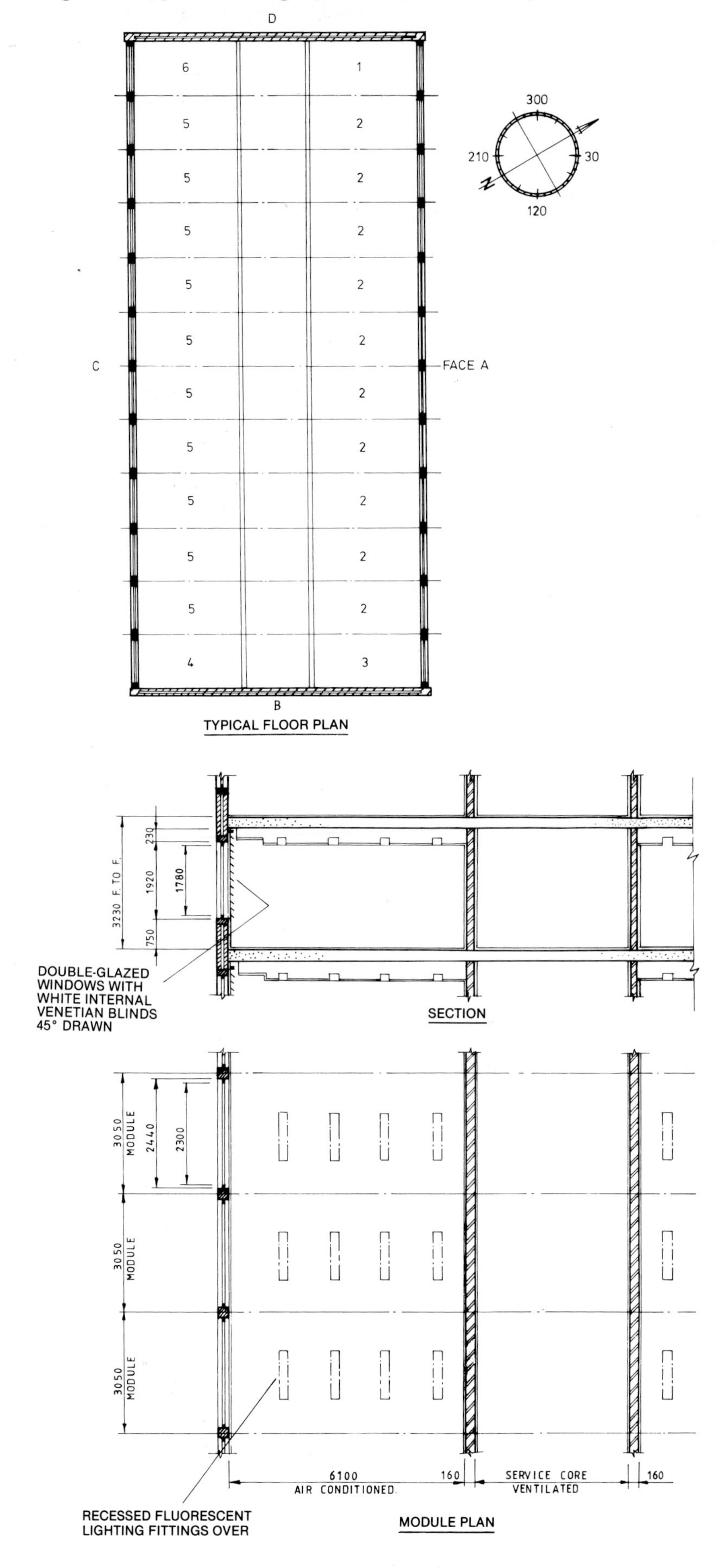

			m^2	(ft^2)
Module areas	– Windows:			
	gross 2.44 × 1.92	=	4.68	(50.4)
	net 2.30 × 1.78	=	4.09	(44.0)
	Module walls 3.05 × 0.98	=	2.98	(32.0)
	End walls 6.10 × 2.67	=	16.28	(175.0)
	Internal walls 3.05 × 2.90	=	8.84	(95.0)
	Floor and ceiling 6.10 × 3.05	=	18.60	(200.0)

Specific weights – Intermediate floors, carpeted
(see p. 45) = 557 kg/m^2
(use 500 kg/m^2 (100 lb/ft^2))

Roof floor:

module wall 2.98 × 430	=	1 281
internal wall 8.84 × 98	=	866
½ floor slab carpeted $18.60 \times \frac{552}{2 \times 2}$	=	2 567
roof slab and ceiling 18.60 × 600	=	11 160
		15 874

$$\frac{15\,874}{18.60} = 853 \text{ kg/m}^2$$

Use 750 kg/m^2 (150 lb/ft^2)

7.3 SOLAR TIME INCIDENCE OF MAXIMUM LOADS

7.3.1 Summer

Face A 30°	– Intermediate floors (see Fig. 6.2, p. 96)	=	15.00 hours July
	Roof floor (see Fig. 6.3, p. 97)	=	17.00 hours July
Face C 210°	– Intermediate floors (Fig. 6.2, p. 96)	=	15.00 hours August
	Roof floor (Fig. 6.3, p. 97)	=	16.00 hours August
Building instantaneous load (Fig. 6.4, p. 99)		=	15.00 hours July

7.3.2 Winter

All faces	– Face peaks and instantaneous	=	08.00 hours January

7.4 DESIGN DATA

Item	Value	Reference
Outdoor temperatures		
Summer	= 28 °C DB/18.5 °C WB (82 °F DB/65 °F WB)	Section 3.1
Winter	= −5.5 °C DB/−6 °C WB (22 °F DB/21 °F WB)	
Indoor temperatures		
Summer, conditioned	= 22 °C DB/45% RH (72 °F DB/45% RH)	Section 3.2
Not conditioned	$= \frac{28+22}{2} = 25$ °C (77 °F)	Eqn. [5.2], p. 85
Winter	= 20 °C DB/45% RH) (68 °F DB/45% RH)	
Population	= 2 per module	
Peak face, no diversity:		
S.ht/person	= 79 W (270 Btu/hr)	Fig. 4.8, p. 70
L.ht/person	= 53 W (180 Btu/hr)	
Instantaneous, 80% diversity:		Table 6.2, p. 100
S.ht/person	= 79 × 0.8 (270 × 0.8)	
L.ht/person	= 53 × 0.8 (180 × 0.8)	
Illumination	= 27.5 W/m^2	Fig. 3.4, p. 27
Peak face	= 27.5 × 18.6 × 1.25 × 0.6	Table 4.2, p. 72
60% diversity	= 384 W	
Instantaneous		Table 6.2, p. 100
80% diversity	= 384 W × 0.8	
Ventilation		
Supply air	= 1.3 litres/sec/m^2 (0.25 cfm/ft^2) 1.3 × 18.6 m^2 = 24 litres/sec (50 cfm)	Fig. 3.5(b), p. 29
Infiltration		
Summer	= nil	
	= 1.5 litres/sec/m^2 window area 1.5 × 4.68 m^2 = 7 litres/sec (15 cfm)	Section 3.7
Fenestration		
Solar radiation	W/m^2 (Btu/hr/ft^2)	
July 30° from north	= 250 (79.5)	Fig. 4.1(b), p. 55
July 210° from north	= 405 (128.5)	Fig. 4.1(b), p. 55
August 30° from north	= 170 (54.0)	Fig. AIII.3, p. 150
August 210° from north	= 475 (151.0)	Fig. AIII.3, p. 150
U-value	= 3.3 W/m^2/°C (0.58 Btu/hr/ft^2/°F)	Table 3.6, p. 36
Shading coefficient	= 0.53	Section 3.8.2 and Appendix II, Table AII.1, p. 146

Structure

U-values — Section 5.1.2

External walls $= 0.52\ \text{W/m}^2/^\circ\text{C}$
$(0.09\ \text{Btu/hr/ft}^2/^\circ\text{F})$

Internal walls
$$= \frac{1}{0.12 + \dfrac{0.114}{0.19} + \dfrac{0.012}{0.50} + \dfrac{0.012}{0.50} + 0.12}$$
$$= 1.13\ \text{W/m}^2/^\circ\text{C}$$
$$(0.2\ \text{Btu/hr/ft}^{2\circ}\text{C})$$

Roof
$$= \frac{1}{0.14 + \dfrac{0.15}{0.16} + \dfrac{0.025}{0.035} + \dfrac{0.019}{0.50} + \dfrac{0.025}{0.16} + 0.25 + 0.04}$$
$$= 0.44\ \text{W/m}^2/^\circ\text{C}$$
$$(0.077\ \text{Btu/hr/ft}^2/^\circ\text{F})$$

Temperature differentials

Summer outdoor/indoor, conditioned

July 15.00 hours	=	5.3 °C (9.5 °F)	Fig. 4.4, p. 60
July 17.00 hours	=	5.3 °C (9.5 °F)	
August 15.00 hours	=	4.7 °C (8.5 °F)	
August 16.00 hours	=	5.0 °C (9.0 °F)	
August 17.00 hours	=	4.7 °C (8.5 °F)	
Indoor non-conditioned/conditioned	=	3.0 °C (5.0 °F)	
Winter outdoor/indoor	=	25.5 °C (46 °F)	

Equivalent temperature differentials — Fig. 4.5, p. 63

Walls 30° from north			
15.00 hours	=	2.4 °C (4.3 °F)	
16.00 hours	=	2.4 °C (4.3 °F)	
17.00 hours	=	2.4 °C (4.3 °F)	
Walls 120° from north			
15.00 hours	=	10.2 °C (18.4 °F)	
16.00 hours	=	9.3 °C (16.7 °F)	
17.00 hours	=	7.9 °C (14.2 °F)	
Walls 210° from north			
15.00 hours	=	7.5 °C (13.5 °F)	
16.00 hours	=	8.8 °C (15.8 °F)	
17.00 hours	=	11.1 °C (20.0 °F)	
Walls 300° from north			
15.00 hours	=	2.2 °C (4.0 °F)	
16.00 hours	=	2.9 °C (5.2 °F)	
17.00 hours	=	4.7 °C (8.5 °F)	
Roof			Fig. 4.6, p. 64
15.00 hours	=	13.5 °C (24.3 °F)	
16.00 hours	=	15.0 °C (27.0 °F)	
17.00 hours	=	16.25 °C (29.3 °F)	

Moisture content differentials — Section 4.2.2

	Outdoor air kg/kg (lb/lb)	Indoor air kg/kg (lb/lb)	Differential kg/kg (lb/lb)
July	0.009 32	0.007 54	0.001 78
August	0.009 72	0.007 54	0.002 18

Storage factors		
Glass 30° from north		Fig. 4.2, p. 56
15.00 hours	= 0.29	
16.00 hours	= 0.26	
17.00 hours	= 0.23	
Glass 210° from north		
15.00 hours	= 0.79	
16.00 hours	= 0.65	
17.00 hours	= 0.46	
Occupants		Fig. 4.9(a), p. 73
15.00 hours (6 hours occupation)	= 0.945	
16.00 hours (7 hours occupation)	= 0.95	
17.00 hours (8 hours occupation)	= 0.96	
Lighting		Fig. AVI.7, p. 194
15.00 hours (7 hours usage)	= 0.91	
16.00 hours (8 hours usage)	= 0.92	
17.00 hours (9 hours usage)	= 0.925	

Using the foregoing data the calculations are made on a suitable job sheet as shown in Table 7.1, sheets 1 to 14, for SI units, and Table 7.2, sheets 1 to 14, for imperial units.

For clarity the calculations have been made in full detail, but, from examination, it will be seen that there is considerable repetition in the line results. Therefore, in practice the extent of the workings can be reduced by simply carrying forward the end results of lines having identical multiplier values.

There are slight discrepancies between the aggregate results of the SI unit calculations and those using imperial, or conventional, units. These are due to the rounding-up of the various component values and factors. However, the differences are sufficiently small to be neglected, e.g.:

	SI units	*Imperial units*	*% difference*
Cooling load	= 206 837 W		
	= 706 348 Btu/hr	703 346 Btu/hr	0.4
Heating load	= 230 496 W		
	= 787 144 Btu/hr	775 104 Btu/hr	1.5

It will be noted that no credit has been given to the instantaneous heating loads for the heat gains from the supply fan and the circulating pump, and no additions have been made for the heat losses from ducts and pipes. It is customary for the former to be omitted in the case of heating calculations, and the latter will depend upon the type of air-conditioning system to be used: both the air and water may be either heated or cooled according to the system design.

Table 7.1 Job sheet for face peak and instantaneous cooling/~~heating~~ loads. SI Units *Sheet No. 1*

Module	Date & time	Load item	Area m^2	Peak Solar radn	Δt or Δt_e °C	U value	Total watts	No. occpts	W/occpnt S.HT.	W/occpnt L.HT.	V l/sec	SF	BF	Δg kg/kg	Factors	Module loads W S.HT.	Module loads W L.HT.	No. mods	Instantaneous loads W S.HT.	Instantaneous loads W L.HT.
No. 1	**Intermediate floors. Face A 30° from North**																B/fd			
Face peak loads																				
	July 1500	Glass solar	4.09	250								0.29	0.53			157				
		Glass condn	4.68		5.3	3.30										81				
		Module wall	2.98		2.4	0.52										4				
		300° end wall	16.28		2.2	0.52										18				
		Internal wall	8.84		3.0	1.13										30				
		Roof	18.00			0.44										—				
		Occupants S.HT.						2	79			0.945				149				
		Occupants L.HT.						2		53						—	106			
		Lighting					384					0.91				349				
		Fresh air S.HT.			5.3						24				× 1.23	156				
		Fresh air L.HT.									24			0.00178	×3012	—	128			
		Infiltration														—				
		Face peak total loads														944	234			
Instantaneous loads																				
	July 1500	Glass solar	4.09	250								0.29	0.53			157				
		Glass condn	4.68		5.3	3.30										81				
		Module wall	2.98		2.4	0.52										4				
		300° end wall	16.28		2.2	0.52										18				
		Internal wall	8.84		3.0	1.13										30				
		Roof	18.60			0.44										—				
		Occupants S.HT.						2	63			0.945				119				
		Occupants L.HT.						2		42						—	84			
		Lighting					307					0.91				279				
		Fresh air S.HT.			5.3						24				× 1.23	156				
		Fresh air L.HT.									24			0.00178	× 3012	—	128			
		Infiltration														—				
		Instantaneous total loads														844	212	5	4220	1060
																	C/fd	5	4220	1060

Δt_e = equivalent temp. difference. SF = storage factor. BF = shade factor.

Table 7.1 Job sheet for face peak and instantaneous cooling/~~heating~~ loads. SI Units — *Sheet No. 2*

Module	*Date & time*	*Load item*	*Area* m^2	*Peak Solar radn*	*Δt or* Δt_e *°C*	*U value*	*Total watts*	*No. occpts*	*W/occpnt*		*V l/sec*	*SF*	*BF*	*Δg kg/kg*	*Factors*	*Module loads W*		*No. mods*	*Instantaneous loads W*	
									S.HT.	*L.HT.*						*S.HT.*	*L.HT.*		*S.HT.*	*L.HT.*
No. 1	**Roof floor. Face A 30° from North**																*B/fd*	5	4220	1060
Face peak loads																				
	July 1700	Glass solar	4.09	250								0.23	0.53			124				
		Glass condn	4.68		5.3	3.30										81				
		Module wall	2.98		2.4	0.52										4				
		300° end wall	16.28		4.7	0.52										39				
		Internal wall	8.84		3.0	1.13										30				
		Roof	18.60		16.25	0.44										133				
		Occupants S.HT.						2	79			0.96				151				
		Occupants L.HT.						2		53						—	106			
		Lighting					384					0.925				355				
		Fresh air S.HT.			5.3						24				× 1.23	156				
		Fresh air L.HT.									24			0.00178	× 3012	—	128			
		Infiltration														—				
		Face peak total loads														1073	234			
Instantaneous loads																				
	July 1500	Glass solar	4.09	250								0.29	0.53			157				
		Glass condn	4.68		5.3	3.30										81				
		Module wall	2.98		2.4	0.52										4				
		300° end wall	16.28		2.2	0.52										18				
		Internal wall	8.84		3.0	1.13										30				
		Roof	18.60		13.5	0.44										110				
		Occupants S.HT.						2	63			0.945				119				
		Occupants L.HT.						2		42						—	84			
		Lighting					307					0.91				279				
		Fresh air S.HT.			5.3						24				× 1.23	156				
		Fresh air L.HT.									24			0.00178	× 3012	—	128			
		Infiltration														—				
		Instantaneous total loads														954	212	1	954	212
																	C/fd	6	5174	1272

Δt_e = equivalent temp. difference. SF = storage factor. BF = shade factor.

Table 7.1 Job sheet for face peak and instantaneous cooling/~~heating~~ loads. SI Units — *Sheet No. 3*

Module	*Date & time*	*Load item*	*Area m^2*	*Peak Solar radn*	*Δt or Δt_e °C*	*U value*	*Total watts*	*No. occpts*	*W/occpnt S.HT.*	*W/occpnt L.HT.*	*V l/sec*	*SF*	*BF*	*Δg kg/kg*	*Factors*	*Module loads W S.HT.*	*Module loads W L.HT.*	*No. mods*	*Instantaneous loads W S.HT.*	*Instantaneous loads W L.HT.*
No. 2	**Intermediate floors. Face A 30° from North**																*B/fd*	6	5174	1272
Face peak loads																				
	July 1500	Glass solar	4.09	250								0.29	0.53			157				
		Glass condn	4.68		5.3	3.30										81				
		Module wall	2.98		2.4	0.52										4				
		—— end wall	16.28			0.52										—				
		Internal wall	8.84		3.0	1.13										30				
		Roof	18.60			0.44										—				
		Occupants S.HT.						2	79			0.945				149				
		Occupants L.HT.						2		53						—	106			
		Lighting					384					0.91				349				
		Fresh air S.HT.			5.3						24				× 1.23	156				
		Fresh air L.HT.									24			0.00178	× 3012	—	128			
		Infiltration														—				
		Face peak total loads														926	234			
Instantaneous loads																				
	July 1500	Glass solar	4.09	250								0.29	0.53			157				
		Glass condn	4.68		5.3	3.30										81				
		Module wall	2.98		2.4	0.52										4				
		—— end wall	16.28			0.52										—				
		Internal wall	8.84		3.0	1.13										30				
		Roof	18.60			0.44										—				
		Occupants S.HT.						2	63			0.945				119				
		Occupants L.HT.						2		42						—	84			
		Lighting					307					0.91				279				
		Fresh air S.HT.			5.3						24				× 1.23	156				
		Fresh air L.HT.									24			0.00178	× 3012	—	128			
		Infiltration														—				
		Instantaneous total loads														826	212	50	41300	10600
																	C/fd	56	46474	11872

Δt_e = equivalent temp. difference. SF = storage factor. BF = shade factor.

Table 7.1 Job sheet for face peak and instantaneous cooling/~~heating~~ loads. SI Units — *Sheet No. 4*

Module	Date & time	Load item	Area m^2	Peak Solar radn	Δt or Δt_e °C	U value	Total watts	No. occpts	W/occpnt		V l/sec	SF	BF	Δg kg/kg	Factors	Module loads W		No. mods	Instantaneous loads W	
									S.HT.	L.HT.						S.HT.	L.HT.		S.HT.	L.HT.
No. 2	Roof floor. Face A 30° from North																B/fd	56	46474	11872
Face peak loads																				
	July 1700	Glass solar	4.09	250								0.23	0.53			124				
		Glass condn	4.68		5.3	3.30										81				
		Module wall	2.98		2.4	0.52										4				
		— end wall	16.28			0.52										—				
		Internal wall	8.84		3.0	1.13										30				
		Roof	18.60		16.25	0.44										133				
		Occupants S.HT.						2	79			0.96				151				
		Occupants L.HT.						2		53						—	106			
		Lighting					384					0.925				355				
		Fresh air S.HT.			5.3						24				× 1.23	156				
		Fresh air L.HT.									24			0.00178	× 3012	—	128			
		Infiltration														—				
		Face peak total loads														1034	234			
Instantaneous loads																				
	July 1500	Glass solar	4.09	250								0.29	0.53			157				
		Glass condn	4.68		5.3	3.30										81				
		Module wall	2.98		2.4	0.52										4				
		— end wall	16.28			0.52										—				
		Internal wall	8.84		3.0	1.13										30				
		Roof	18.60		13.5	0.44										110				
		Occupants S.HT.						2	63			0.945				119				
		Occupants L.HT.						2		42						—	84			
		Lighting					307					0.91				279				
		Fresh air S.HT.			5.3						24				× 1.23	156				
		Fresh air L.HT.									24			0.00178		—	128			
		Infiltration														—				
		Instantaneous total loads														936	212	10	9360	2120
																	C/fd	66	55834	13992

Δt_e = equivalent temp. difference. SF = storage factor. BF = shade factor.

Table 7.1 Job sheet for face peak and instantaneous cooling/~~heating~~ loads. SI Units *Sheet No. 5*

Module	*Date & time*	*Load item*	*Area m²*	*Peak Solar radn*	*Δt or Δt_e °C*	*U value*	*Total watts*	*No. occpts*	*W/occpnt*		*V l/sec*	*SF*	*BF*	*Δg kg/kg*	*Factors*	*Module loads W*		*No. mods*	*Instantaneous loads W*	
									S.HT.	*L.HT.*						*S.HT.*	*L.HT.*		*S.HT.*	*L.HT.*
No. 3	**Intermediate floors. Face A 30° from North**																*B/fd*	66	55834	13992
Face peak loads																				
	July 1500	Glass solar	4.09	250								0.29	0.53			157				
		Glass condn	4.68		5.3	3.30										81				
		Module wall	2.98		2.4	0.52										4				
		120° end wall	16.28		10.2	0.52										86				
		Internal wall	8.84		3.0	1.13										30				
		Roof	18.60			0.44										—				
		Occupants S.HT.						2	79			0.945				149				
		Occupants L.HT.						2		53						—	106			
		Lighting					384					0.91				349				
		Fresh air S.HT.			5.3						24				× 1.23	156				
		Fresh air L.HT.									24			0.00178	× 3012	—	128			
		Infiltration														—				
		Face peak total loads														1012	234			
Instantaneous loads																				
	July 1500	Glass solar	4.09	250								0.29	0.53			157				
		Glass condn	4.68		5.3	3.30										81				
		Module wall	2.98		2.4	0.52										4				
		120° end wall	16.28		10.2	0.52										86				
		Internal wall	8.84		3.0	1.13										30				
		Roof	18.60			0.44										—				
		Occupants S.HT.						2	63			0.945				119				
		Occupants L.HT.						2		42						—	84			
		Lighting					307					0.91				279				
		Fresh air S.HT.			5.3						24				× 1.23	156				
		Fresh air L.HT.									24			0.00178	× 3012	—	128			
		Infiltration														—				
		Instantaneous total loads														912	212	5	4560	1060
																	C/fd	71	60394	15052

Δt_e = equivalent temp. difference. SF = storage factor. BF = shade factor.

Table 7.1 Job sheet for face peak and instantaneous cooling/~~heating~~ loads. SI Units — *Sheet No. 6*

Module	Date & time	Load item	Area m^2	Peak Solar radn	Δt or $\Delta t_e\,^\circ C$	U value	Total watts	No. occpts	W/occpnt S.HT.	W/occpnt L.HT.	V l/sec	SF	BF	Δg kg/kg	Factors	Module loads W S.HT.	Module loads W L.HT.	No. mods	Instantaneous loads W S.HT.	Instantaneous loads W L.HT.
No. 3	**Roof floor. Face A 30° from North**																B/fd	71	60394	15052
Face peak loads																				
	July 1700	Glass solar	4.09	250								0.23	0.53			124				
		Glass condn	4.68		5.3	3.30										81				
		Module wall	2.98		2.4	0.52										4				
		120° end wall	16.28		7.9	0.52										66				
		Internal wall	8.84		3.0	1.13										30				
		Roof	18.60		16.25	0.44										133				
		Occupants S.HT.						2	79			0.96				151				
		Occupants L.HT.						2		53						—	106			
		Lighting					384					0.925				355				
		Fresh air S.HT.			5.3						24				× 1.23	156				
		Fresh air L.HT.									24			0.00178	× 3012	—	128			
		Infiltration														—				
		Face peak total loads														1100	234			
Instantaneous loads																				
	July 1500	Glass solar	4.09	250								0.29	0.53			157				
		Glass condn	4.68		5.3	3.30										81				
		Module wall	2.98		2.4	0.52										4				
		120° end wall	16.28		10.2	0.52										86				
		Internal wall	8.84		3.0	1.13										30				
		Roof	18.60		13.5	0.44										110				
		Occupants S.HT.						2	63			0.945				119				
		Occupants L.HT.						2		42						—	84			
		Lighting					307					0.91				279				
		Fresh air S.HT.			5.3						24				× 1.23	156				
		Fresh air L.HT.									24			0.00178	× 3012	—	128			
		Infiltration														—				
		Instantaneous total loads														1022	212	1	1022	212
																	C/fd	72	61416	15264

Δt_e = equivalent temp. difference. SF = storage factor. BF = shade factor.

Table 7.1 Job sheet for face peak and instantaneous cooling/~~heating~~ loads. SI Units — *Sheet No. 7*

Module	Date & time	Load item	Area m^2	Peak Solar radn	Δt or Δt_e °C	U value	Total watts	No. occpts	W/occpnt		V l/sec	SF	BF	Δg kg/kg	Factors	Module loads W		No. mods	Instantaneous loads W	
									S.HT.	L.HT.						S.HT.	L.HT.		S.HT.	L.HT.
No. 4	**Intermediate floors. Face C 210° from North**																*B/fd*	72	61416	15264
Face peak loads																				
	Aug 1500	Glass solar	4.09	475								0.79	0.53			813				
		Glass condn	4.68		4.7	3.30										72				
		Module wall	2.98		7.5	0.52										11				
		120° end wall	16.28		10.2	0.52										86				
		Internal wall	8.84		3.0	1.13										30				
		Roof	18.60			0.44										—				
		Occupants S.HT.						2	79			0.945				149				
		Occupants L.HT.						2		53						—	106			
		Lighting					384					0.91				349				
		Fresh air S.HT.			4.7						24				× 1.23	138				
		Fresh air L.HT.									24			0.00218	× 3012	—	157			
		Infiltration														—				
		Face peak total loads														1648	263			
Instantaneous loads																				
	July 1500	Glass solar	4.09	405								0.79	0.53			693				
		Glass condn	4.68		5.3	3.30										81				
		Module wall	2.98		7.5	0.52										11				
		120° end wall	16.28		10.2	0.52										86				
		Internal wall	8.84		3.0	1.13										30				
		Roof	18.60			0.44										—				
		Occupants S.HT.						2	63			0.945				119				
		Occupants L.HT.						2		42						—	84			
		Lighting					307					0.91				279				
		Fresh air S.HT.			5.3						24				× 1.23	156				
		Fresh air L.HT.									24			0.00178	× 3012	—	128			
		Infiltration														—				
		Instantaneous total loads														1455	212	5	7275	1060
																	C/fd	77	68691	16324

Δt_e = equivalent temp. difference. SF = storage factor. BF = shade factor.

Table 7.1 Job sheet for face peak and instantaneous cooling/~~heating~~ loads. SI Units *Sheet No. 8*

Module	*Date & time*	*Load item*	*Area m^2*	*Peak Solar radn*	*Δt or Δt_e °C*	*U value*	*Total watts*	*No. occpts*	*W/occpnt*		*V l/sec*	*SF*	*BF*	*Δg kg/kg*	*Factors*	*Module loads W*		*No. mods*	*Instantaneous loads W*	
									S.HT.	*L.HT.*						*S.HT.*	*L.HT.*		*S.HT.*	*L.HT.*
No. 4	**Roof floor. Face C 210° from North**																*B/fd*	77	68691	16324
Face peak loads																				
	Aug 1600	Glass solar	4.09	475								0.65	0.53			669				
		Glass condn	4.68		5.0	3.30										77				
		Module wall	2.98		8.8	0.52										13				
		120° end wall	16.28		9.3	0.52										78				
		Internal wall	8.84		3.0	1.13										30				
		Roof	18.60		15.0	0.44										123				
		Occupants S.HT.						2	79			0.95				150				
		Occupants L.HT.						2		53						—	106			
		Lighting					384					0.92				353				
		Fresh air S.HT.			5.0						24				× 1.23	147				
		Fresh air L.HT.									24			0.00218	× 3012	—	157			
		Infiltration														—				
		Face peak total loads														1640	263			
Instantaneous loads																				
	July 1500	Glass solar	4.09	405								0.79	0.53			693				
		Glass condn	4.68		5.3	3.30										81				
		Module wall	2.98		7.5	0.52										11				
		120° end wall	16.28		10.2	0.52										86				
		Internal wall	8.84		3.0	1.13										30				
		Roof	18.60		15.0	0.44										123				
		Occupants S.HT.						2	63			0.945				119				
		Occupants L.HT.						2		42						—	84			
		Lighting					307					0.91				279				
		Fresh air S.HT.			5.3						24				× 1.23	156				
		Fresh air L.HT.									24			0.00178	× 3012	—	128			
		Infiltration														—				
		Instantaneous total loads														1578	212	1	1578	212
																	C/fd	78	70269	16536

Δt_e = equivalent temp. difference. SF = storage factor. BF = shade factor.

Table 7.1 Job sheet for face peak and instantaneous cooling/~~heating~~ loads. SI Units *Sheet No. 9*

Module	*Date & time*	*Load item*	*Area m^2*	*Peak Solar radn*	*Δt or Δt_e °C*	*U value*	*Total watts*	*No. occpts*	*W/occpnt*		*V l/sec*	*SF*	*BF*	*Δg kg/kg*	*Factors*	*Module loads W*		*No. mods*	*Instantaneous loads W*	
									S.HT.	*L.HT.*						*S.HT.*	*L.HT.*		*S.HT.*	*L.HT.*
No. 5	**Intermediate floors. Face C 210° from North**																*B/fd*	78	70269	16536
Face peak loads																				
	Aug 1500	Glass solar	4.09	475								0.79	0.53			813				
		Glass condn	4.68		4.7	3.30										72				
		Module wall	2.98		7.5	0.52										11				
		— end wall	16.28			0.52										—				
		Internal wall	8.84		3.0	1.13										30				
		Roof	18.60			0.44										—				
		Occupants S.HT.						2	79			0.945				149				
		Occupants L.HT.						2		53						—	106			
		Lighting					384					0.91				349				
		Fresh air S.HT.			4.7						24				× 1.23	138				
		Fresh air L.HT.									24			0.00218	× 3012	—	157			
		Infiltration														—				
		Face peak total loads														1562	263			
Instantaneous loads																				
	July 1500	Glass solar	4.09	405								0.79	0.53			693				
		Glass condn	4.68		5.3	3.30										81				
		Module wall	2.98		7.5	0.52										11				
		— end wall	16.28			0.52										—				
		Internal wall	8.84		3.0	1.13										30				
		Roof	18.60			0.44										—				
		Occupants S.HT.						2	63			0.945				119				
		Occupants L.HT.						2		42						—	84			
		Lighting					307					0.91				279				
		Fresh air S.HT.			5.3						24				× 1.23	156				
		Fresh air L.HT.									24			0.00178	× 3012	—	128			
		Infiltration														—				
		Instantaneous total loads														1369	212	50	68450	10600
																	C/fd	128	138719	27136

Δt_e = equivalent temp. difference. SF = storage factor. BF = shade factor.

Table 7.1 Job sheet for face peak and instantaneous cooling/~~heating~~ loads. SI Units — *Sheet No. 10*

Module	Date & time	Load item	Area m^2	Peak Solar radn	Δt or Δt_e °C	U value	Total watts	No. occpts	W/occpnt		V l/sec	SF	BF	Δg kg/kg	Factors	Module loads W		No. mods	Instantaneous loads W	
									S.HT.	L.HT.						S.HT.	L.HT.		S.HT.	L.HT.
No. 5	**Roof floor. Face C 210° from North**																*B/fd*	128	138719	27136
Face peak loads																				
	Aug 1600	Glass solar	4.09	475								0.65	0.53			669				
		Glass condn	4.68		5.0	3.30										77				
		Module wall	2.98		8.8	0.52										13				
		— end wall	16.28			0.52										—				
		Internal wall	8.84		3.0	1.13										30				
		Roof	18.60		15.0	0.44										123				
		Occupants S.HT.						2	79			0.95				150				
		Occupants L.HT.						2		53						—	106			
		Lighting					384					0.92				353				
		Fresh air S.HT.			5.0						24				× 1.23	147				
		Fresh air L.HT.									24			0.00218	× 3012	—	157			
		Infiltration														—				
		Face peak total loads														1562	263			
Instantaneous loads																				
	July 1500	Glass solar	4.09	405								0.79	0.53			693				
		Glass condn	4.68		5.3	3.30										81				
		Module wall	2.98		7.5	0.52										11				
		— end wall	16.28			0.52										—				
		Internal wall	8.84		3.0	1.13										30				
		Roof	18.60		15.0	0.44										123				
		Occupants S.HT.						2	63			0.945				119				
		Occupants L.HT.						2		42						—	84			
		Lighting					307					0.91				279				
		Fresh air S.HT.			5.3						24				× 1.23	156				
		Fresh air L.HT.									24			0.00178	× 3012	—	128			
		Infiltration														—				
		Instantaneous total loads														1492	212	10	14920	2120
																	C/fd	138	153639	29256

Δt_e = equivalent temp. difference. SF = storage factor. BF = shade factor.

Table 7.1 Job sheet for face peak and instantaneous cooling/~~heating~~ loads. SI Units *Sheet No. 11*

Module	*Date & time*	*Load item*	*Area m^2*	*Peak Solar radn*	*Δt or Δt_e °C*	*U value*	*Total watts*	*No. occpts*	*W/occpnt*		*V l/sec*	*SF*	*BF*	*Δg kg/kg*	*Factors*	*Module loads W*		*No. mods*	*Instantaneous loads W*	
									S.HT.	*L.HT.*						*S.HT.*	*L.HT.*		*S.HT.*	*L.HT.*
No. 6	**Intermediate floors. Face C 210° from North**																*B/fd*	138	153639	29256
Face peak loads																				
	Aug 1500	Glass solar	4.09	475								0.79	0.53			813				
		Glass condn	4.68		4.7	3.30										72				
		Module wall	2.98		7.5	0.52										11				
		300° end wall	16.28		2.2	0.52										18				
		Internal wall	8.84		3.0	1.13										30				
		Roof	18.60			0.44										—				
		Occupants S.HT.						2	79			0.945				149				
		Occupants L.HT.						2		53						—	106			
		Lighting					384					0.91				349				
		Fresh air S.HT.			4.7						24				× 1.23	138				
		Fresh air L.HT.									24			0.00218	× 3012	—	157			
		Infiltration														—				
		Face peak total loads														1580	263			
Instantaneous loads																				
	July 1500	Glass solar	4.09	405								0.79	0.53			693				
		Glass condn	4.68		5.3	3.30										81				
		Module wall	2.98		7.5	0.52										11				
		300° end wall	16.28		2.2	0.52										18				
		Internal wall	8.84		3.0	1.13										30				
		Roof	18.60			0.44										—				
		Occupants S.HT.						2	63			0.945				119				
		Occupants L.HT.						2		42						—	84			
		Lighting					307					0.91				279				
		Fresh air S.HT.			5.3						24				× 1.23	156				
		Fresh air L.HT.									24			0.00178	× 3012	—	128			
		Infiltration														—				
		Instantaneous total loads														1387	212	5	6935	1060
																	C/fd	143	160574	30316

Δt_e = equivalent temp. difference. SF = storage factor. BF = shade factor.

Table 7.1 Job sheet for face peak and instantaneous cooling/~~heating~~ loads. SI Units — *Sheet No. 12*

Module	*Date & time*	*Load item*	*Area* m^2	*Peak Solar radn*	Δt *or* Δt_e °*C*	*U value*	*Total watts*	*No. occpts*	*W/occpnt*		*V l/sec*	*SF*	*BF*	Δg *kg/kg*	*Factors*	*Module loads W*		*No. mods*	*Instantaneous loads W*	
									S.HT.	*L.HT.*						*S.HT.*	*L.HT.*		*S.HT.*	*L.HT.*
No. 6	**Roof floor. Face C 210° from North**																*B/fd*	143	160574	30316
Face peak loads																				
	Aug 1600	Glass solar	4.09	475								0.65	0.53			669				
		Glass condn	4.68		5.0	3.30										77				
		Module wall	2.98		8.8	0.52										13				
		300° end wall	16.28		2.9	0.52										24				
		Internal wall	8.84		3.0	1.13										30				
		Roof	18.60		15.0	0.44										123				
		Occupants S.HT.						2	79			0.95				150				
		Occupants L.HT.						2		53						—	106			
		Lighting					384					0.92				353				
		Fresh air S.HT.			5.0						24				× 1.23	147				
		Fresh air L.HT.									24			0.00218	× 3012	—	157			
		Infiltration														—				
		Face peak total loads														1586	263			
Instantaneous loads																				
	July 1500	Glass solar	4.09	405								0.79	0.53			693				
		Glass condn	4.68		5.3	3.30										81				
		Module wall	2.98		7.5	0.52										11				
		300° end wall	16.28		2.2	0.52										18				
		Internal wall	8.84		3.0	1.13										30				
		Roof	18.60		15.0	0.44										123				
		Occupants S.HT.						2	63			0.945				119				
		Occupants L.HT.						2		42						—	84			
		Lighting					307					0.91				279				
		Fresh air S.HT.			5.3						24				× 1.23	156				
		Fresh air L.HT.									24			0.00178	× 3012	—	128			
		Infiltration														—				
		Instantaneous total loads														1510	212	1	1510	212
																	C/fd	144	162084	30528

Δt_e = equivalent temp. difference. SF = storage factor. BF = shade factor.

Table 7.1 Job sheet for instantaneous cooling loads. SI Units

Sheet No. 13

Date & time	*Load item*	*Calculation*			*No. mods*	*Instantaneous loads W*	
						S.HT.	*L.HT.*
Building instantaneous cooling load				*B/fd*	144	162084	30528
July 1500	Duct gains	Section 4.7.1 p.79					
		25 mm thick insulation					
		Indoor air temperature	= 22°C				
		Duct air temperature assume	= 13°C				
		$\Delta t = 22 - 13$	= 9°C				
		Percentage gain = 9/2.8	= 3.2%	=		5187	
	Pipe gains	Section 4.7.2 p. 80					
		25 mm to 32 mm insulation					
		Water mean temperature assume	= 10°C				
		$\Delta t = 22 - 10$	= 12°C				
		Percentage gain = 12/5.6	= 2.1%	=		3404	
	Supply fan	$Q_S = 1.43$ VP. Eqn 4.12 p. 78					
		External motor and drive					
		V = 144 × 24 + 5% for leakage	= 3628 l/sec				
		P – assume 0.6 kpa swg					
		$Q_S = 1.43 \times 3628 \times 0.6$		=		3112	
	Circulating pump	$Q_S = 1.54$ VP. Eqn 4.16 p. 79					
		V – assume 9.15 l/sec					
		P – assume 179 kpa head					
		$Q_S = 1.54 \times 9.15 \times 179$		=		2522	
						176309 30528	30528
	Instantaneous load	Total heat, watts		=		206837	

Table 7.1 Job sheet for face peak and instantaneous ~~cooling~~/heating loads. SI Units *Sheet No. 14*

Module	*Date & time*	*Load item*	*Area* m^2	*Peak Solar radn*	*Δt or Δt_e °C*	*U value*	*Total watts*	*No. occpts*	*W/occpnt*		*V l/sec*	*SF*	*BF*	*Δg kg/kg*	*Factors*	*Module loads W*		*No. mods*	*Instantaneous loads W*	
									S.HT.	*L.HT.*						*S.HT.*	*L.HT.*		*S.HT.*	*L.HT.*
Intermediate modules																				
	Jan 08.00	Glass condn	4.68		25.5	3.30										393				
		Module wall	2.98		25.5	0.52										39				
		Internal wall	8.84		12.75	1.13										127				
		Fresh air			25.5						24				× 1.23	752				
		Infiltration			25.5						7				× 1.23	219				
		Intermediate modules totals														1530		100	153000	
End modules																				
	Jan 08.00	Glass condn	4.68		25.5	3.30										393				
		Module wall	2.98		25.5	0.52										39				
		End wall	16.28		25.5	0.52										215				
		Internal wall	8.84		12.75	1.13										127				
		Fresh air			25.5						24				× 1.23	752				
		Infiltration			25.5						7				× 1.23	219				
		End modules totals														1745		20	34900	
Roof intermediate modules																				
	Jan 08.00	Glass condn	4.68		25.5	3.30										393				
		Module wall	2.98		25.5	0.52										39				
		Internal wall	8.84		12.75	1.13										127				
		Roof	18.60		25.5	0.44										209				
		Fresh air			25.5						24				× 1.23	752				
		Infiltration			25.5						7				× 1.23	219				
		Roof intermediate modules totals														1739		20	34780	
Roof end modules																				
	Jan 08.00	Glass condn	4.68		25.5	3.30										393				
		Module wall	2.98		25.5	0.52										39				
		End wall	16.28		25.5	0.52										215				
		Internal wall	8.84		12.75	1.13										127				
		Roof	18.60		25.5	0.44										209				
		Fresh air			25.5						24				× 1.23	752				
		Infiltration			25.5						7				× 1.23	219				
		Roof end modules totals														1954		4	7816	
Building total heating load, watts																		144	230496	

Δt_e = equivalent temp. difference. SF = storage factor. BF = shade factor.

Table 7.2 Job sheet for face peak and instantaneous cooling/~~heating~~ loads. Imperial Units. *Sheet No. 1*

Module	Date & time	Load item	Area ft^2	Peak Solar radn	Δt or Δt_e °F	U value	Total watts	No. occpts	BTU/hr/occpt		V cfm	SF	BF	Δg lb/lb	Factors	Module loads BTU/hr		No. mods	Instant. loads BTU/hr	
									S.HT.	L.HT.						S.HT.	L.HT.		S.HT.	L.HT.
No. 1	**Intermediate floors. Face A 30° from North**																			
Face Peak Loads																				
	July 1500	Glass solar	44.0	79.5								0.29	0.53			538				
		Glass condn	50.4		9.5	0.58										278				
		Module wall	32.0		4.3	0.09										12				
		300° end wall	175.0		4.0	0.09										63				
		Internal wall	95.0		5.0	0.20										95				
		Roof	200.0			0.077										—				
		Occupants S.HT.						2	270			0.945				510				
		Occupants L.HT.						2		180						—	360			
		Lighting					384					0.91			X 3.415	1193				
		Fresh air S.HT.			9.5						50				X 1.08	513				
		Fresh air L.HT.									50			0.00178	X 4830	—	430			
		Infiltration														—				
		Face peak total loads														3202	790			
Instantaneous loads																				
	July 1500	Glass solar	44.0	79.5								0.29	0.53			538				
		Glass condn	50.4		9.5	0.58										278				
		Module wall	32.0		4.3	0.09										12				
		300° end wall	175.0		4.0	0.09										63				
		Internal wall	95.0		5.0	0.20										95				
		Roof	200.0			0.077										—				
		Occupants S.HT.						2	216			0.945				408				
		Occupants L.HT.						2		144						—	288			
		Lighting					307					0.91			X 3.415	954				
		Fresh air S.HT.			9.5						50				X 1.08	513				
		Fresh air L.HT.									50			0.00178	X 4830	—	430			
		Infiltration														—				
		Instantaneous total loads														2861	718	5	14305	3590
																	C/fd	5	14305	3590

Δt_e = equivalent temp. difference. SF = storage factor. BF = shade factor.

Table 7.2 Job sheet for face peak and instantaneous cooling/~~heating~~ loads. Imperial Units. *Sheet No. 2*

Module	Date & time	Load item	Area ft^2	Peak Solar radn	Δt or Δt_e °F	U value	Total watts	No. occpts	BTU/hr/occpt S.HT.	BTU/hr/occpt L.HT.	V cfm	SF	BF	Δg lb/lb	Factors	Module loads BTU/hr S.HT.	Module loads BTU/hr L.HT.	No. mods	Instant. loads BTU/hr S.HT.	Instant. loads BTU/hr L.HT.
No. 1	**Roof floor. Face A 30° from North**																*B/fd*	5	14305	3590
Face peak loads																				
	July 1700	Glass solar	44.0	79.5								0.23	0.53			426				
		Glass condn	50.4		9.5	0.58										278				
		Module wall	32.0		4.3	0.09										12				
		300° end wall	175.0		8.5	0.09										134				
		Internal wall	95.0		5.0	0.20										95				
		Roof	200.0		29.3	0.077										451				
		Occupants S.HT.						2	270			0.96				518				
		Occupants L.HT.						2		180						—	360			
		Lighting					384					0.925			X 3.415	1213				
		Fresh air S.HT.			9.5						50				X 1.08	513				
		Fresh air L.HT.									50			0.00178	X 4830	—	430			
		Infiltration														—				
		Face peak total loads														3640	790			
Instantaneous loads																				
	July 1500	Glass solar	44.0	79.5								0.29	0.53			538				
		Glass condn	50.4		9.5	0.58										278				
		Module wall	32.0		4.3	0.09										12				
		300° end wall	175.0		4.0	0.09										63				
		Internal wall	95.0		5.0	0.20										95				
		Roof	200.0		24.3	0.077										374				
		Occupants S.HT.						2	216			0.945				408				
		Occupants L.HT.						2		144						—	288			
		Lighting					307					0.91			X 3.415	954				
		Fresh air S.HT.			9.5						50				X 1.08	513				
		Fresh air L.HT.									50			0.00178	X 4830	—	430			
		Infiltration														—				
		Instantaneous total loads														3235	718	1	3235	718
																	C/fd	6	17540	4308

Δt_e = equivalent temp. difference. SF = storage factor. BF = shade factor.

Table 7.2 Job sheet for face peak and instantaneous cooling/~~heating~~ loads. Imperial Units. *Sheet No. 3*

Module	*Date & time*	*Load item*	*Area* ft^2	*Peak Solar radn*	Δt *or* $\Delta t_e\,°F$	*U value*	*Total watts*	*No. occpts*	*BTU/hr/occpt*		*V cfm*	*SF*	*BF*	Δg *lb/lb*	*Factors*	*Module loads BTU/hr*		*No. mods*	*Instant. loads BTU/hr*	
									S.HT.	*L.HT.*						*S.HT.*	*L.HT.*		*S.HT.*	*L.HT.*
No. 2	**Intermediate floors. Face A 30° from North**																*B/fd*	6	17540	4308
Face peak loads																				
	July 1500	Glass solar	44.0	79.5								0.29	0.53			538				
		Glass condn	50.4		9.5	0.58										278				
		Module wall	32.0		4.3	0.09										12				
		— end wall	175.0			0.09										—				
		Internal wall	95.0		5.0	0.20										95				
		Roof	200.0			0.077										—				
		Occupants S.HT.						2	270			0.945				510				
		Occupants L.HT.						2		180						—	360			
		Lighting					384					0.91			× 3.415	1193				
		Fresh air S.HT.			9.5						50				× 1.08	513				
		Fresh air L.HT.									50			0.00178	× 4830	—	430			
		Infiltration														—				
		Face peak total loads														3139	790			
Instantaneous loads																				
	July 1500	Glass solar	44.0	79.5								0.29	0.53			538				
		Glass condn	50.4		9.5	0.58										278				
		Module wall	32.0		4.3	0.09										12				
		— end wall	175.0			0.09										—				
		Internal wall	95.0		5.0	0.20										95				
		Roof	200.0			0.077										—				
		Occupants S.HT.						2	216			0.945				408				
		Occupants L.HT.						2		144						—	288			
		Lighting					307					0.91			× 3.415	954				
		Fresh air S.HT.			9.5						50				× 1.08	513				
		Fresh air L.HT.									50			0.00178	× 4830	—	430			
		Infiltration														—				
		Instantaneous total loads														2798	718	50	139900	35900
																	C/fd	56	157440	40208

Δt_e = equivalent temp. difference. SF = storage factor. BF = shade factor.

Table 7.2 Job sheet for face peak and instantaneous cooling/~~heating~~ loads. Imperial Units. *Sheet No. 4*

Module	Date & time	Load item	Area ft^2	Peak Solar radn	Δt or $\Delta t_e\,^\circ F$	U value	Total watts	No. occpts	BTU/hr/occpt S.HT.	BTU/hr/occpt L.HT.	V cfm	SF	BF	Δg lb/lb	Factors	Module loads BTU/hr S.HT.	Module loads BTU/hr L.HT.	No. mods	Instant. loads BTU/hr S.HT.	Instant. loads BTU/hr L.HT.
No. 2	**Roof floor. Face A 30° from North**																*B/fd*	56	157440	40208
Face peak loads																				
	July 1700	Glass solar	44.0	79.5								0.23	0.53			426				
		Glass condn	50.4		9.5	0.58										278				
		Module wall	32.0		4.3	0.09										12				
		— end wall	175.0			0.09										—				
		Internal wall	95.0		5.0	0.20										95				
		Roof	200.0		29.3	0.077										451				
		Occupants S.HT.						2	270			0.96				518				
		Occupants L.HT.						2		180						—	360			
		Lighting					384					0.925			× 3.415	1213				
		Fresh air S.HT.			9.5						50				× 1.08	513				
		Fresh air L.HT.									50			0.00178	× 4830	—	430			
		Infiltration														—				
		Face peak total loads														3506	790			
Instantaneous loads																				
	July 1500	Glass solar	44.0	79.5								0.29	0.53			538				
		Glass condn	50.4		9.5	0.58										278				
		Module wall	32.0		4.3	0.09										12				
		— end wall	175.0			0.09										—				
		Internal wall	95.0		5.0	0.20										95				
		Roof	200.0		24.3	0.077										374				
		Occupants S.HT.						2	216			0.945				408				
		Occupants L.HT.						2		144						—	288			
		Lighting					307					0.91			× 3.415	954				
		Fresh air S.HT.			9.5						50				× 1.08	513				
		Fresh air L.HT.									50			0.00178	× 4830	—	430			
		Infiltration														—				
		Instantaneous total loads														3172	718	10	31720	7180
																	C/fd	66	189160	47388

Δt_e = equivalent temp. difference. SF = storage factor. BF = shade factor.

Table 7.2 Job sheet for face peak and instantaneous cooling/~~heating~~ loads. Imperial Units. *Sheet No. 5*

Module	Date & time	Load item	Area ft^2	Peak Solar radn	Δt or Δt_e °F	U value	Total watts	No. occpts	BTU/hr/occpt S.HT.	BTU/hr/occpt L.HT.	V cfm	SF	BF	Δg lb/lb	Factors	Module loads BTU/hr S.HT.	Module loads BTU/hr L.HT.	No. mods	Instant. loads BTU/hr S.HT.	Instant. loads BTU/hr L.HT.
No. 3	**Intermediate floors. Face A 30° from North**																*B/fd*	66	189160	47388
Face peak loads																				
	July 1500	Glass solar	44.0	79.5								0.29	0.53			538				
		Glass condn	50.4		9.5	0.58										278				
		Module wall	32.0		4.3	0.09										12				
		120° end wall	175.0		18.4	0.09										290				
		Internal wall	95.0		5.0	0.20										95				
		Roof	200.0			0.077										—				
		Occupants S.HT.						2	270			0.945				510				
		Occupants L.HT.						2		180						—	360			
		Lighting					384					0.91			× 3.415	1193				
		Fresh air S.HT.			9.5						50				× 1.08	513				
		Fresh air L.HT.									50			0.00178	× 4830	—	430			
		Infiltration														—				
		Face peak total loads														3429	790			
Instantaneous loads																				
	July 1500	Glass solar	44.0	79.5								0.29	0.53			538				
		Glass condn	50.4		9.5	0.58										278				
		Module wall	32.0		4.3	0.09										12				
		120° end wall	175.0		18.4	0.09										290				
		Internal wall	95.0		5.0	0.20										95				
		Roof	200.0			0.077										—				
		Occupants S.HT.						2	216			0.945				408				
		Occupants L.HT.						2		144						—	288			
		Lighting					307					0.91			× 3.415	954				
		Fresh air S.HT.			9.5						50				× 1.08	513				
		Fresh air L.HT.									50			0.00178	× 4830	—	430			
		Infiltration														—				
	Instantaneous total loads															3088	718	5	15440	3590
																	C/fd	71	204600	50978

Δt_e = equivalent temp. difference. SF = storage factor. BF = shade factor.

Table 7.2 Job sheet for face peak and instantaneous cooling/~~heating~~ loads. Imperial Units. *Sheet No. 6*

Module	*Date & time*	*Load item*	*Area ft^2*	*Peak Solar radn*	*Δt or Δt_e °F*	*U value*	*Total watts*	*No. occpts*	*BTU/hr/occpt S.HT.*	*BTU/hr/occpt L.HT.*	*V cfm*	*SF*	*BF*	*Δg lb/lb*	*Factors*	*Module loads BTU/hr S.HT.*	*Module loads BTU/hr L.HT.*	*No. mods*	*Instant. loads BTU/hr S.HT.*	*Instant. loads BTU/hr L.HT.*
No. 3	**Roof floor. Face A 30° from North**																*B/fd*	71	204600	50978
Face peak loads																				
	July 1700	Glass solar	44.0	79.5								0.23	0.53			426				
		Glass condn	50.4		9.5	0.58										278				
		Module wall	32.0		4.3	0.09										12				
		120° end wall	175.0		14.2	0.09										224				
		Internal wall	95.0		5.0	0.20										95				
		Roof	200.0		29.3	0.077										451				
		Occupants S.HT.						2	270			0.96				518				
		Occupants L.HT.						2		180						—	360			
		Lighting					384					0.925			× 3.415	1213				
		Fresh air S.HT.			9.5						50				× 1.08	513				
		Fresh air L.HT.									50			0.00178	× 4830	—	430			
		Infiltration														—				
		Face peak total loads														3730	790			
Instantaneous loads																				
	July 1500	Glass solar	44.0	79.5								0.29	0.53			538				
		Glass condn	50.4		9.5	0.58										278				
		Module wall	32.0		4.3	0.09										12				
		120° end wall	175.0		18.4	0.09										290				
		Internal wall	95.0		5.0	0.20										95				
		Roof	200.0		24.3	0.077										374				
		Occupants S.HT.						2	216			0.945				408				
		Occupants L.HT.						2		144						—	288			
		Lighting					307					0.91			× 3.415	954				
		Fresh air S.HT.			9.5						50				× 1.08	513				
		Fresh air L.HT.									50			0.00178	× 4830	—	430			
		Infiltration														—				
		Instantaneous total loads														3462	718	1	3462	718
																	C/fd	72	208062	51696

Δt_e = equivalent temp. difference. SF = storage factor. BF = shade factor.

Table 7.2 Job sheet for face peak and instantaneous cooling/~~heating~~ loads. Imperial Units.

Sheet No. 7

Module	Date & time	Load item	Area ft^2	Peak Solar radn	Δt or Δt_e °F	U value	Total watts	No. occpts	BTU/hr/occpt S.HT.	BTU/hr/occpt L.HT.	V cfm	SF	BF	Δg lb/lb	Factors	Module loads BTU/hr S.HT.	Module loads BTU/hr L.HT.	No. mods	Instant. loads BTU/hr S.HT.	Instant. loads BTU/hr L.HT.
No. 4	**Intermediate floors. Face C 210° from North**																B/fd	72	208062	51696
Face peak loads																				
	Aug 1500	Glass solar	44.0	151								0.79	0.53			2782				
		Glass condn	50.4		8.5	0.58										248				
		Module wall	32.0		13.5	0.09										39				
		120° end wall	175.0		18.4	0.09										290				
		Internal wall	95.0		5.0	0.20										95				
		Roof	200.0			0.077										—				
		Occupants S.HT.						2	270			0.945				510				
		Occupants L.HT.						2		180						—	360			
		Lighting					384					0.91			× 3.415	1193				
		Fresh air S.HT.			8.5						50				× 1.08	459				
		Fresh air L.HT.									50			0.00218	× 4830	—	526			
		Infiltration														—				
		Face peak total loads														5616	886			
Instantaneous loads																				
	July 1500	Glass solar	44.0	128.5								0.79	0.53			2367				
		Glass condn	50.4		9.5	0.58										278				
		Module wall	32.0		13.5	0.09										39				
		120° end wall	175.0		18.4	0.09										290				
		Internal wall	95.0		5.0	0.20										95				
		Roof	200.0			0.077										—				
		Occupants S.HT.						2	216			0.945				408				
		Occupants L.HT.						2		144						—	288			
		Lighting					307					0.91			× 3.415	954				
		Fresh air S.HT.			9.5						50				× 1.08	513				
		Fresh air L.HT.									50			0.00178	× 4830	—	430			
		Infiltration														—				
		Instantaneous total loads														4944	718	5	24720	3590
																	C/fd	77	232782	55286

Δt_e = equivalent temp. difference. SF = storage factor. BF = shade factor.

Table 7.2 Job sheet for face peak and instantaneous cooling/~~heating~~ loads. Imperial Units. *Sheet No. 8*

Module	*Date & time*	*Load item*	*Area ft^2*	*Peak Solar radn*	*Δt or Δt_e °F*	*U value*	*Total watts*	*No. occpts*	*BTU/hr/occpt*		*V cfm*	*SF*	*BF*	*Δg lb/lb*	*Factors*	*Module loads BTU/hr*		*No. mods*	*Instant. loads BTU/hr*	
									S.HT.	*L.HT.*						*S.HT.*	*L.HT.*		*S.HT.*	*L.HT.*
No. 4	**Roof floor. Face C 210° from North**																*B/fd*	77	232782	55286
Face peak loads																				
	Aug 1600	Glass solar	44.0	151								0.65	0.53			2289				
		Glass condn	50.4		9.0	0.58										263				
		Module wall	32.0		15.8	0.09										46				
		120° end wall	175.0		16.7	0.09										263				
		Internal wall	95.0		5.0	0.20										95				
		Roof	200.0		27.0	0.077										416				
		Occupants S.HT.						2	270			0.95				513				
		Occupants L.HT.						2		180						—	360			
		Lighting					384					0.92			× 3.415	1206				
		Fresh air S.HT.			9.0						50				× 1.08	486				
		Fresh air L.HT.									50			0.00218	× 4830	—	526			
		Infiltration														—				
		Face peak total loads														5577	886			
Instantaneous loads																				
	July 1500	Glass solar	44.0	128.5								0.79	0.53			2367				
		Glass condn	50.4		9.5	0.58										278				
		Module wall	32.0		13.5	0.09										39				
		120° end wall	175.0		18.4	0.09										290				
		Internal wall	95.0		5.0	0.20										95				
		Roof	200.0		24.3	0.077										374				
		Occupants S.HT.						2	216			0.945				408				
		Occupants L.HT.						2		144						—	288			
		Lighting					307					0.91			× 3.415	954				
		Fresh air S.HT.			9.5						50				× 1.08	513				
		Fresh air L.HT.									50			0.00178	× 4830	—	430			
		Infiltration														—				
		Instantaneous total loads														5318	718	1	5318	718
																	C/fd	78	238100	56004

Δt_e = equivalent temp. difference. SF = storage factor. BF = shade factor.

Table 7.2 Job sheet for face peak and instantaneous cooling/~~heating~~ loads. Imperial Units. *Sheet No. 9*

Module	Date & time	Load item	Area ft^2	Peak Solar radn	Δt or Δt_e °F	U value	Total watts	No. occpts	BTU/hr/occpt S.HT.	BTU/hr/occpt L.HT.	V cfm	SF	BF	Δg lb/lb	Factors	Module loads BTU/hr S.HT.	Module loads BTU/hr L.HT.	No. mods	Instant. loads BTU/hr S.HT.	Instant. loads BTU/hr L.HT.
No. 5	**Intermediate floors. Face C 210° from North**																*B/fd*	78	238100	56004
Face peak loads																				
	Aug 1500	Glass solar	44.0	151								0.79	0.53			2782				
		Glass condn	50.4		8.5	0.58										248				
		Module wall	32.0		13.5	0.09										39				
		— end wall	175.0			0.09										—				
		Internal wall	95.0		5.0	0.20										95				
		Roof	200.0			0.077										—				
		Occupants S.HT.						2	270			0.945				510				
		Occupants L.HT.						2		180						—	360			
		Lighting					384					0.91			X 3.415	1193				
		Fresh air S.HT.			8.5						50				X 1.08	459				
		Fresh air L.HT.									50			0.00218	X 4830	—	526			
		Infiltration														—				
		Face peak total loads														5326	886			
Instantaneous loads																				
	July 1500	Glass solar	44.0	128.5								0.79	0.53			2367				
		Glass condn	50.4		9.5	0.58										278				
		Module wall	32.0		13.5	0.09										39				
		— end wall	175.0			0.09										—				
		Internal wall	95.0		5.0	0.20										95				
		Roof	200.0			0.077										—				
		Occupants S.HT.						2	216			0.945				408				
		Occupants L.HT.						2		144						—	288			
		Lighting					307					0.91			X 3.415	954				
		Fresh air S.HT.			9.5						50				X 1.08	513				
		Fresh air L.HT.									50			0.00178		—	430			
		Infiltration														—				
	Instantaneous total loads															4654	718	50	232700	35900
																	C/fd	128	470800	91904

Δt_e = equivalent temp. difference. SF = storage factor. BF = shade factor.

Table 7.2 Job sheet for face peak and instantaneous cooling/~~heating~~ loads. Imperial Units.

Sheet No. 10

Module	*Date & time*	*Load item*	*Area ft^2*	*Peak Solar radn*	*Δt or Δt_e °F*	*U value*	*Total watts*	*No. occpts*	*BTU/hr/occpt*		*V cfm*	*SF*	*BF*	*Δg lb/lb*	*Factors*	*Module loads BTU/hr*		*No. mods*	*Instant. loads BTU/hr*	
									S.HT.	*L.HT.*						*S.HT.*	*L.HT.*		*S.HT.*	*L.HT.*
No. 5	**Roof floor. Face C 210° from North**																*B/fd*	128	470800	91904
Face peak loads																				
	Aug 1600	Glass solar	44.0	151								0.65	0.53			2289				
		Glass condn	50.4		9.0	0.58										263				
		Module wall	32.0		15.8	0.09										46				
		— end wall	175.0			0.09										—				
		Internal wall	95.0		5.0	0.20										95				
		Roof	200.0		27.0	0.077										416				
		Occupants S.HT.						2	270			0.95				513				
		Occupants L.HT.						2		180						—	360			
		Lighting					384					0.92			× 3.415	1206				
		Fresh air S.HT.			9.0						50				× 1.08	486				
		Fresh air L.HT.									50			0.00218	× 4830	—	526			
		Infiltration														—				
		Face peak total loads														4930	886			
Instantaneous loads																				
	July 1500	Glass solar	44.0	128.5								0.79	0.53			2367				
		Glass condn	50.4		9.5	0.58										278				
		Module wall	32.0		13.5	0.09										39				
		— end wall	175.0			0.09										—				
		Internal wall	95.0		5.0	0.20										95				
		Roof	200.0		24.3	0.077										374				
		Occupants S.HT.						2	216			0.945				408				
		Occupants L.HT.						2		144						—	288			
		Lighting					307					0.91			× 3.415	954				
		Fresh air S.HT.			9.5						50				× 1.08	513				
		Fresh air L.HT.									50			0.00178	× 4830	—	430			
		Infiltration														—				
		Instantaneous total loads														5028	718	10	50280	7180
																	C/fd	138	521080	99084

Δt_e = equivalent temp. difference. SF = storage factor. BF = shade factor.

Table 7.2 Job sheet for face peak and instantaneous cooling/~~heating~~ loads. Imperial Units. *Sheet No. 11*

Module	Date & time	Load item	Area ft^2	Peak Solar radn	Δt or Δt_e °F	U value	Total watts	No. occpts	BTU/hr/occpt		V cfm	SF	BF	Δg lb/lb	Factors	Module loads BTU/hr		No. mods	Instant. loads BTU/hr	
									S.HT.	L.HT.						S.HT.	L.HT.		S.HT.	L.HT.
No. 6	**Intermediate floors. Face C 210° from North**																*B/fd*	138	521080	99084
Face peak loads																				
	Aug 1500	Glass solar	44.0	151								0.79	0.53			2782				
		Glass condn	50.4		8.5	0.58										248				
		Module wall	32.0		13.5	0.09										39				
		300° end wall	175.0		4.0	0.09										63				
		Internal wall	95.0		5.0	0.20										95				
		Roof	200.0			0.077										—				
		Occupants S.HT.						2	270			0.945				510				
		Occupants L.HT.						2		180						—	360			
		Lighting					384					0.91			× 3.415	1193				
		Fresh air S.HT.			8.5						50				× 1.08	459				
		Fresh air L.HT.									50			0.00218	× 4830	—	526			
		Infiltration														—				
		Face peak total loads														5389	886			
Instantaneous loads																				
	July 1500	Glass solar	44.0	128.5								0.79	0.53			2367				
		Glass condn	50.4		9.5	0.58										278				
		Module wall	32.0		13.5	0.09										39				
		300° end wall	175.0		4.0	0.09										63				
		Internal wall	95.0		5.0	0.20										95				
		Roof	200.0			0.077										—				
		Occupants S.HT.						2	216			0.945				408				
		Occupants L.HT.						2		144						—	288			
		Lighting					307					0.91			× 3.415	954				
		Fresh air S.HT.			9.5						50				× 1.08	513				
		Fresh air L.HT.									50			0.00178	× 4830	—	430			
		Infiltration														—				
		Instantaneous total loads														4717	718	5	23585	3590
																	C/fd	143	544665	102674

Δt_e = equivalent temp. difference. SF = storage factor. BF = shade factor.

Table 7.2 Job sheet for face peak and instantaneous cooling/~~heating~~ loads. Imperial Units. *Sheet No. 12*

Module	Date & time	Load item	Area ft^2	Peak Solar radn	Δt or Δt_e °F	U value	Total watts	No. occpts	BTU/hr/occpt S.HT.	BTU/hr/occpt L.HT.	V cfm	SF	BF	Δg lb/lb	Factors	Module loads BTU/hr S.HT.	Module loads BTU/hr L.HT.	No. mods	Instant. loads BTU/hr S.HT.	Instant. loads BTU/hr L.HT.
No. 6	**Roof floor. Face C 210° from North**																B/fd	143	544665	102674
Face peak loads																				
	Aug 1600	Glass solar	44.0	151								0.65	0.53			2289				
		Glass condn	50.4		9.0	0.58										263				
		Module wall	32.0		15.8	0.09										46				
		300° end wall	175.0		5.2	0.09										82				
		Internal wall	95.0		5.0	0.20										95				
		Roof	200.0		27.0	0.077										416				
		Occupants S.HT.						2	270			0.95				513				
		Occupants L.HT.						2		180						—	360			
		Lighting					384					0.92			X 3.415	1206				
		Fresh air S.HT.			9.0						50				X 1.08	486				
		Fresh air L.HT.									50			0.00218	X 4830	—	526			
		Infiltration														—				
		Face peak total loads														5396	886			
Instantaneous loads																				
	July 1500	Glass solar	44.0	128.5								0.79	0.53			2367				
		Glass condn	50.4		9.5	0.58										278				
		Module wall	32.0		13.5	0.09										39				
		300° end wall	175.0		4.0	0.09										63				
		Internal wall	95.0		5.0	0.20										95				
		Roof	200.0		24.3	0.077										374				
		Occupants S.HT.						2	216			0.945				408				
		Occupants L.HT.						2		144						—	288			
		Lighting					307					0.91			X 3.415	954				
		Fresh air S.HT.			9.5						50				X 1.08	513				
		Fresh air L.HT.									50			0.00178	X 4830	—	430			
		Infiltration														—				
		Instantaneous total loads														5091	718	1	5091	718
																	C/fd	144	549756	103392

Δt_e = equivalent temp. difference. SF = storage factor. BF = shade factor.

Table 7.2 Job sheet for instantaneous cooling loads. Imperial Units. *Sheet No. 13*

Date & time	*Load item*	*Calculation*			*No. mods*	*Instant. loads BTU/hr*	
						S.HT.	*L.HT.*
Building instantaneous cooling load				*B/fd*	144	549756	103392
July 1500	Duct gains	Section 4.7.1 p. 79 1 in thick insulation Indoor air temperature Duct air temperature assume $\Delta t = 72 - 55$ Percentage gain = 17/5	 = 72°F = 55°F = 17°F = 3.4%	=		18692	
	Pipe gains	Section 4.7.2 p. 80 1 in to 1¼ in thick insulation Water mean temperature assume $\Delta t = 72 - 50$ Percentage gain = 22/10	 = 50°F = 22°F = 2.2%	=		12095	
	Supply fan	$Q_S = 0.57$ VP. Equation 4.12 p. 78 External motor and drive V = 144 × 50 + 5% for leakage P – assume 2.5 in swg $Q_S = 0.57 \times 7560 \times 2.5$	 = 7560	=		10773	
	Circulating pump	$Q_S = 1.18$ VP. Equation 4.16 p. 79 V – assume 122 galls/min P – assume 60 ft head $Q_S = 1.18 \times 122 \times 60$		=		8638	
						599954 103392	103392
	Instantaneous load	Total heat, BTU/hour Tons refrigeration = 703346/12000		= =		703346 58.61 T.R.	

Table 7.2 Job sheet for face peak and instantaneous ~~cooling~~/heating loads. Imperial Units. *Sheet No. 14*

Module	*Date & time*	*Load item*	*Area ft^2*	*Peak Solar radn*	*Δt or Δt_e °F*	*U value*	*Total watts*	*No. occpts*	*BTU/hr/occpt*		*V cfm*	*SF*	*BF*	*Δg lb/lb*	*Factors*	*Module loads BTU/hr*		*No. mods*	*Instant. loads BTU/hr*	
									S.HT.	*L.HT.*						*S.HT.*	*L.HT.*		*S.HT.*	*L.HT.*
Intermediate modules																	*B/fd*			
	Jan 08.00	Glass condn	50.4		46	0.58										1345				
		Module wall	32.0		46	0.09										133				
		Internal wall	95.0		23	0.20										437				
		Fresh air			46						50				× 1.08	2484				
		Infiltration			46						15				× 1.08	745				
		Intermediate modules totals														5144		100	514400	
End modules																				
	Jan 08.00	Glass condn	50.4		46	0.58										1345				
		Module wall	32.0		46	0.09										133				
		End wall	175.0		46	0.09										724				
		Internal wall	95.0		23	0.20										437				
		Fresh air			46						50				× 1.08	2484				
		Infiltration			46						15				× 1.08	745				
		End modules totals														5868		20	117360	
Roof intermediate modules																				
	Jan 08.00	Glass condn	50.4		46	0.58										1345				
		Module wall	32.0		46	0.09										133				
		Internal wall	95.0		23	0.20										437				
		Roof	200.0		46	0.077										708				
		Fresh air			46						50				× 1.08	2484				
		Infiltration			46						15				× 1.08	745				
		Roof intermediate modules totals														5852		20	117040	
Roof end modules																				
	Jan 08.00	Glass condn	50.4		46	0.58										1345				
		Module wall	32.0		46	0.09										133				
		End wall	175.0		46	0.09										724				
		Internal wall	95.0		23	0.20										437				
		Roof	200.0		46	0.077										708				
		Fresh air			46						50				× 1.08	2484				
		Infiltration			46						15				× 1.08	745				
		Roof end modules totals														6576		4	26304	
Building total heating load, BTU per hour																		144	775104	

Δt_e = equivalent temp. difference. SF = storage factor. BF = shade factor.

Appendix I
Comparison of alternative methods of calculation of cooling loads

Fig. AI.1 Typical building module

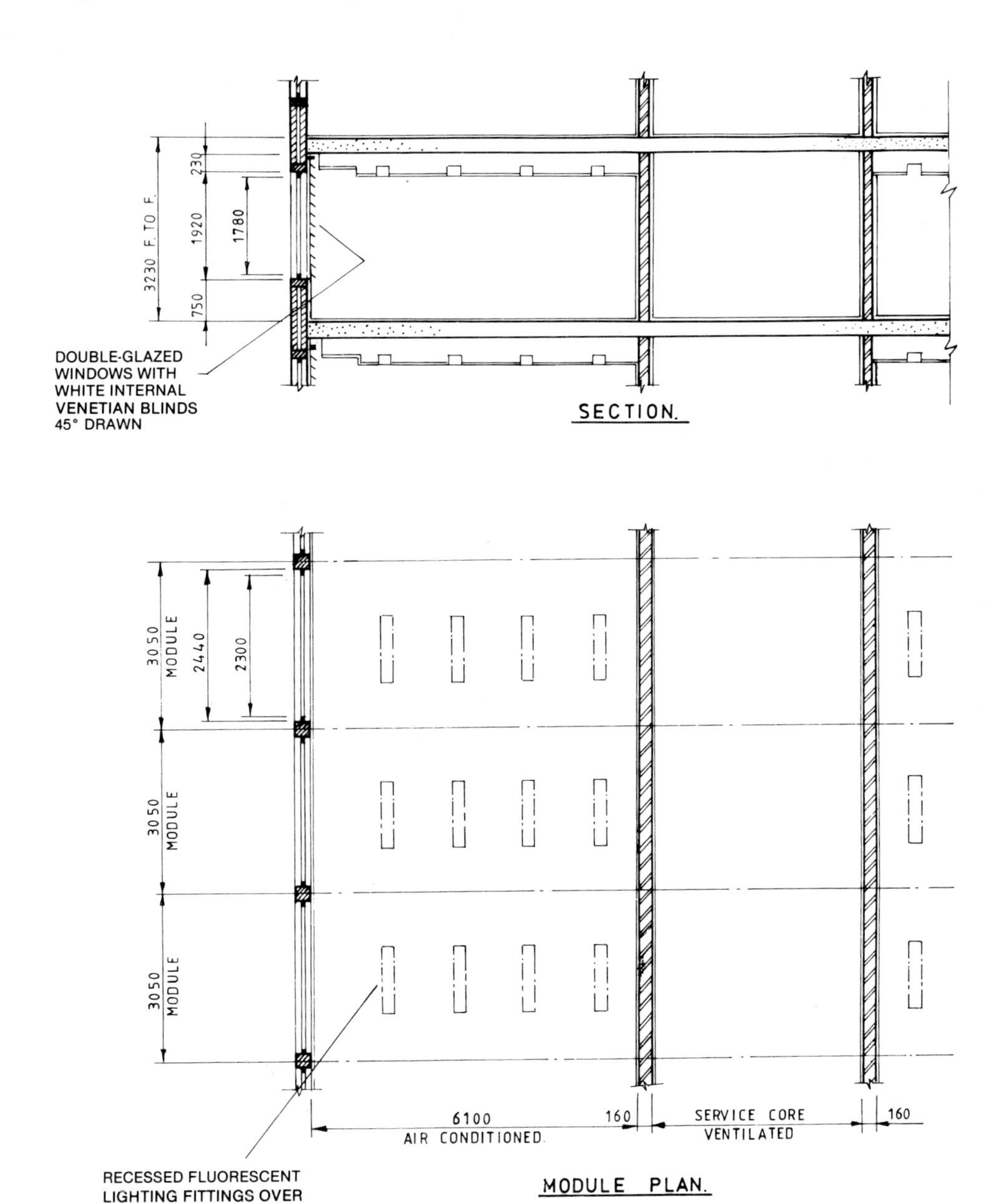

DESIGN DATA –
General

Surface	*Weight*		*Dimensions*	*Areas*	*U*-values
	(kg/m²)	(lb/ft²)	(m)	(m²)	(W/m²/°C)
Windows					
Gross	—	—	2.44 × 1.92	4.68	3.85
Nett	—	—	2.30 × 1.78	4.09	—
Perimeter wall	430	88	3.05 × 0.98	2.98	0.49
Internal wall	98	20	3.05 × 2.90	8.84	1.40
Floor	552	113	6.10 × 3.05	18.60	1.70
Ceiling	28	6	6.10 × 3.05	18.60	1.70

Latitude – 50°N
Aspect – Southwest
Date and time – August, 16.00 hours.

Temperatures
Outdoor
max. – 27 °C at 16.00 hours
mean – 22.5 °C at 23.00 hours
Indoor – 22 °C DB/50% RH constant

Fenestration
Double-glazed units, 6 mm glass with 12 mm air gap; aluminium frame with thermal break; white internal venetian blinds 45° drawn.

Perimeter walls – Light-coloured.

Specific weight of structure

	m²		kg/m²		kg
Floor slab	½ (18.60	×	552)	=	5 134
Ceiling slab	½ (18.60	×	552)	=	5 134
Perimeter wall	2.98	×	430	=	1 281
Internal wall	8.84	×	98	=	866
Suspended ceiling	18.60	×	28	=	521
					12 936

Specific weight $\frac{12\,936}{18.6}$ = 695 kg/m² floor area
(142 lb/ft² floor area)

Lighting
Fluorescent fittings recessed into non-ventilated suspended ceiling. Output 21.5 W/m² floor area.

Occupants (per module)
Two (one male, one female) seated at light desk work.

Infiltration
Well-sealed windows. Hence, neglect infiltration in summer but include in winter.

BASES OF CALCULATION

For a typical 6 m × 3 m nominal module of Fig. AI.1 and the foregoing relevant design data, cooling load calculations are set out below for the three authorities:

(a) Chartered Institution of Building Services.
(b) American Society of Heating, Refrigerating and Air-conditioning Engineers.
(c) Carrier Air-conditioning Company.

(a) Chartered institution of building services (CIBS)

For the calculation of thermal loads in buildings, Sections A of the CIBS *Guide* are used.

The following typical calculation refers to the building module of Fig. AI.1 and to the CIBS *Guide*, Sections A listed below and annotated in the procedural steps of the calculation; SI units are used to conform with the CIBS *Guide* and current general practice.

A2, 1982.	Weather and solar data.
A3, 1980.	Thermal properties of building structures.
A5, 1979.	Thermal response of buildings.
A7, 1971.	Casual gains.
A9, 1979.	Estimation of plant capacity.
A9,	Supplement, June 1983.

In Section A9 two methods of calculation are discussed based upon the alternative designated internal conditions of inside air temperature or dry resultant temperature.

Inside air temperature (t_{ai}) is the average of the air temperature of an enclosed space which, for practical purposes, may be regarded as measured by a dry-bulb thermometer at the centre of the space, shielded from radiation.

Dry resultant temperature (t_c) is recommended by the CIBS as an acceptable index temperature for comfort. Hence, this is the basis of the typical calculation.

In most practical situations the dry resultant temperature is the average of the air temperature and either the mean surface temperature (t_m) or the mean radiant temperature (t_r):

$$t_c = \tfrac{1}{2}t_{ai} + \tfrac{1}{2}t_m$$ Section A5, eqn. A5.3

where t_m approximates to t_r at the room centre and t_{ai} is the air temperature at the same point.

CIBS load calculations for the building module of Fig. AI.1

Factors used	**CIBS reference**
Fabric Coefficients	Section A3

Surface	Area A (m^2)	U-value ($W/m^2/°C$)	AU	Y-value ($W/m^2/°C$)	AY	Decrement factor (f)	Time-lag (hr)	
External wall	2.98	0.49	1.46	4.30	12.81	0.2	9	Table A3.17 5(e)
Internal wall	8.84	1.40	—	4.40	38.89	—	—	Table A3.20 4(b)
Floor	18.60	1.70	—	5.20	96.72	—	—	Table A3.21 2(a)
Ceiling	18.60	1.70	—	2.20	40.92	—	—	Table A3.21 2(a)
Window gross	4.68	3.85	18.01	3.85	18.01	1.0	0	Table A3.14
Window nett	(4.09)							
Totals (Σ)	53.70		19.47		207.35			

Temperatures

Dry resultant (t_c) — Section A9

From p. 136: t_c = 22 °C

Outside air (t_{ao}) — Section A2

t_{ao} mean $= \bar{t}_{ao}$ = 16.5 °C — Table A2.33(f)

t_{ao} cyclic $= \tilde{t}_{ao}$ = 21.5 °C at 16.00 hours — Table A2.33(f)

Sol-air (t_{eo}) — Section A2

t_{eo} mean $= \bar{t}_{eo}$ = 19.5 °C — Table A2.33(f)

t_{eo} cyclic $= \tilde{t}_{eo}$ = 13.0 °C at 07.00 hours (16.00 – 09.00) — Table A2.33(f)

Cooling-load factor (S_a) — Sections A5, A9

S_a August 16.00 = 318 W/m^2 — Table A9.31

Shading coefficient (S_c) — Sections A5, A9

S_c for venetian blind, 45° closed

= 0.5(0.95 + 0.74) = 0.84 — Table A9.31

Heat-transfer coefficients — Section A5

h_{ec} = 18.0 $W/m^2/°C$ — appendix 3

h_{ac} = 6.0 $W/m^2/°C$ — appendix 3

h_a = 4.5 $W/m^2/°C$ — appendix 3

Room factors — Section A5,

$$F_u = \frac{h_{ec}\,\Sigma(A)}{h_{ec}\,\Sigma(A) + \Sigma(AU)}$$ — Eqn. A5.19

$$= \frac{18 \times 53.7}{(18 \times 53.7) + 19.47}$$

$$= 0.98$$

$$F_v = \frac{h_{ac}\,\Sigma(A)}{h_{ac}\,\Sigma(A) + \tfrac{1}{3}NV}$$ — Eqn. A5.18

NV = infiltration rate

= 0 Therefore F_v = 1.0

Factors used		CIBS reference
$F_y = \dfrac{h_{ec}\,\Sigma(A)}{h_{ec}\,\Sigma(A) + \Sigma(AY)}$		Eqn. A5.36
$= \dfrac{18 \times 53.7}{(18 \times 53.7) + 207.35}$	$= 0.82$	
Total light wattage = floor area × W/m^2 × ballast factor = 18.6 × 21.5 × 1.25	= 500 W	Not quoted standard formula used
Use factor = ratio of wattage in use to wattage installed	= 1.0	Not quoted factor of 1.0 assumed
Distribution factor	= 0.55	Table A7.5
Occupants Sensible heat emission per occupant	= 90 W	Table A7.1
Male/female proportion factor	= 0.93	Table A7.2
Load Components	**Watts**	
Window solar gain = net area × S_a × S_c = 4.09 m^2 × 318 × 0.84	= 1093	Not quoted formula assumed
Window conduction gains Mean conduction gain		Section A9 and Supplement A9
$= \text{gross area} \times \left(\dfrac{F_u}{F_v}\right) \times U(\bar{t}_{ao} - t_c)$		Eqn. A9.25
$= 4.68\left(\dfrac{0.98}{1.0}\right) \times 3.85\,(16.5 - 22)$	= −97	
Cyclic conduction gain		
$= \text{gross area}\left(\dfrac{F_y}{F_v}\right) \times U(\tilde{t}_{ao} - \bar{t}_{ao}) \times f$		Eqn. A9.26
$= 4.68\left(\dfrac{0.82}{1.0}\right) \times 3.85\,(21.5 - 16.5) \times 1.0$	= 74	
External wall conduction gains Mean conduction gain		
$= \text{area}\left(\dfrac{F_u}{F_v}\right) \times U(\bar{t}_{eo} - t_c)$		Eqn. A9.25
$= 2.98\left(\dfrac{0.98}{1.0}\right) \times 0.49\,(19.5 - 22)$	= −4	
	c/f 1066	

Load Components **Carrier reference**

Cyclic conduction gain	b/f 1066	
$= \text{area}\left(\frac{F_y}{F_v}\right) \times U(\tilde{t}_{eo} - \bar{t}_{eo}) \times f$		Eqn. A9.26
$= 2.98\left(\frac{0.82}{1.0}\right) \times 0.49\,(13 - 19.5) \times 0.2$	$= \quad -2$	
Internal wall conduction gain		Not quoted formula assumed
$= \text{area} \times U\left[\left(\frac{t_{ao} + t_c}{2}\right) - t_c\right]$		
$= 8.84 \times 1.4\,(24.5 - 22)$	$= \quad 31$	
Heat gain from lighting = watts × use factor × distribution factor = 500 × 1.0 × 0.55	$= \quad 275$	Not quoted formula assumed
Heat gain from occupants = number × emission rate × proportion factor = 2 × 90 × 0.93	$= \quad 167$	Not quoted formula assumed
Total sensible heat gain	$= \quad 1537$	

(b) American Society of Heating, Refrigerating and Air-Conditioning Engineers (ASHRAE)

The typical calculation which follows relates to the building module of Fig. AI.1 and Chapters 26 and 27 of ASHRAE Guide F (*Fundamentals Handbook*).

Guide F presents data in SI and imperial units; SI units are used in the calculation.

Factors used		**ASHRAE reference**
Outside air temperature (t_o) From p. 136 maximum mean	 = 27 °C = 22.5 °C	Ch. 26, eqn. 8
Indoor air temperature (t_i) From p. 136 t_i	 = 22 °C	Ch. 26, eqn. 8
Maximum solar heat gain factor (SHGF) SHGF for August	 = 662 W/m^2	Ch. 26, Table 11 interpolated for 50°N
Cooling-load factor (CLF) CLF for southwest glass at 16.00 hours internally shaded	 = 0.81	Ch. 26 Table 14
Shading coefficient (SC) SC for double clear glass internally shaded	 = 0.51	Ch. 27 Table 35
Cooling load temperature difference (CLTD) Window glass CLTD = 8 + (25.5 − 22) − (29.4 − 22.5)	 = 4.6 °C	Ch. 26 Table 10
External wall CLTD = (9 + 2.3) × 1.0 + (25.5 − 22) + (22.5 − 29.4)	 = 7.9 °C	Table 7. Group B corrected

Factors used		**ASHRAE reference**
Interior wall temperature difference $(t_b - t_i)$		Ch. 26. eqn. 13
$t_b = t_o - 2.8$		
$= 27 - 2.8$	= 24.2 °C	
Total light wattage		Ch. 26, eqn. 14
= installed lighting load		
= floor area × 21.5 W/m^2		
= 18.6 m^2 × 21.5	= 400 W	
Use factor (UF)		Ch. 26. eqn. 14
= ratio of wattage in use to wattage installed		
= 1.0 in this case		
Special allowance factor (SAF)		Ch. 26, eqn. 14
= 1.25 for fluorescent lights		
Cooling-load factor (CLF)		Ch. 26, eqn. 14
CLF lighting on for 10 hours	= 0.75	Ch. 26, Table 17B
Sensible heat gain from occupants (SHG)		Ch. 26, Table 18
SHG per occupant	= 65 W	
Cooling-load factor (CLF)		Ch. 26, Table 19
CLF occupants	= 0.82	

Load Components	**Watts**	
Window solar gain		
= net area × SHGF × CLF × SC		Ch. 26, Table 1
= 4.09 m^2 × 662 × 0.81 × 0.51	= 1119	
Window conduction gain		
= gross area × CLTD × U-value		Ch. 26, Table 1
= 4.68 m^2 × 4.6 × 3.85	= 83	
External wall conduction gain		
= area × CLTD × U-value		Ch. 26, Table 1
= 2.98 m^2 × 7.9 × 0.49	= 12	
Internal wall conduction gain		
= area × $(t_b - t_i)$ × U-value		Ch. 26, eqn. 13
= 8.84 m^2 × (24.2 − 22) × 1.4	= 27	
Heat gain from lighting		
= total wattage × UF × SAF × CLF		Ch. 26, eqn. 14
400 × 1.0 × 1.25 × 0.75	= 375	
Heat gain from occupants		
= number × SHG × CLF		Ch. 26, Table 1
= 2 × 65 × 0.82	= 107	
Total sensible heat gain	= 1723	

(c) Carrier Handbook of Air-Conditioning System Design

The following typical calculation relates to the building module of Fig. AI.1 and to the sections of the Carrier *Handbook* listed below and referred to in the procedural steps of the calculation.

Carrier *Handbook*, Part 1:

Chapter 3	Heat storage diversity and stratification.
Chapter 4	Solar heat gain thru glass.
Chapter 5	Heat and water vapor flow thru structures.
Chapter 7	Internal and system heat gain.

The Carrier *Handbook* uses conventional (imperial) units only. The calculation conforms to this, with conversions made to SI units for comparison with the results of the other authorities.

Factors used		**Carrier reference**
Outdoor air temperature (t_o) From p. 136: t_o	= 27 °C (80.6 °F)	
Indoor air temperature (t_i) From p. 136: t_i	= 22 °C DB/50% RH = 71.6 °F DB/50% RH	
Dewpoint temperature	= 52.3 °F	
Equivalent temperature difference (Δt_e) Δt_e for southwest wall at 16.00 hours; 88 lb/ft^2, light-coloured and corrected for latitude and daily range	= 40 °F	Ch. 5, Table 19
Temperature difference at internal walls $t = t_o - t_i - 5$ °F $= 80.6 - 71.6 - 5$	= 4.0 °F	Ch. 5, Table 25
Peak solar heat gain factor Solar factor for southwest window in August, corrected for metal frame and dewpoint temperature $= 157 \times 1.17 \times 1.1$	= 202 Btu/hr/ft^2	Ch. 3, Table 6
Shading factor Shading factor for double glass with light-coloured inside venetian blind at 45°	= 0.54	Ch. 4, Table 16
Specific weight of module From p. 136	= 142 lb/ft^2	Ch. 3
Storage factor (structure) Storage factor for 12-hour operation; internal shade; sp. wt. 142 lb/ft^2	= 0.69	Ch. 3, Table 11
Total light wattage = floor area × W/m^2 × ballast factor $= 18.6 \times 21.5 \times 1.25$	= 500 W	Ch. 7, Table 49

Factors used		**Carrier reference**
Use factor = ratio of wattage in use to wattage installed	= 1.0	Ch. 3
Storage factor (lights) Storage factor for recessed fluorescent lights; 12-hour operation; sp. wt. 142 lb/ft^2; lights on 8 hours	= 0.94	Ch. 3, Table 12
Distribution factor 50% heat stratified	= 0.50	Ch. 3
Sensible heat gain from occupants Gain per person at 71.6 °F	= 269 Btu/hr	Ch. 7, Table 48
Storage factor (occupants) Storage factor for 12-hour operation; sp. wt. 142 lb/ft^2; 7 hours occupation	= 0.95	Ch. 3, Table 12 for exposed fluorescents

Transmittance coefficients (*U*)

From p. 136:

U glass	= 3.85 W/m^2/°C	= 0.67 Btu/hr/ft^2/°F
U ext. wall	= 0.49 W/m^2/°C	= 0.08 Btu/hr/ft^2/°F
U int. wall	= 1.40 W/m^2/°C	= 0.24 Btu/hr/ft^2/°F

Surface areas

From p. 136:

Glass areas:

Gross	= 4.68 m^2	= 50.35 ft^2
Nett	= 4.09 m^2	= 44.00 ft^2
Ext. wall	= 2.98 m^2	= 32.06 ft^2
Int. wall	= 8.84 m^2	= 95.11 ft^2

Load components	**Btu/hr**	**Watts**	
Window solar gain = net area × solar factor × shading factor × storage factor = 44 × 202 × 0.54 × 0.69	= 3312	970	Ch. 3, Tables 7–11
Window conduction gain = gross area × *U*-value × $(t_o - t_i)$ = 50.35 × 0.67 (80.6 – 71.6)	= 304	89	Ch. 5 Standard formula used
External wall conduction gain = area × *U*-value × Δt_e = 32.06 × 0.08 × 40	= 103	30	Ch. 5, p. 1–59
Internal wall conduction gain = area × *U*-value × Δt = 95.11 × 0.24 × 4.0	= 91	27	Ch. 5, Table 25
	c/f 3810	1116	

Load components			**Carrier reference**
	b/f 3810	1116	
Heat gain from lighting			Ch. 7, Table 49
= total wattage × use factor × storage factor × distribution factor × 3.415			
= 500 × 1.0 × 0.94 × 0.50 × 3.415	= 803	235	
Heat gain from occupants			Ch. 7, Table 48
= number × gain per person × storage factor			
= 2 × 269 × 0.95	= 511	150	
	5124	1501	

Comparison of calculated loads

	CIBS (W)	ASHRAE (W)	Carrier (W)
Window solar	1093	1119	970
Window conduction		83	89
Mean	−97		
Cyclic	74		
Ext. wall conduction		12	30
Mean	−4		
Cyclic	−2		
Internal wall	31	27	27
Lighting	275	375	235
Occupants	167	107	150
	1537	1723	1501

Appendix II
Shading coefficients

Table AII.1 Shading coefficients for Pilkington glasses. Reproduced from *Thermal Transmission of Windows*

Window design			*Shading coefficient*		
			Short-wave	*Long-wave**	*Total*
Single					
Clear glass	4 mm		0.94	0.04	0.98
Clear float	6 mm		0.90	0.05	0.95
'Spectrafloat'	6 mm	51/65 (bronze)	0.62	0.13	0.75
'Antisun' float	6 mm	75/61 (green)	0.53	0.17	0.70
	6 mm	41/60 (grey)	0.51	0.18	0.69
	6 mm	50/60 (bronze)	0.51	0.18	0.69
'Reflectafloat'	6 mm	33/52 (silver)	0.49	0.11	0.60
'Solarshield'	6.4 mm	20/18 (deep gold)	0.08	0.13	0.21
	6.4 mm	38/38 (gold)	0.29	0.15	0.44
Coolray	6.4 mm	14/33 (silver blue)	0.17	0.21	0.38
Single with internal venetian blind†					
Clear glass	4 mm		0.11	0.44	0.55
Clear float	6 mm		0.10	0.44	0.54
'Spectrafloat'	6 mm	51/65 (bronze)	0.07	0.42	0.49
'Antisun' float	6 mm	75/61 (green)	0.06	0.43	0.49
	6 mm	41/60 (grey)	0.06	0.42	0.48
	6 mm	50/60 (bronze)	0.06	0.42	0.48
'Reflectafloat'	6 mm	33/52 (silver)	0.06	0.36	0.42
'Solarshield'	6.4 mm	20/18 (deep gold)	0.01	0.18	0.19
	6.4 mm	38/38 (gold)	0.03	0.31	0.34
Coolray	6.4 mm	14/33 (silver blue)	0.02	0.30	0.32
Double‡					
Clear glass	4 mm		0.74	0.11	0.85
Clear float	6 mm		0.70	0.12	0.82
'Spectrafloat'	6 mm	51/65 (bronze)	0.49	0.13	0.62
'Antisun' float	6 mm	75/61 (green)	0.41	0.15	0.56
	6 mm	41/60 (grey)	0.39	0.15	0.54
	6 mm	50/60 (bronze)	0.39	0.15	0.54
'Reflectafloat'	6 mm	33/52 (silver)	0.40	0.10	0.50
'Solarshield'	6.4 mm	20/18 (deep gold)	0.06	0.08	0.14
	6.4 mm	38/38 (gold)	0.23	0.11	0.34
Coolray	6.4 mm	14/33 (silver blue)	0.14	0.13	0.27
'SunCool' 'Insulight'		37/28 (azure)	0.23	0.09	0.32
		18/16 (coral gold)	0.11	0.07	0.18

Table AII.1 Shading coefficients for Pilkington glasses. Reproduced from *Thermal Transmission of Windows*

Double with venetian blind between †‡					
Clear glass	4 mm		0.09	0.19	0.28
Clear Float	6 mm		0.08	0.20	0.28
'Spectrafloat'	6 mm	51/65 (bronze)	0.05	0.20	0.25
'Antisun' Float	6 mm	75/61 (green)	0.04	0.21	0.25
	6 mm	41/60 (grey)	0.05	0.20	0.25
	6 mm	50/60 (bronze)	0.05	0.20	0.25
'Reflectafloat'	6 mm	33/52 (silver)	0.05	0.17	0.22
'Solarshield'	6.4 mm	20/18 (deep gold)	0.01	0.09	0.10
	6.4 mm	38/38 (gold)	0.03	0.15	0.18
Coolray	6.4 mm	14/33 (silver blue)	0.02	0.15	0.17
Double with internal venetian blind†‡					
Clear glass	4 mm		0.09	0.46	0.55
Clear Float	6 mm		0.08	0.45	0.53
'Spcctrafloat'	6 mm	51/65 (bronze)	0.06	0.37	0.43
'Antisun' Float	6 mm	75/61 (green)	0.05	0.35	0.40
	6 mm	41/60 (grey)	0.05	0.34	0.39
	6 mm	50/60 (bronze)	0.05	0.34	0.39
'Reflectafloat'	6 mm	33/52 (silver)	0.05	0.32	0.37
'Solarshield'	6.4 mm	20/18 (deep gold)	0.01	0.12	0.13
	6.4 mm	38/38 (gold)	0.03	0.24	0.27
Coolray	6.4 mm	14/33 (silver blue)	0.02	0.20	0.22
'Suncool' 'Insulight'		37/28 (azure)	0.03	0.22	0.25
		18/16 (coral gold)	0.02	0.14	0.16

* Includes long-wavelength radiation and convected heat, calculated for an outdoor wind velocity of 2 m/sec.
† Properties of blind: reflectance, 0.50; absorptance, 0.39; transmittance, 0.11. It is assumed that the louvers are set at 45° and that radiation is nearly normal to the plane of the glass.
‡ The inner glass is 6 mm clear Float. The air space is 12 mm wide except when the blind is between the panes when it is 50 mm.

Table AII.2 General shading coefficients. Reproduced from Carrier *Handbook of Air-conditioning System Design*, Chapter 4, Part 1. Outdoor wind velocity, 5 mph; Angle of incidence, 30°; Shading devices fully covering window.

Type of glass	*Glass factor no shade*	*Inside venetian blind (45° horiz. or vertical) or roller shade*			*Outside venetian blind (45° horiz. slats)*		*Outside shading screen (17° horiz. slats)*		*Outside awning (vent. sides and top)*	
		Light colour	*Medium colour*	*Dark colour*	*Light colour*	*Light on outside dark on inside*	*Medium colour*	*Dark colour*	*Light colour*	*Medium or dark colour*
Ordinary glass	1.00	0.56	0.65	0.75	0.15	0.13	0.22	0.15	0.20	0.25
Regular plate (¼ in.)	0.94	0.56	0.65	0.74	0.14	0.12	0.21	0.14	0.19	0.24
Heat-absorbing glass										
40 to 48% absorbing	0.80	0.56	0.62	0.72	0.12	0.11	0.18	0.12	0.16	0.20
48 to 56% absorbing	0.73	0.53	0.59	0.62	0.11	0.10	0.16	0.11	0.15	0.18
56 to 70% absorbing	0.62	0.51	0.54	0.56	0.10	0.10	0.14	0.10	0.12	0.16
Double pane										
Ordinary glass	0.90	0.54	0.61	0.67	0.14	0.12	0.20	0.14	0.18	0.22
Regular plate	0.80	0.52	0.59	0.65	0.12	0.11	0.18	0.12	0.16	0.20
48 to 56% absorbing outside; ordinary glass inside.	0.52	0.36	0.39	0.43	0.10	0.10	0.11	0.10	0.10	0.13
48 to 56% absorbing outside; regular plate inside.	0.50	0.36	0.39	0.43	0.10	0.10	0.11	0.10	0.10	0.12
Triple pane										
Ordinary glass	0.83	0.48	0.56	0.64	0.12	0.11	0.18	0.12	0.16	0.20
Regular plate	0.69	0.47	0.52	0.57	0.10	0.10	0.15	0.10	0.14	0.17
Painted glass										
Light colour	0.28									
Medium colour	0.39									
Dark colour	0.50									
Stained glass										
Amber colour	0.70									
Dark red	0.56									
Dark blue	0.60									
Dark green	0.32									
Greyed green	0.46									
Light opalescent	0.43									
Dark opalescent	0.37									

Appendix III
Charts of peak solar radiation through common glass

Fig. No.	Page	Latitude (N and S)	Months N Latitude	S Latitude
AIII.1	149	50°	June	Dec.
AIII.2	149	50°	July, May	Jan., Nov.
AIII.3	150	50°	Aug., April	Feb., Oct.
AIII.4	150	50°	Sept., March	March, Sept.
AIII.5	151	40°	June	Dec.
AIII.6	151	40°	July, May	Jan., Nov.
AIII.7	152	40°	Aug., April	Feb., Oct.
AIII.8	152	40°	Sept., March	March, Sept.
AIII.9	153	30°	June	Dec.
AIII.10	153	30°	July, May	Jan., Nov.
AIII.11	154	30°	Aug., April	Feb., Oct.
AIII.12	154	30°	Sept., March	March, Sept.
AIII.13	155	20°	June	Dec.
AIII.14	155	20°	July, May	Jan., Nov.
AIII.15	156	20°	Aug., April	Feb., Oct.
AIII.16	156	20°	Sept., March	March, Sept.
AIII.17	157	10°	June	Dec.
AIII.18	157	10°	July, May	Jan., Nov.
AIII.19	158	10°	Aug., April	Feb., Oct.
AIII.20	158	10°	Sept., March	March, Sept.
AIII.21	159	0°	June	Dec.
AIII.22	159	0°	July, May	Jan., Nov.
AIII.23	160	0°	Aug., April	Feb., Oct.
AIII.24	160	0°	Sept., March	March, Sept.

Fig. AIII.1 Peak solar radiation through common glass; 50° N and S latitudes

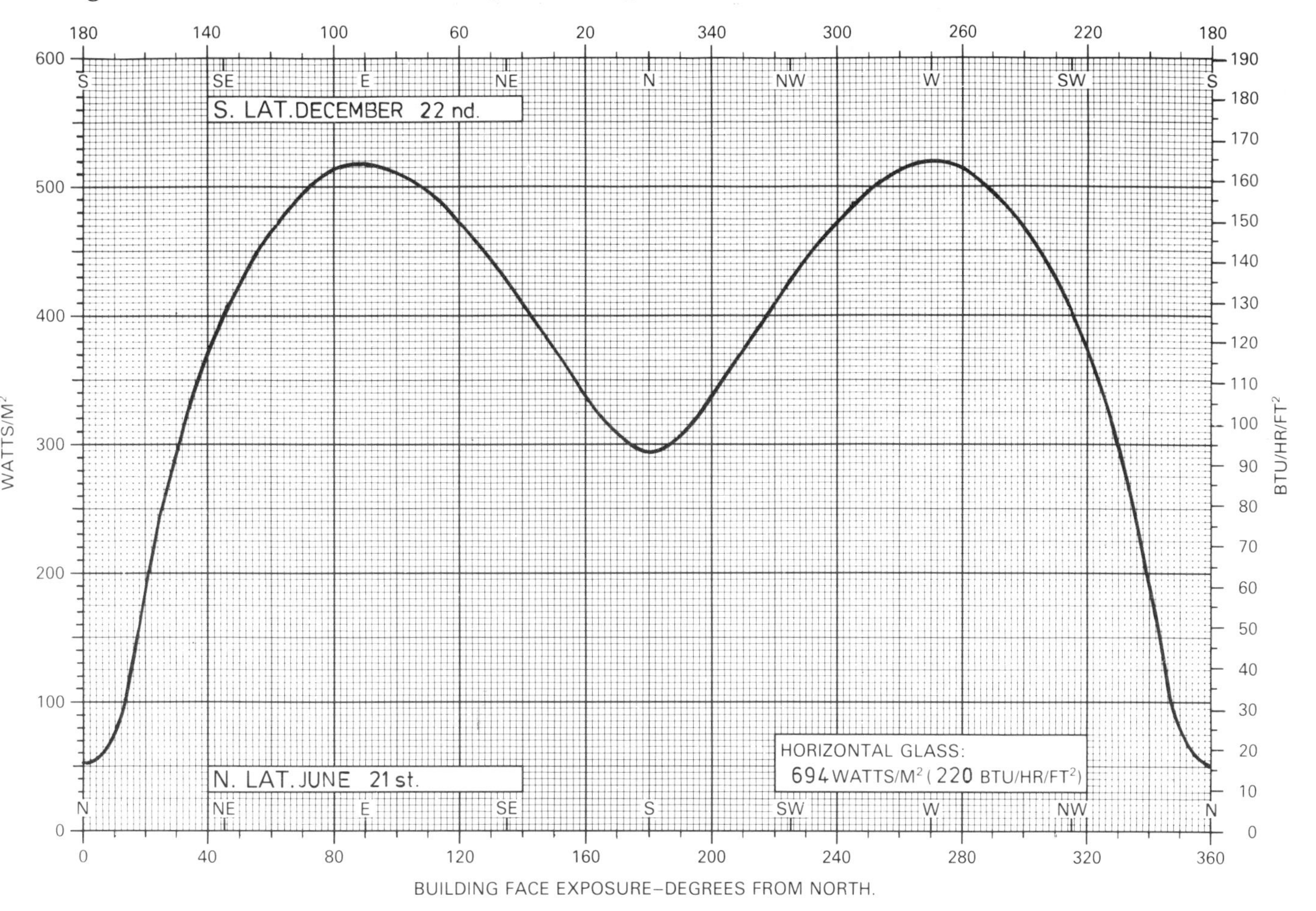

Fig. AIII.2 50° N and S latitudes

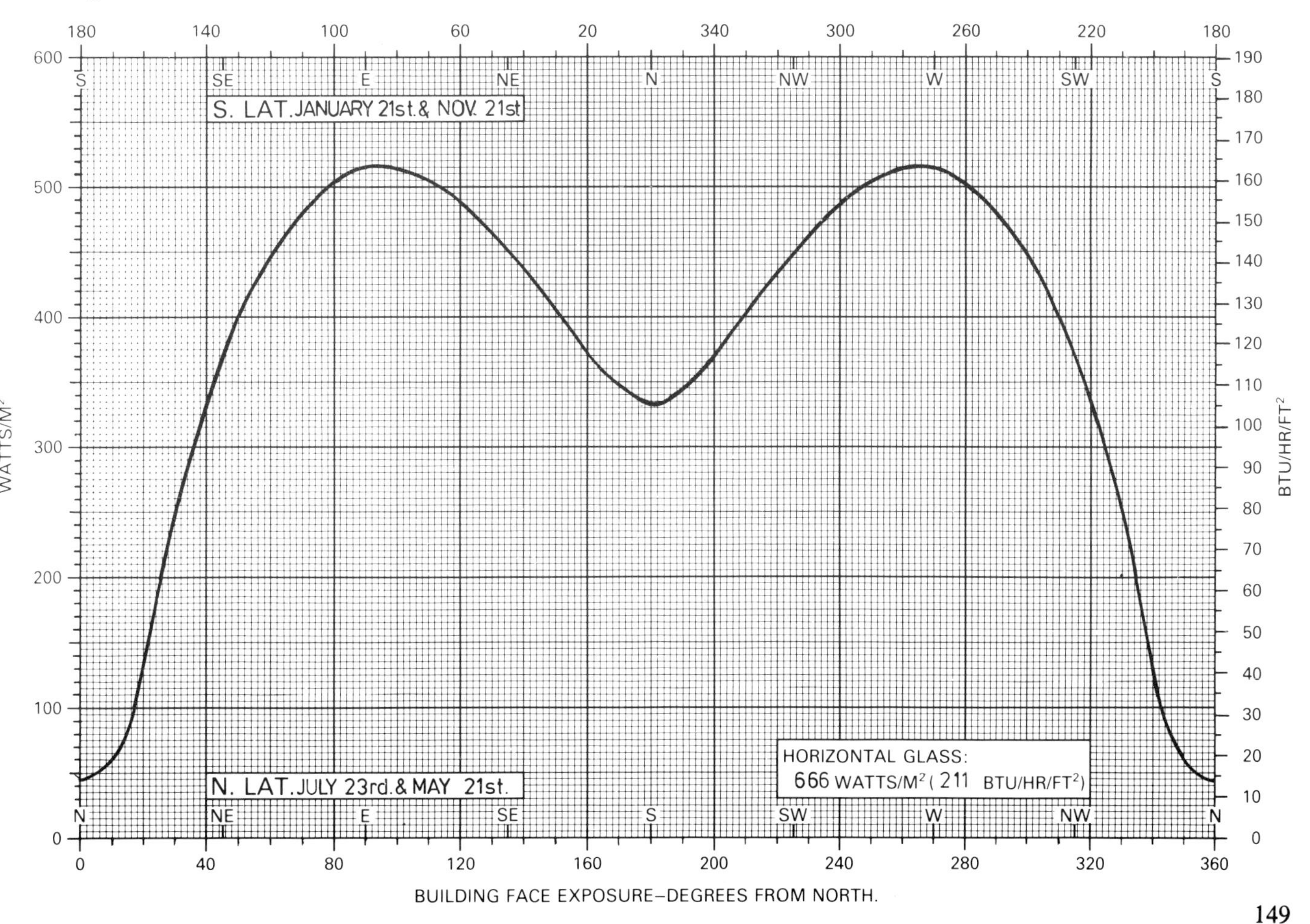

Fig. AIII.3 50° N and S latitudes

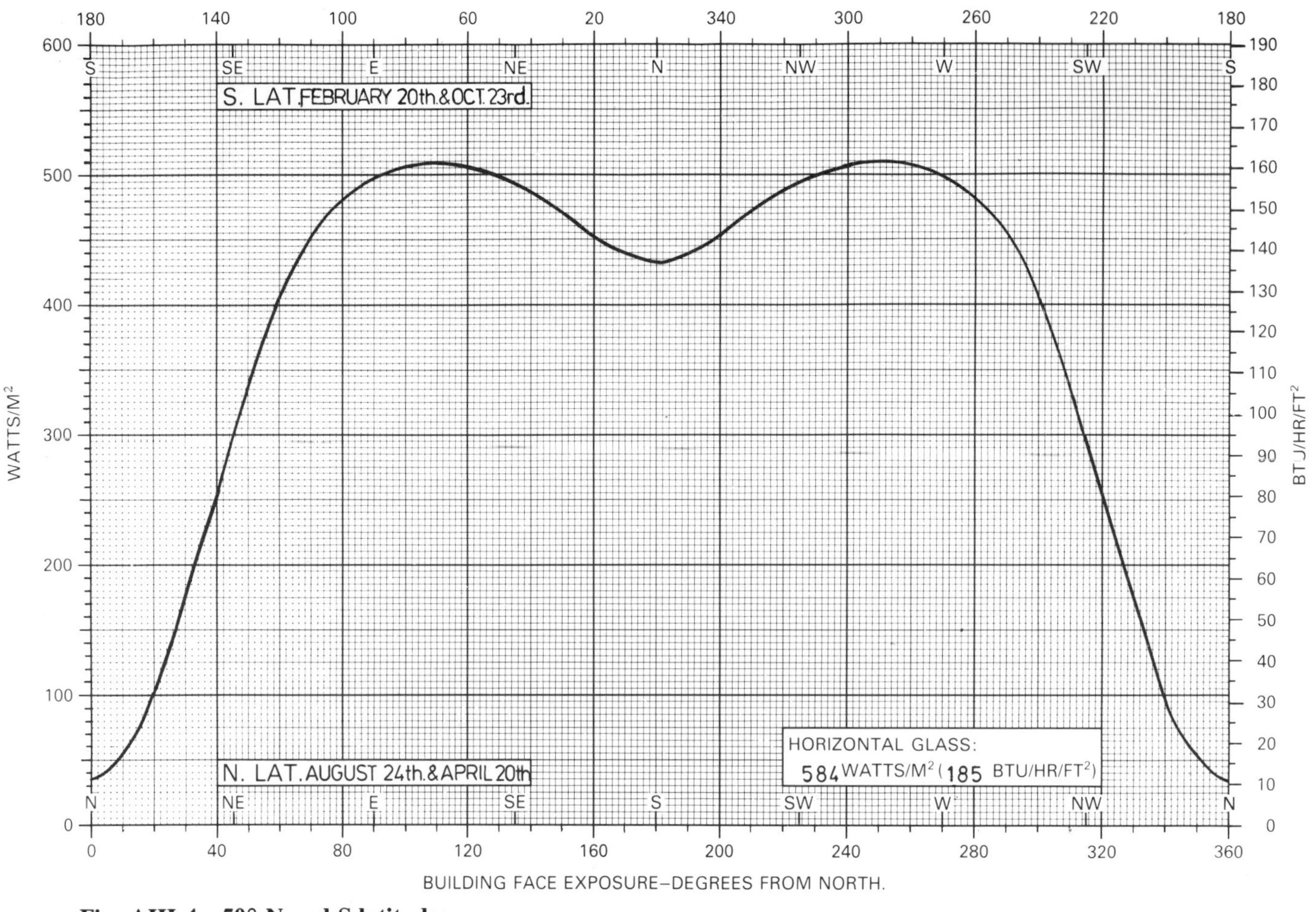

Fig. AIII.4 50° N and S latitudes

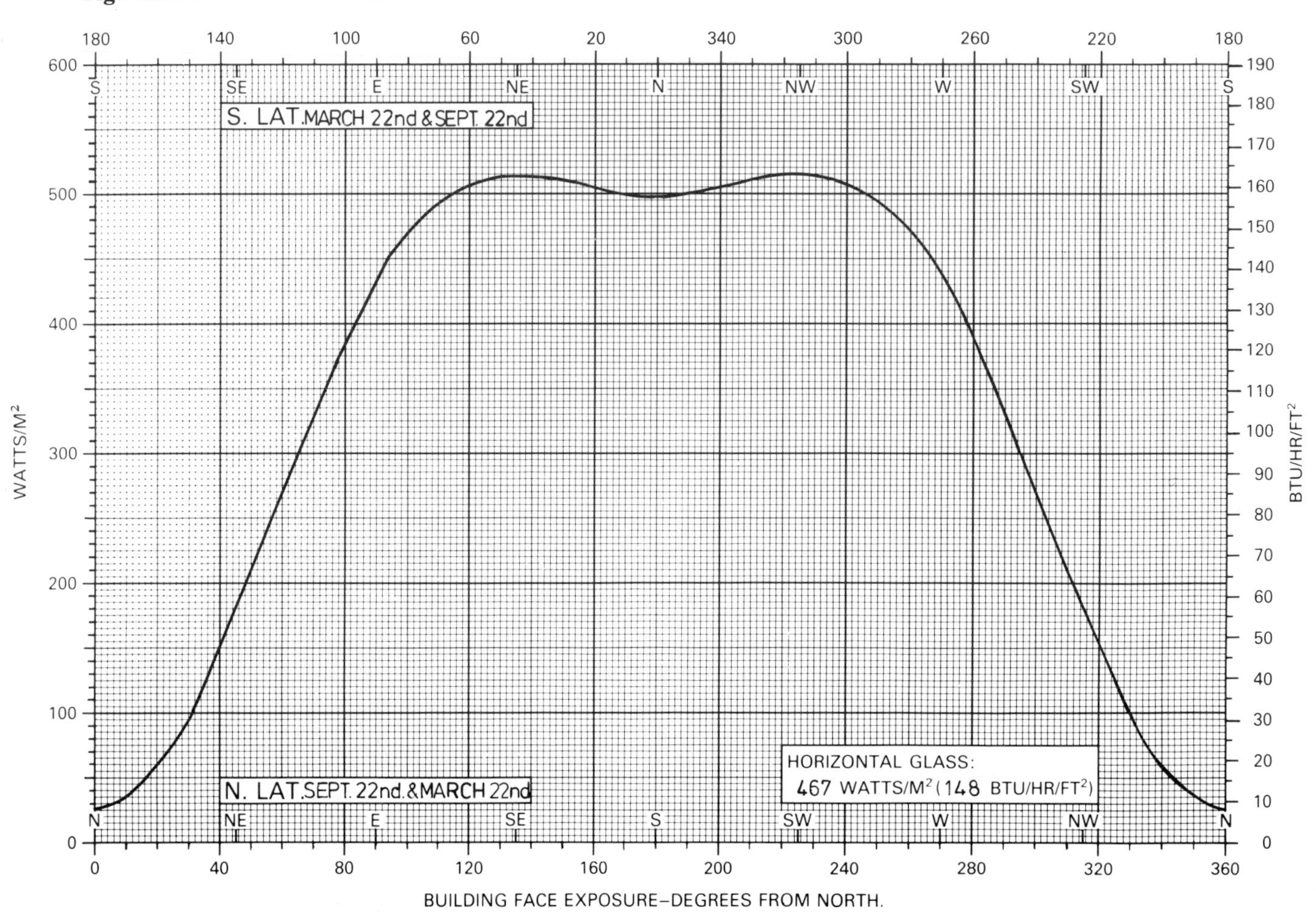

Fig. AIII.5 40° N and S latitudes

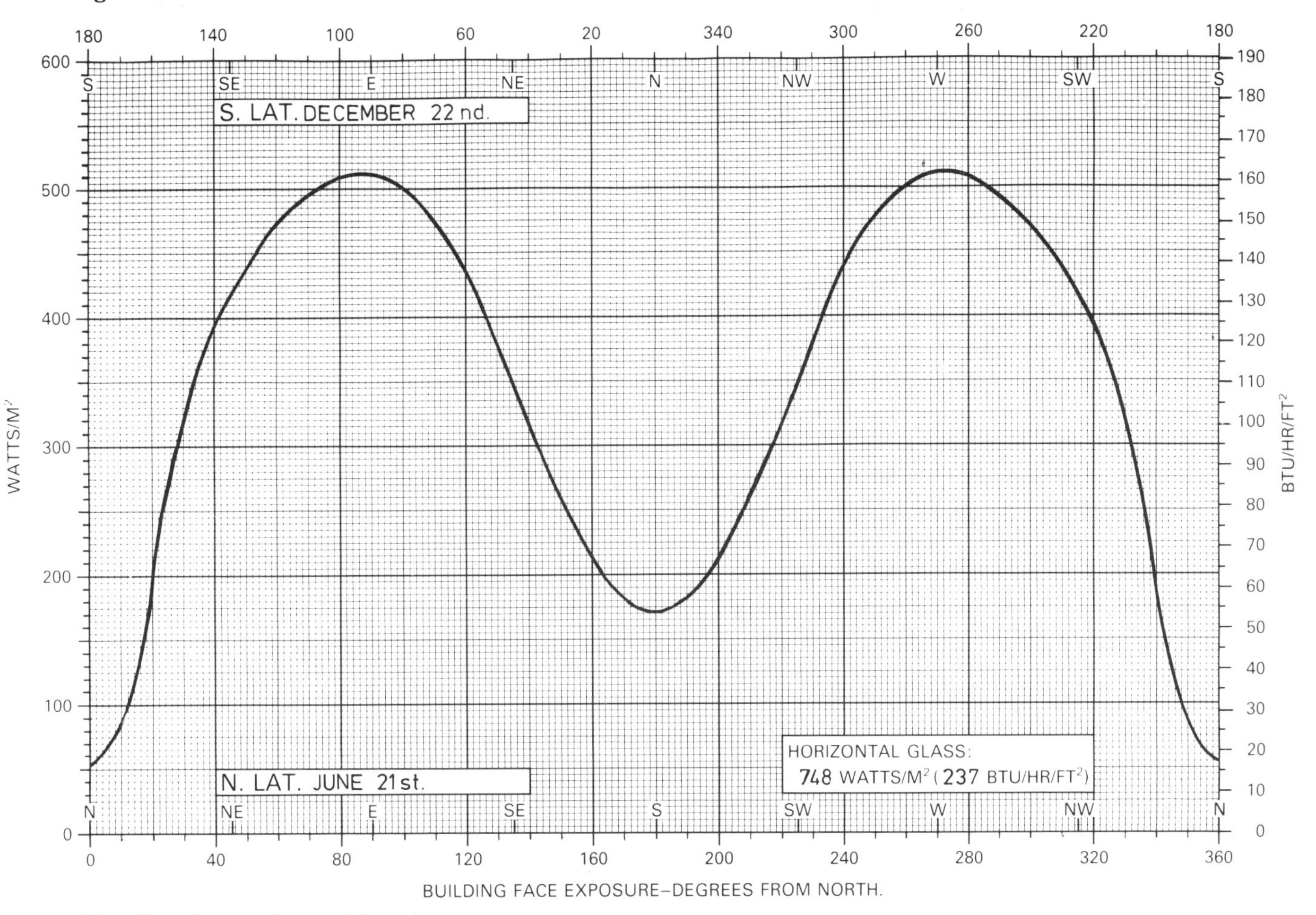

Fig. AIII.6 40° N and S latitudes

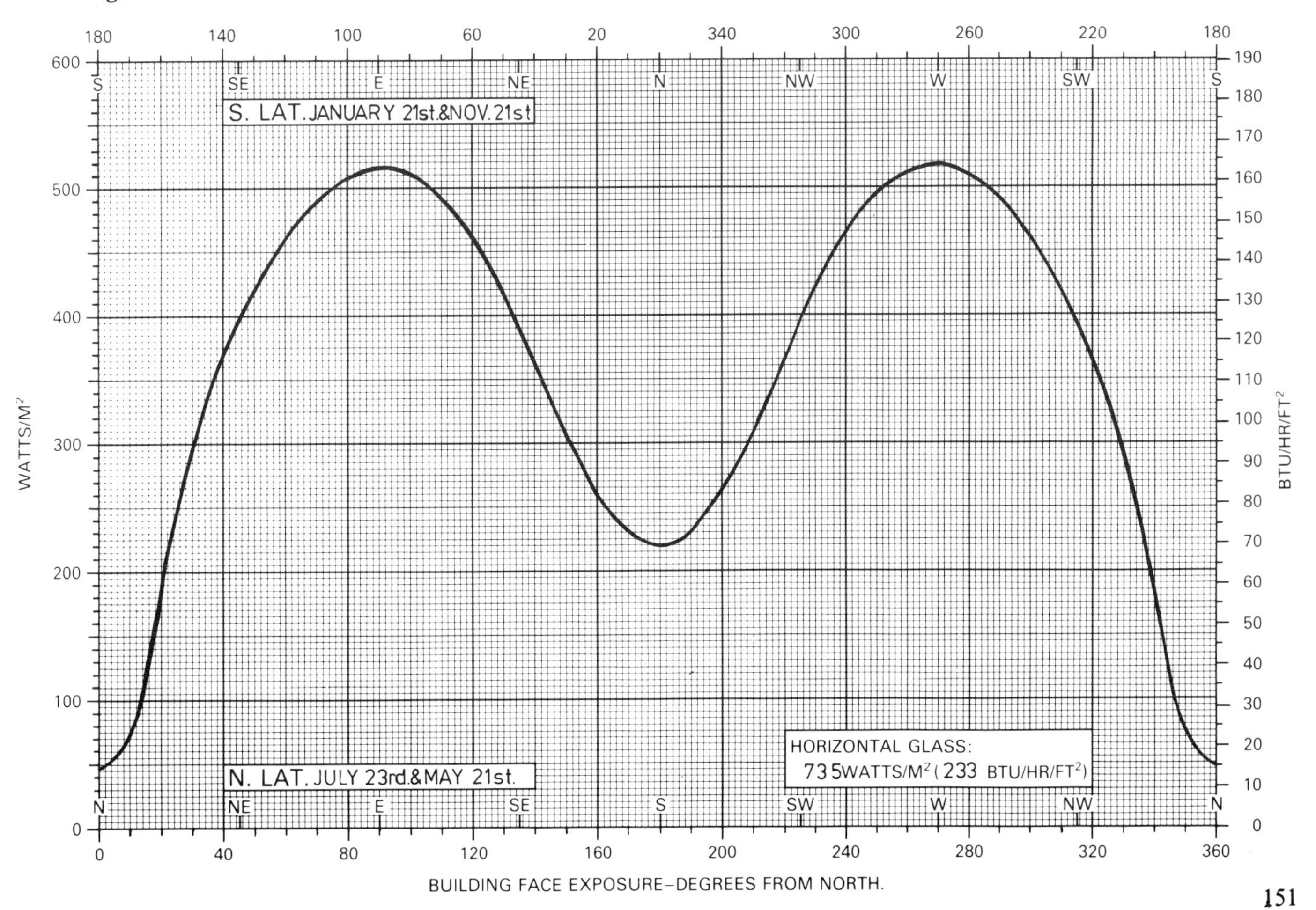

Fig. AIII.7 40° N and S latitudes

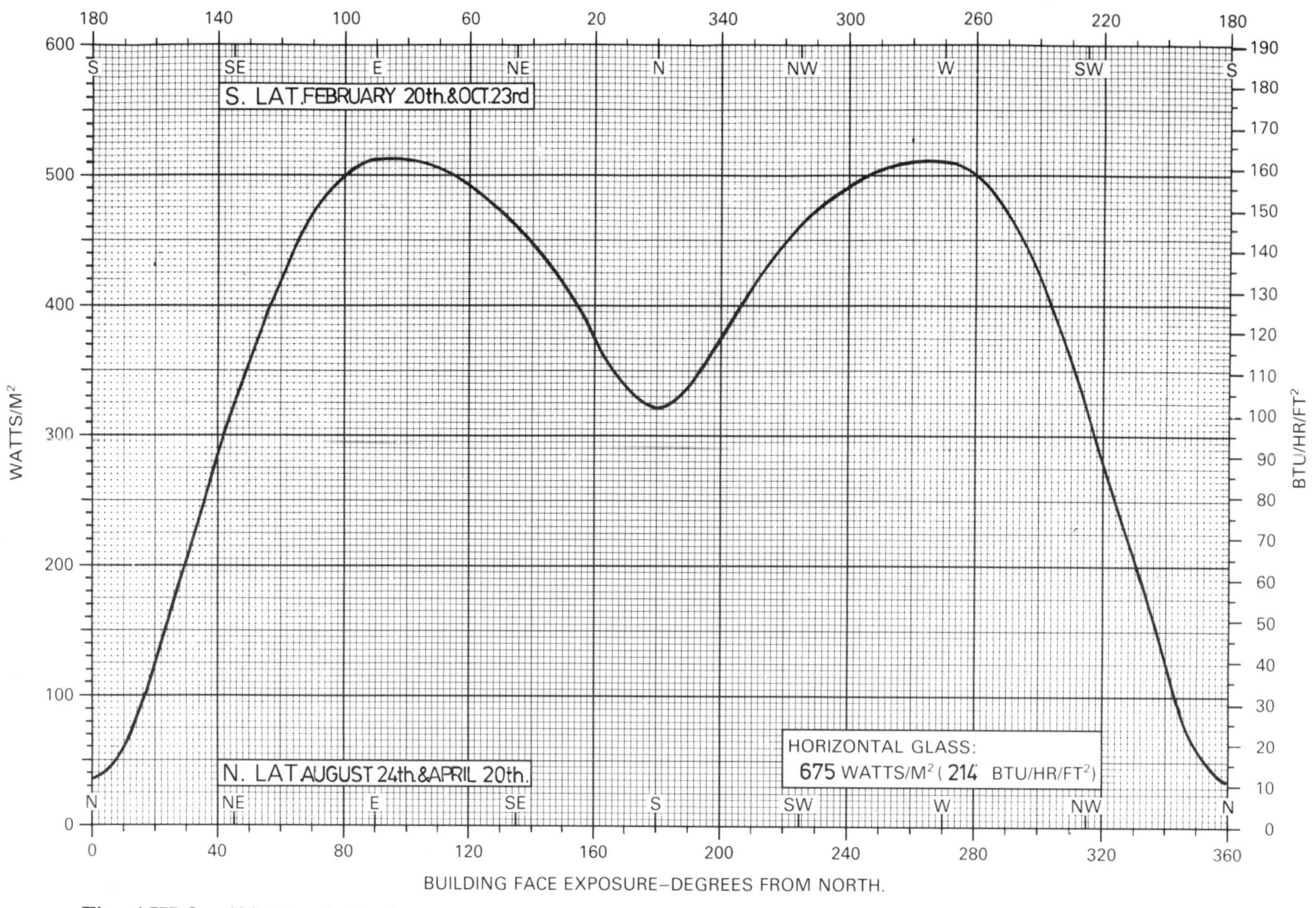

Fig. AIII.8 40° N and S latitudes

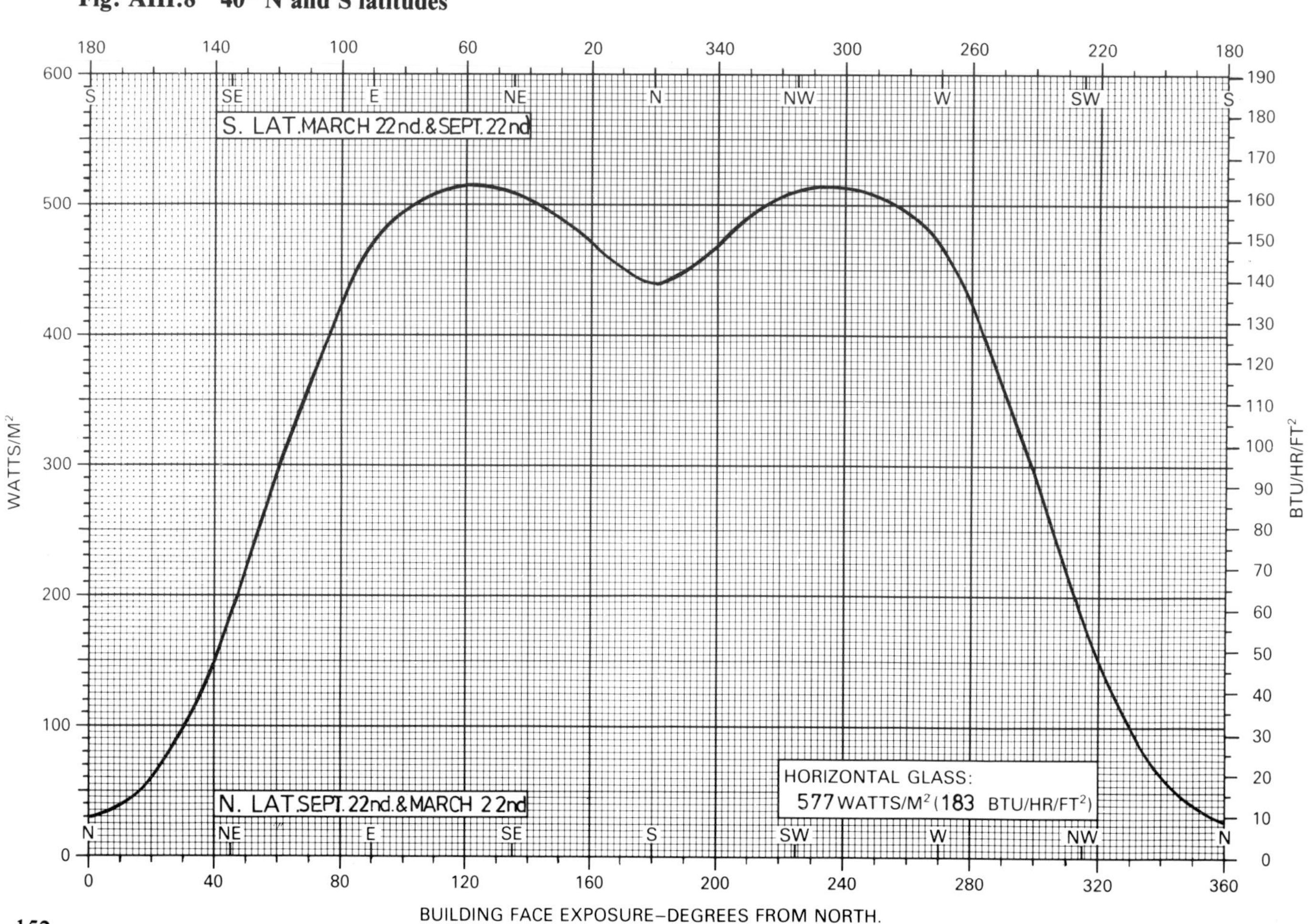

Fig. AIII.9 30° N and S latitudes

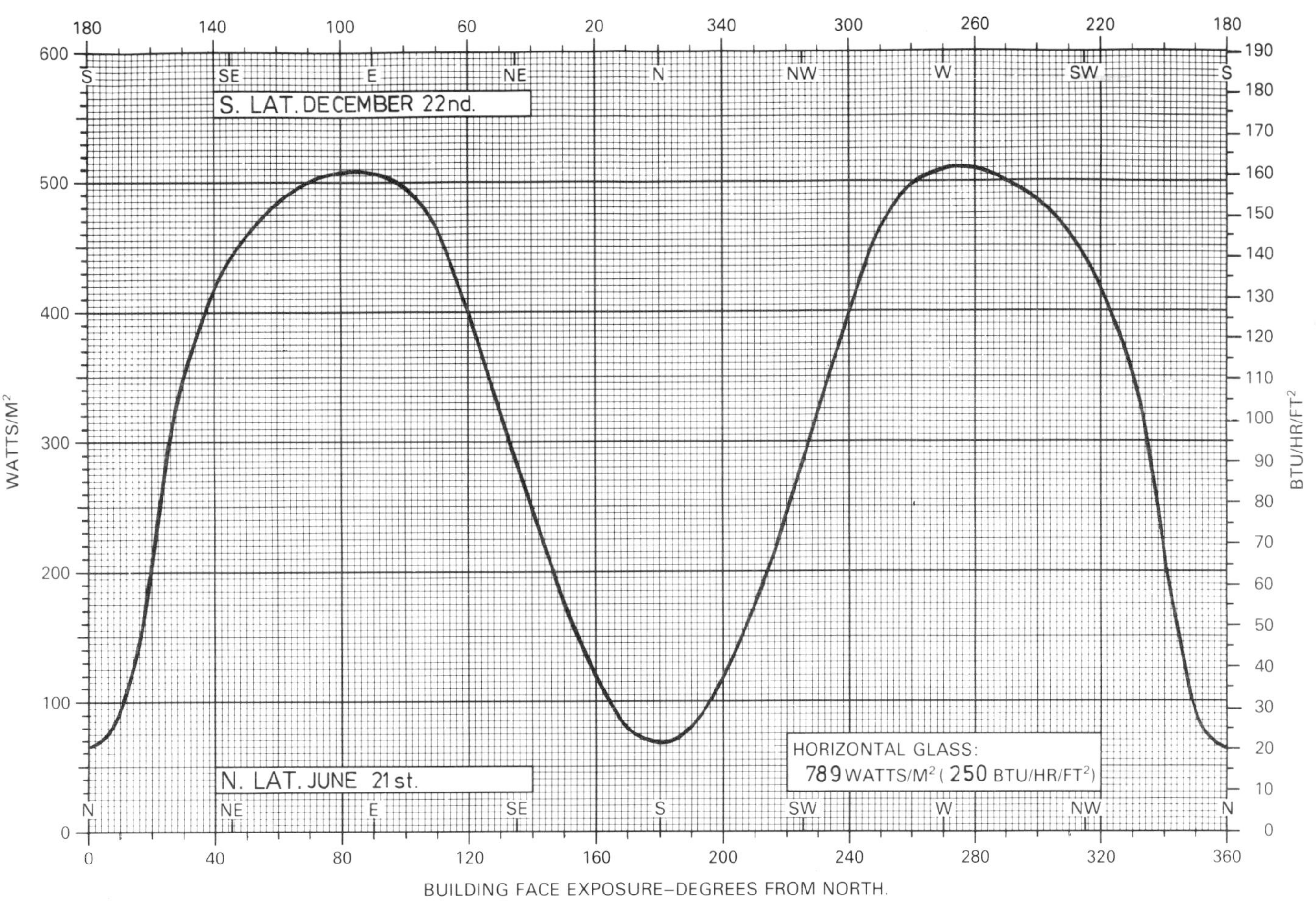

Fig. AIII.10 30° N and S latitudes

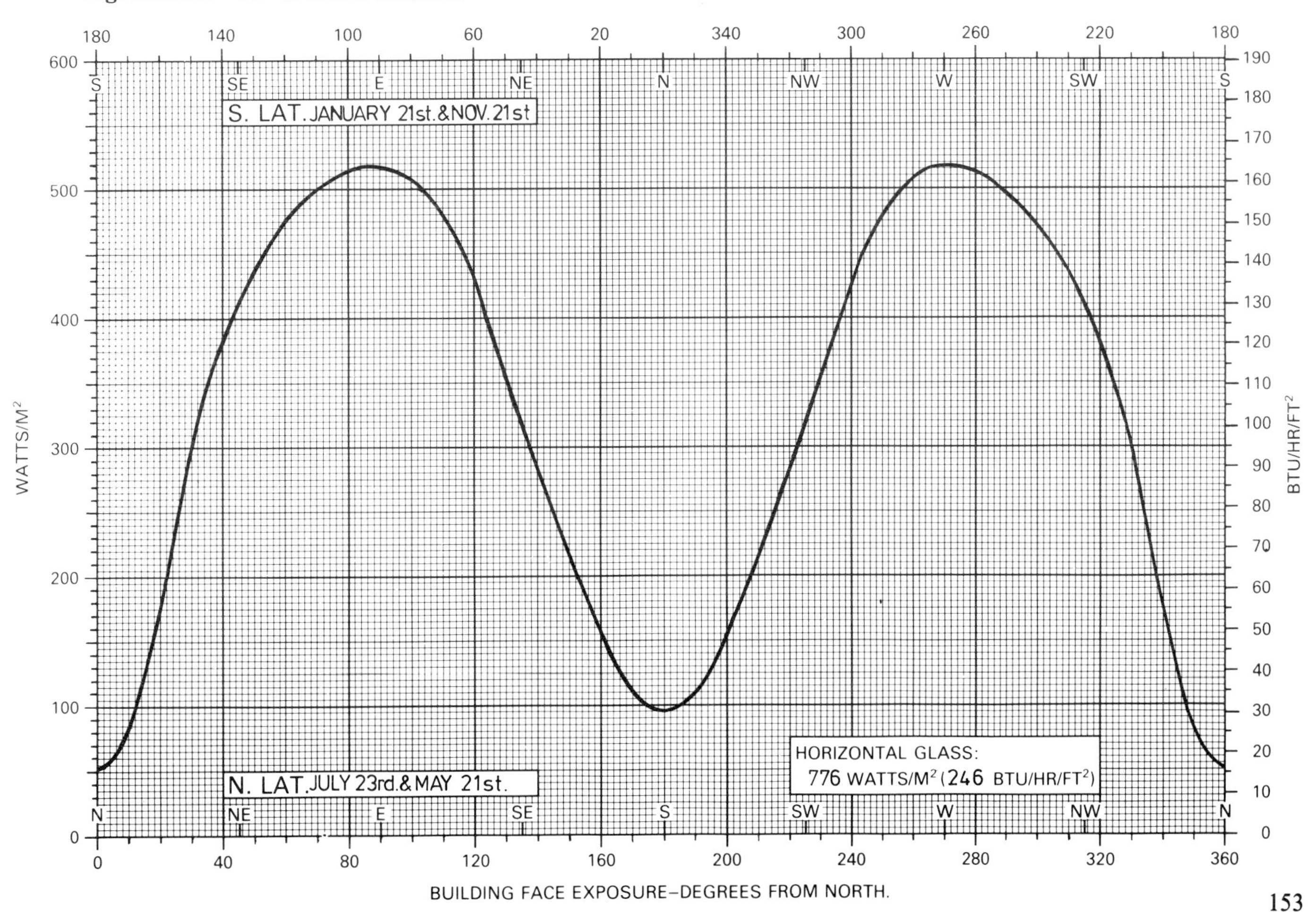

Fig. AIII.11 30° N and S latitudes

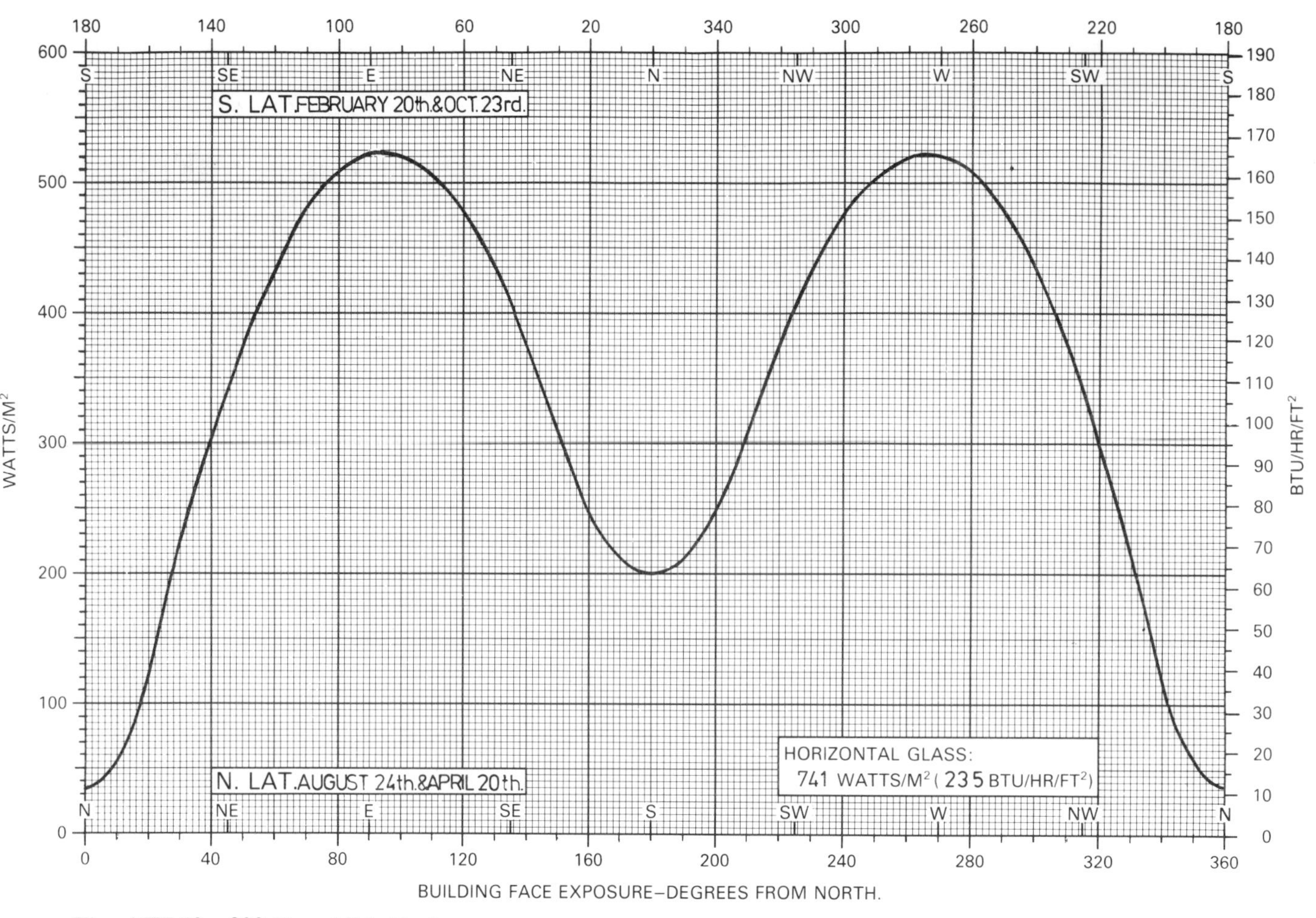

Fig. AIII.12 30° N and S latitudes

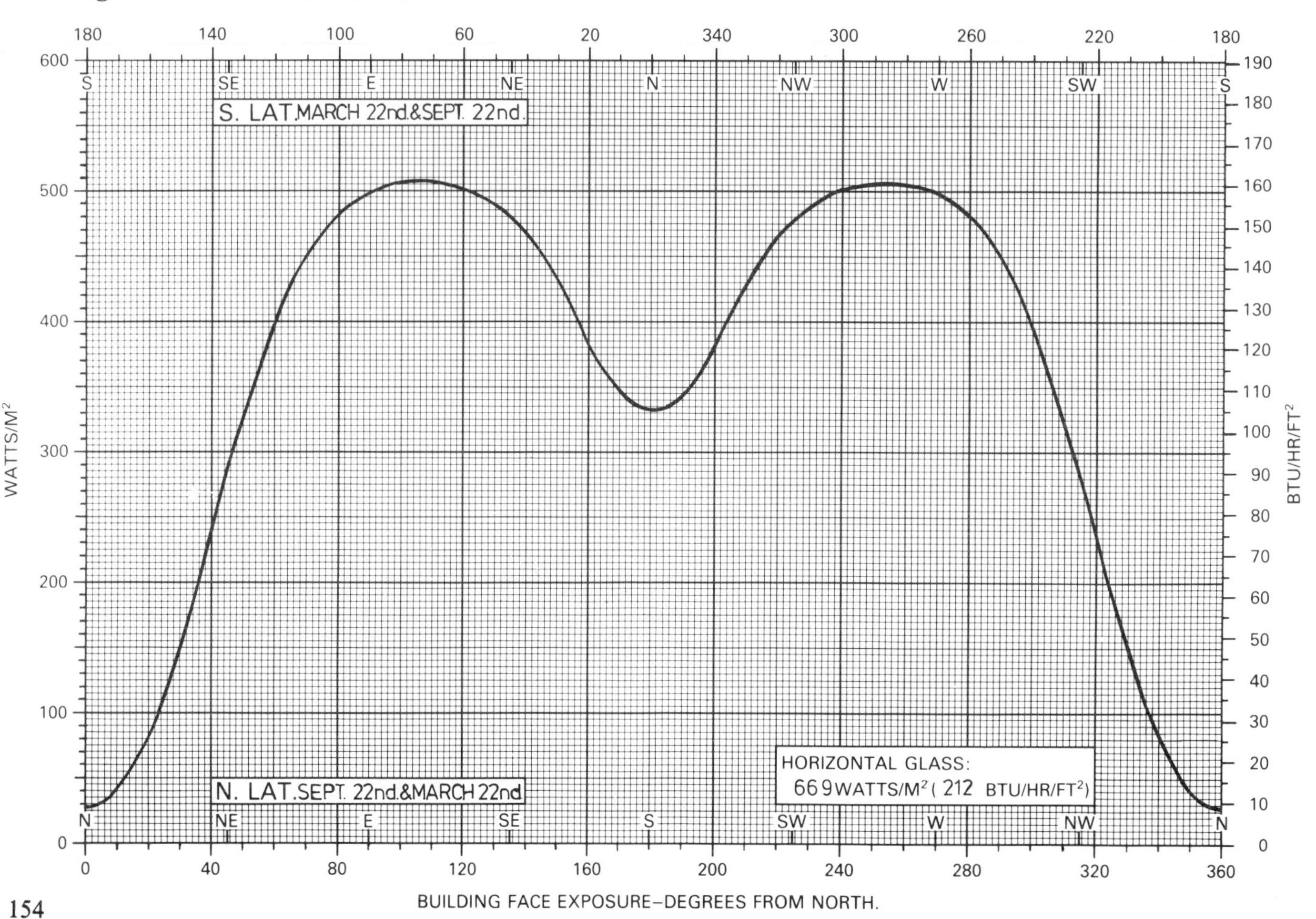

Fig. AIII.13 20° N and S latitudes

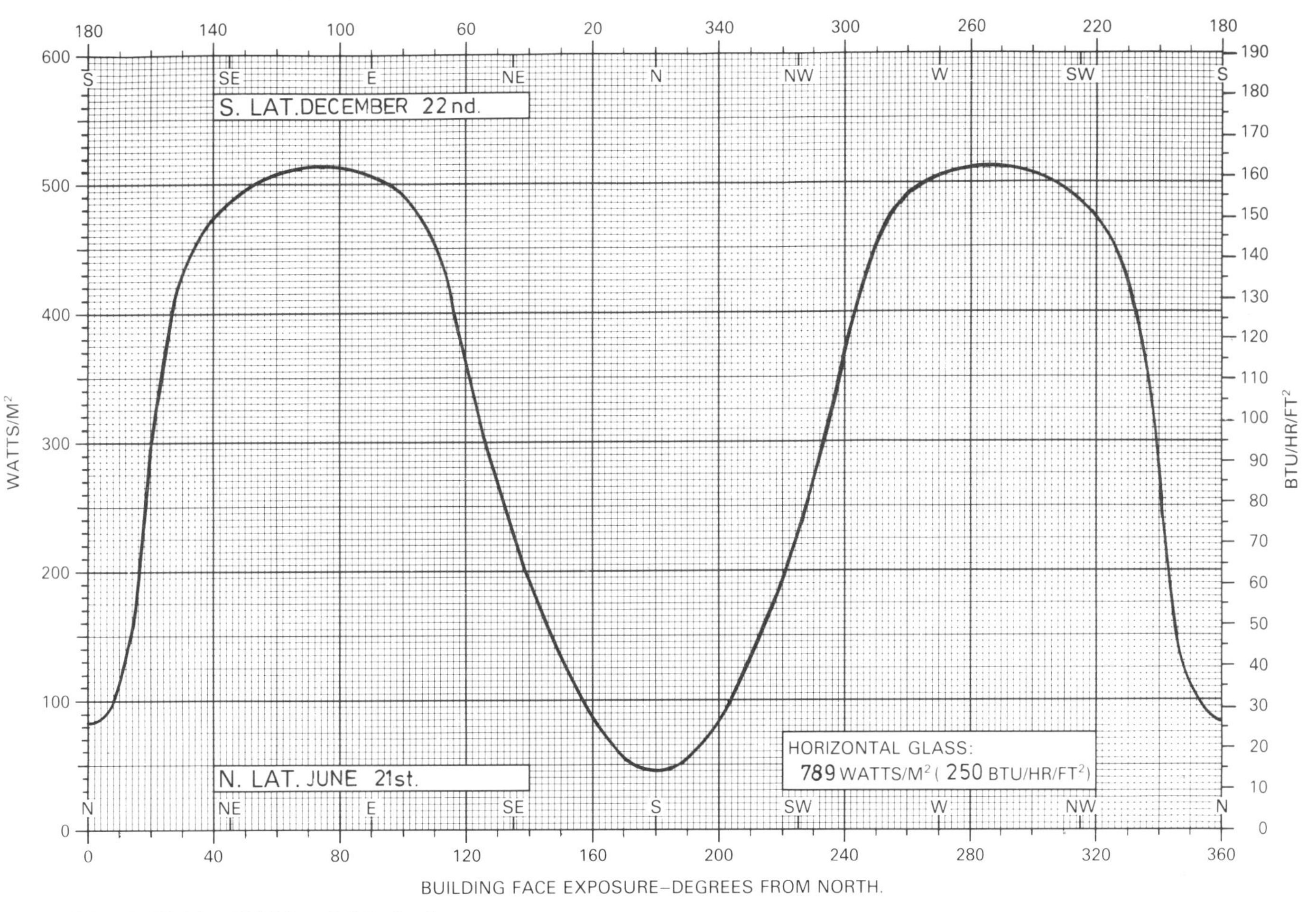

Fig. AIII.14 20° N and S latitudes

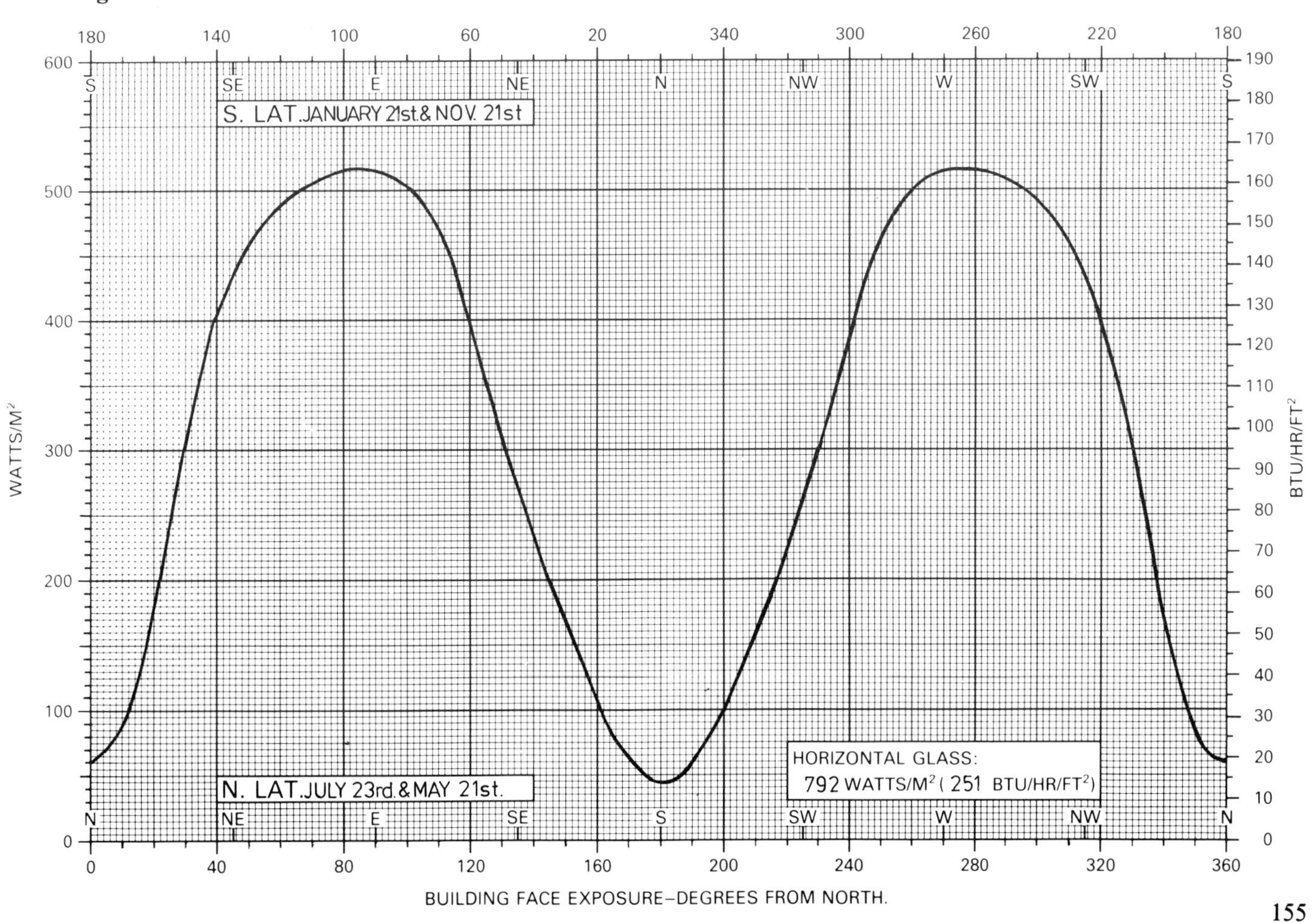

Fig. AIII.15 20° N and S latitudes

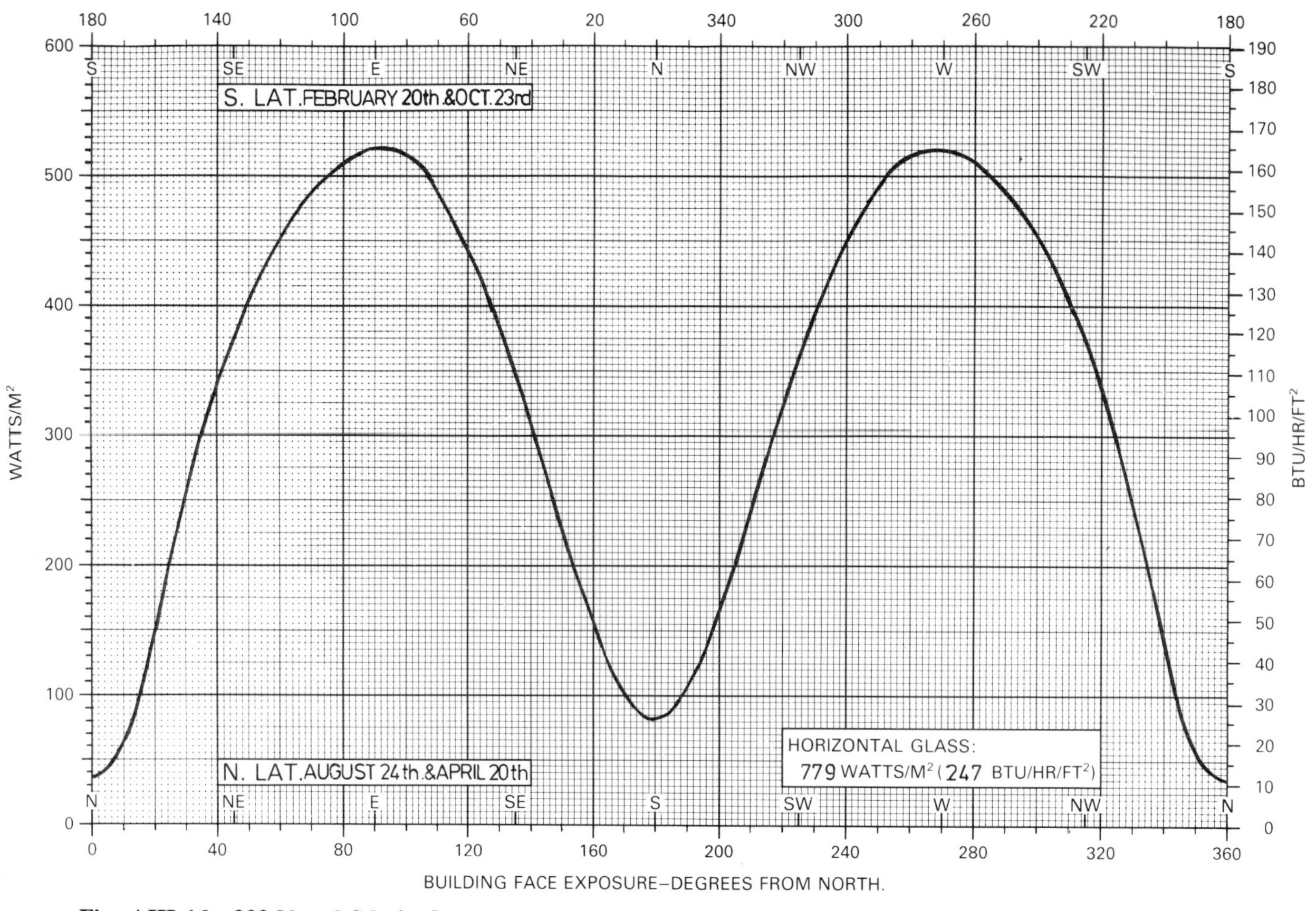

Fig. AIII.16 20° N and S latitudes

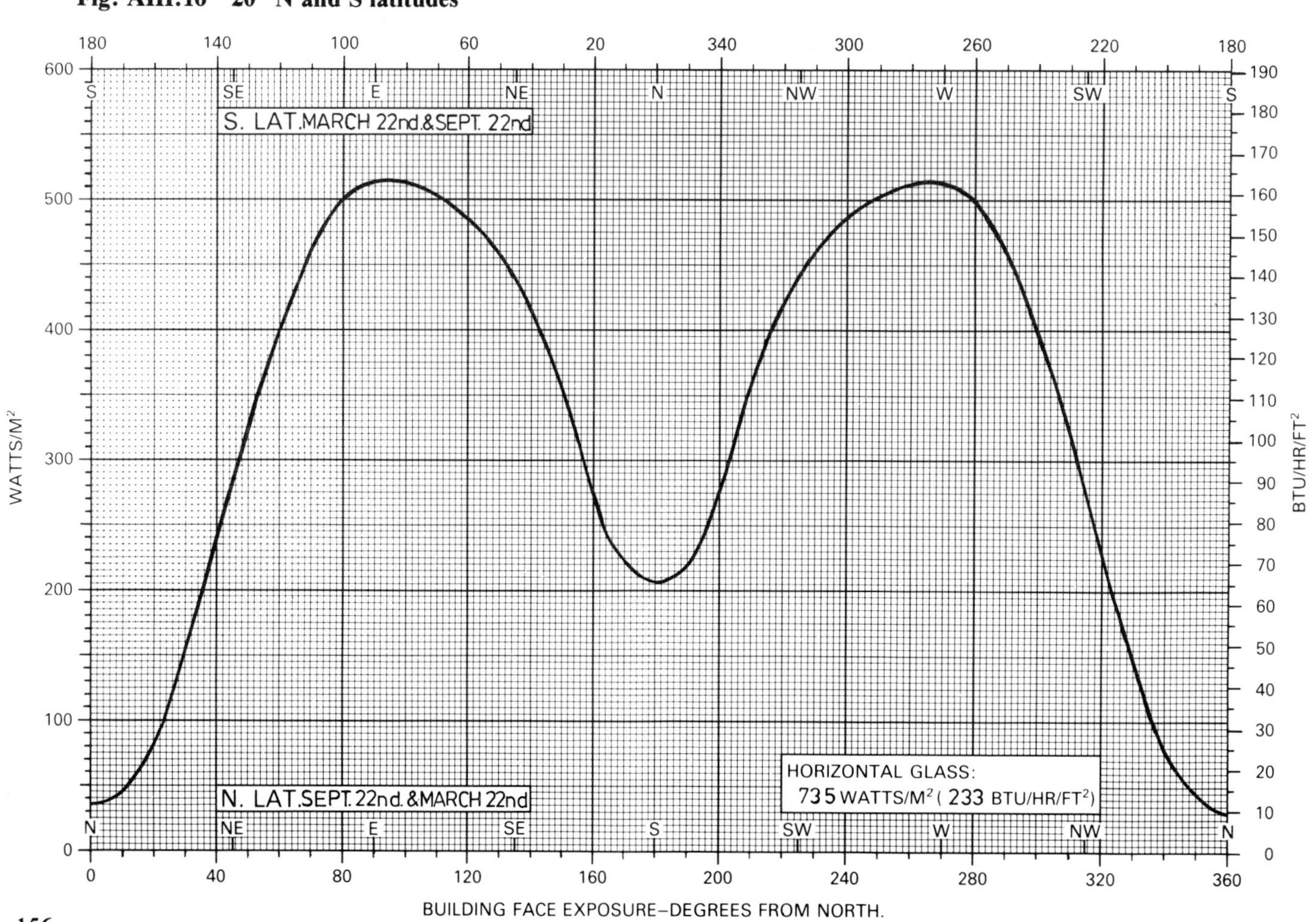

Fig. AIII.17 10° N and S latitudes

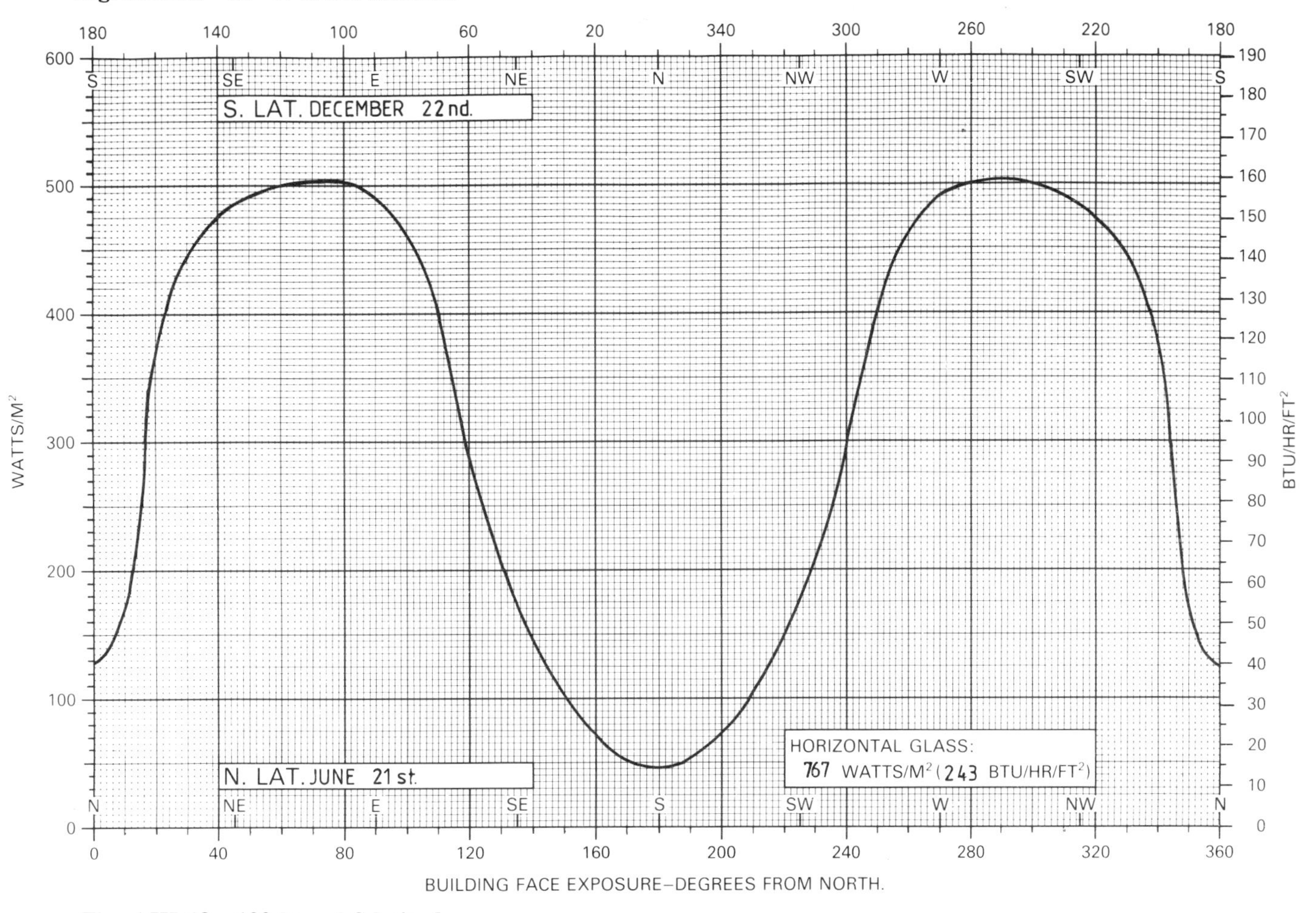

Fig. AIII.18 10° N and S latitudes

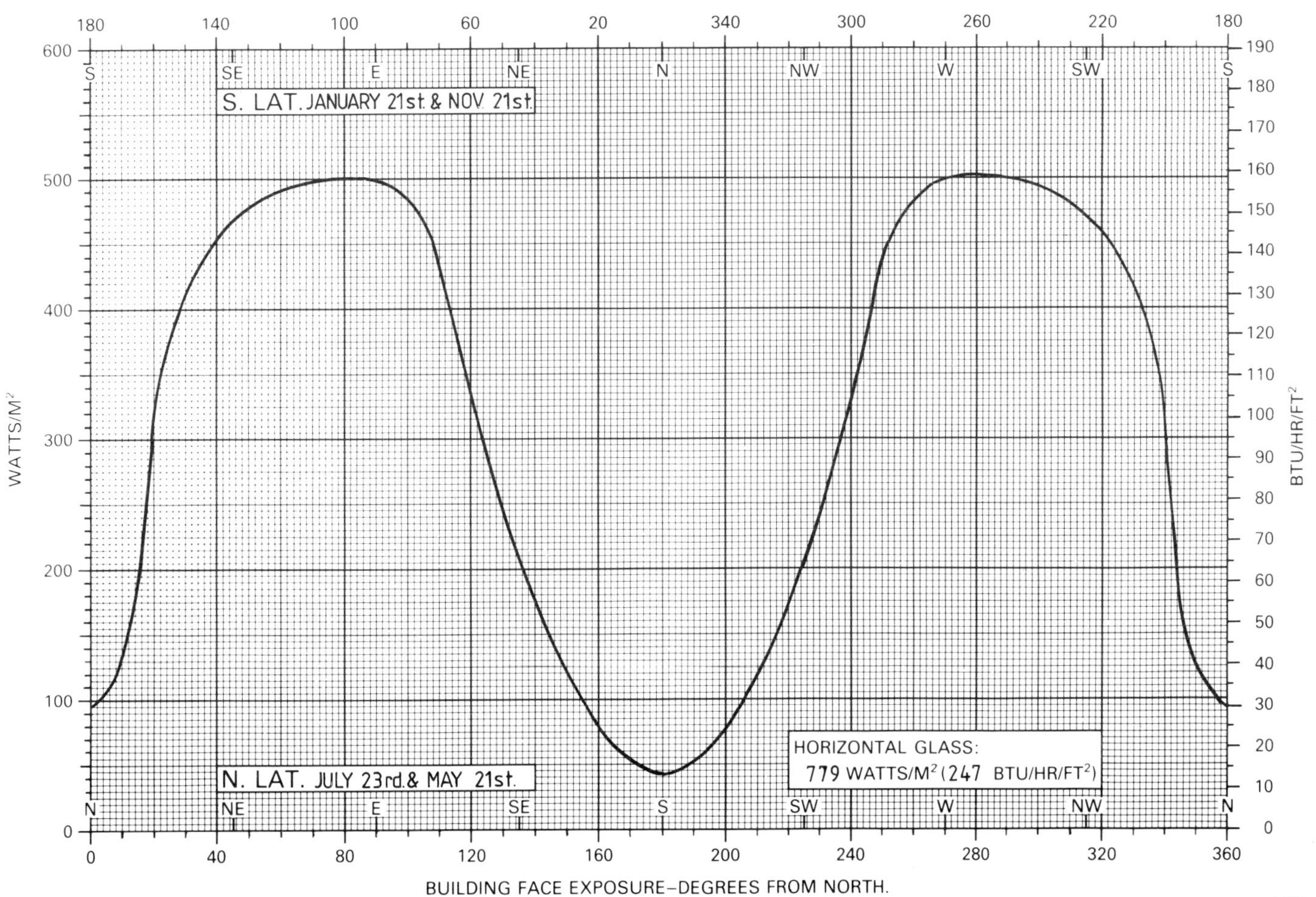

Fig. AIII.19 10° N and S latitudes

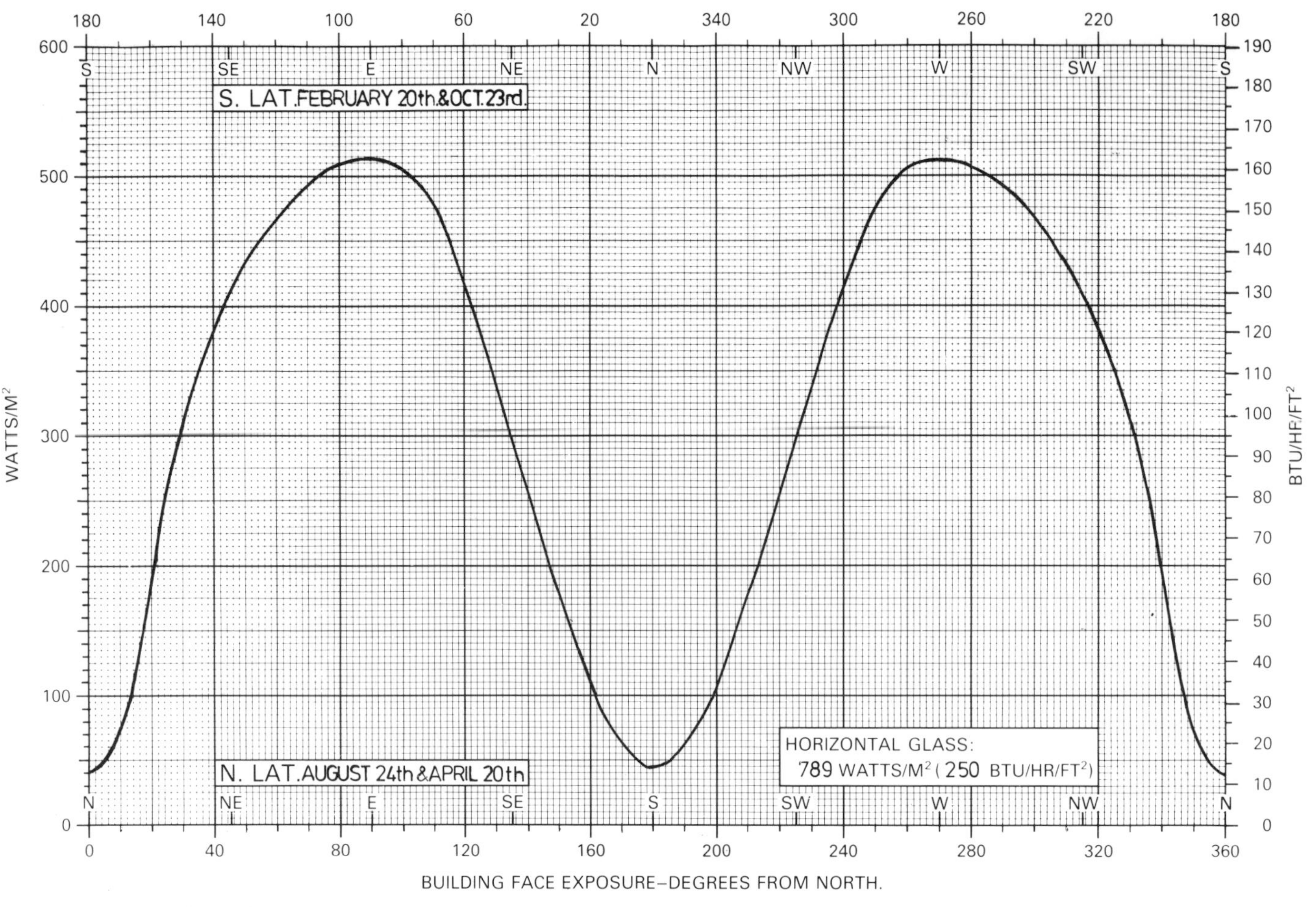

Fig. AIII.20 10° N and S latitudes

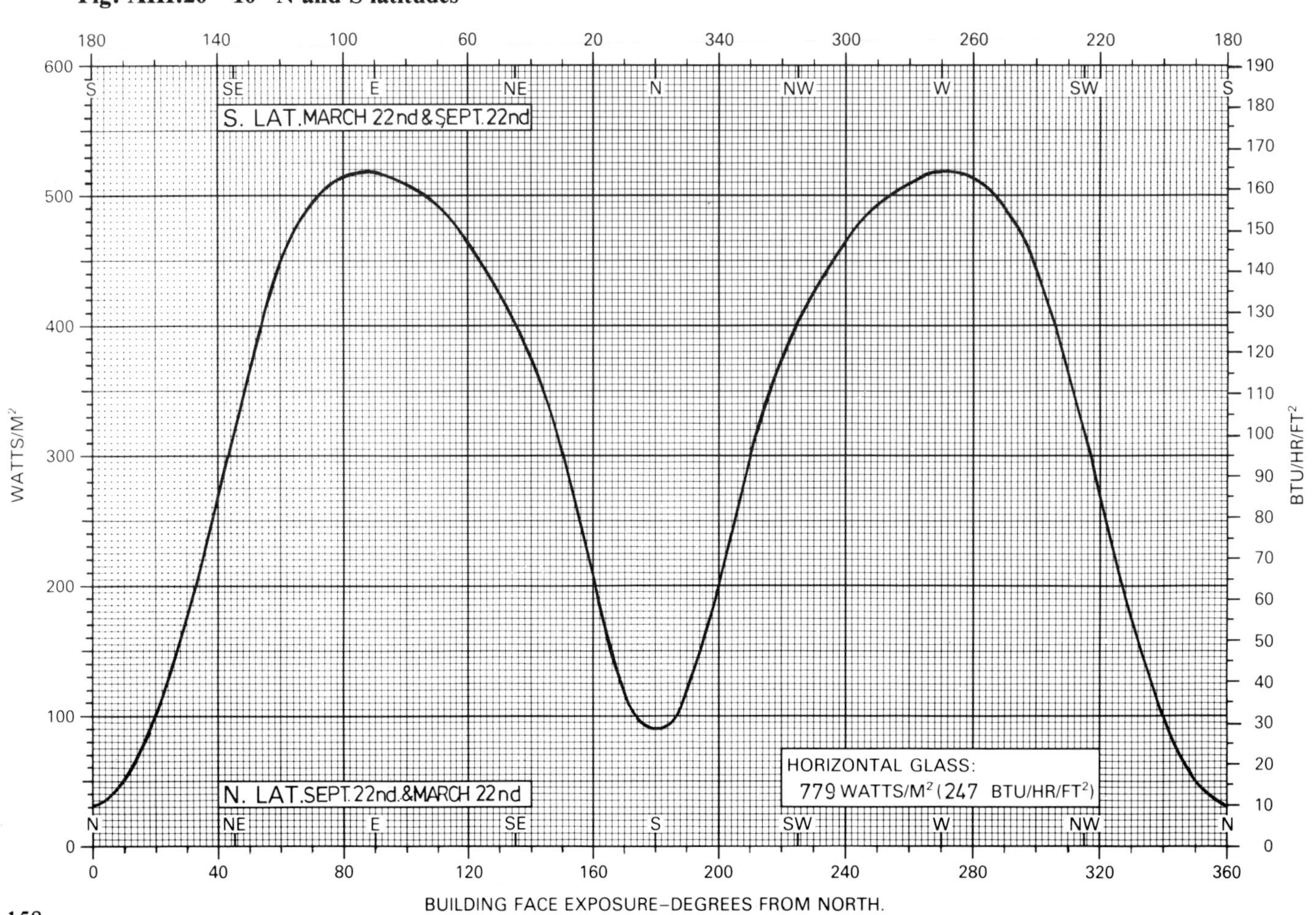

Fig. AIII.21 0° N and S latitudes

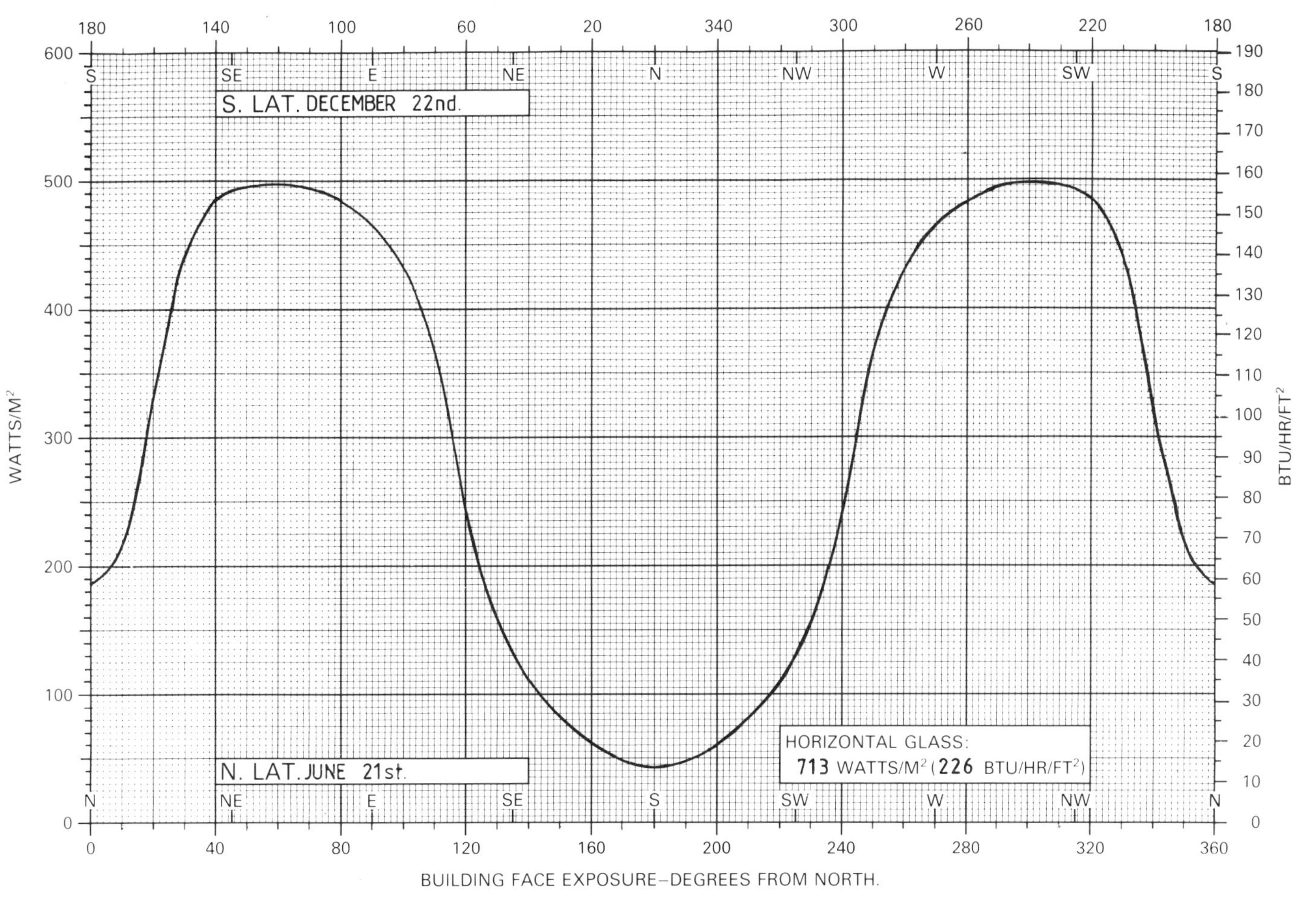

Fig. AIII.22 0° N and S latitudes

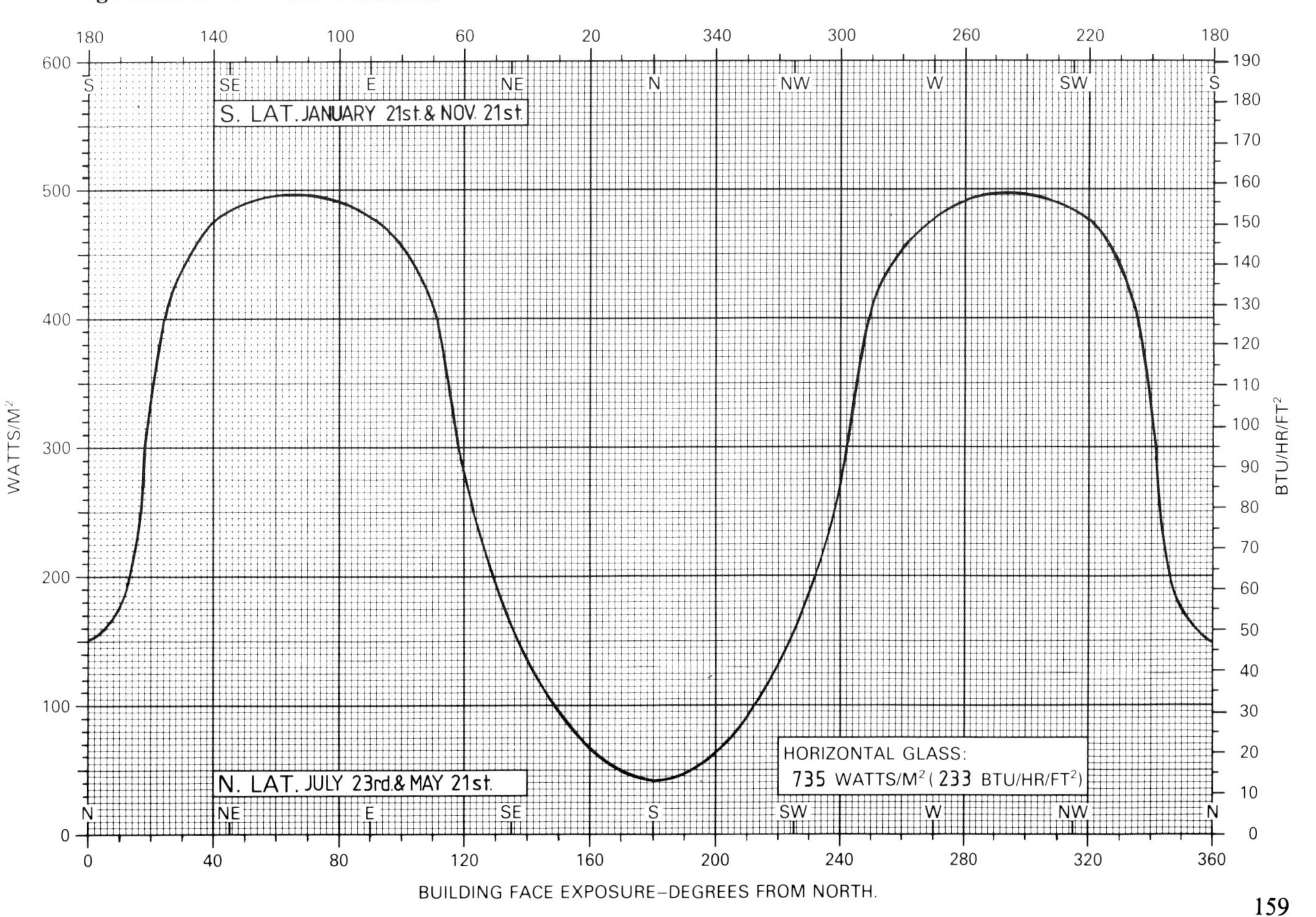

Fig. AIII.23 0° N and S latitudes

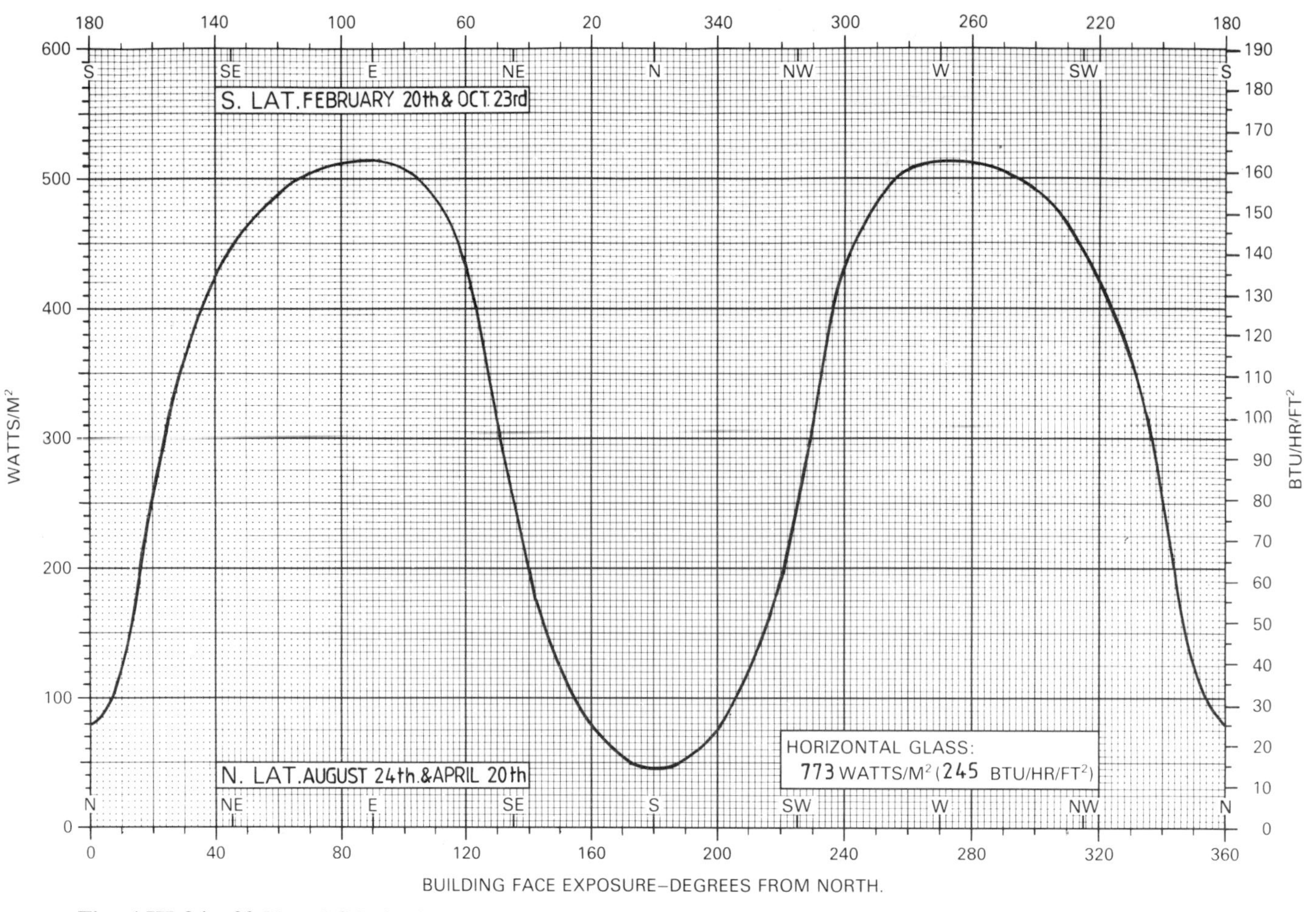

Fig. AIII.24 0° N and S latitudes

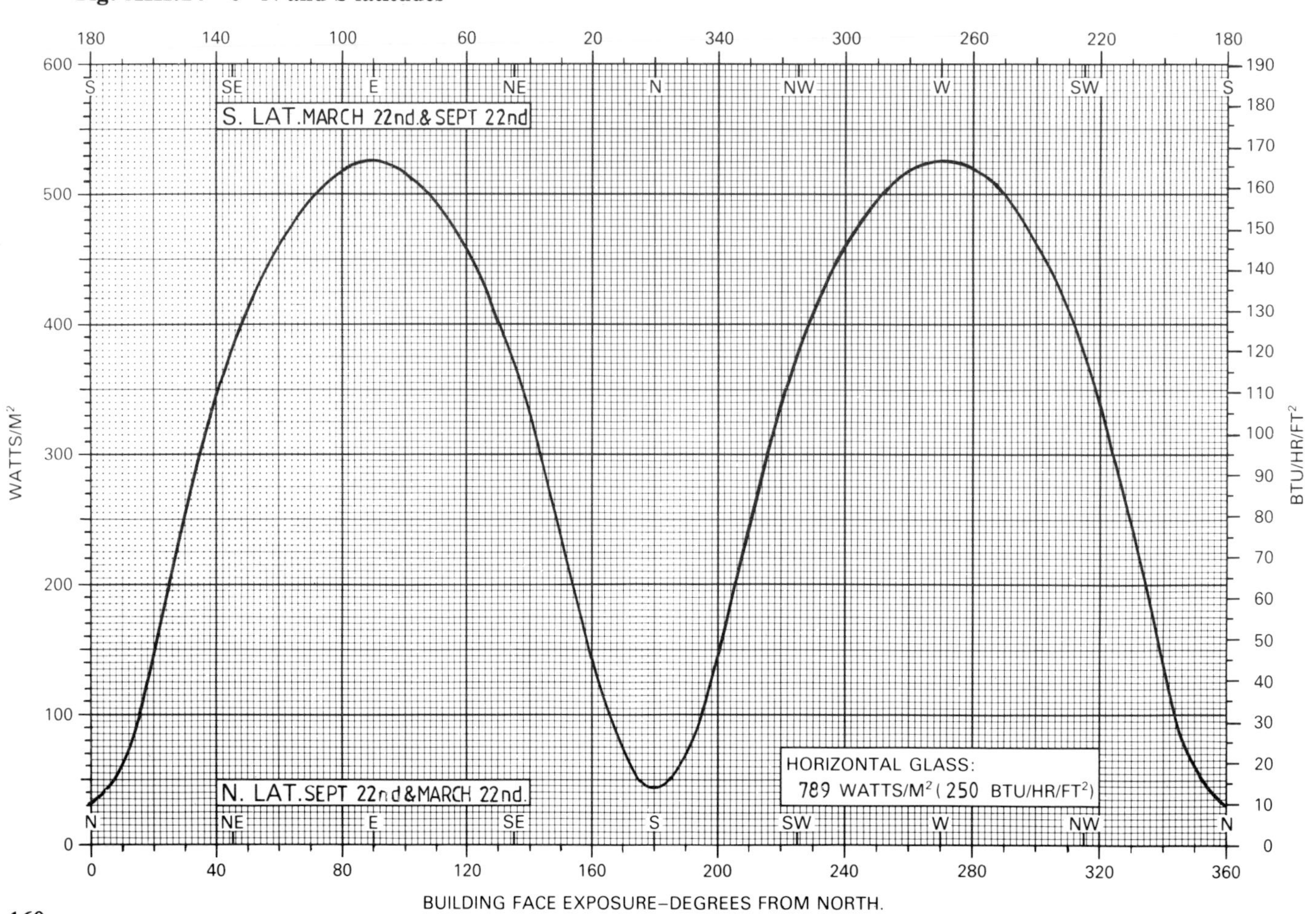

Appendix IV
Storage load factors for solar radiation through glass

Fig. No.	*Page*	*Plant cooling period (hours)*	*Shades*	*Spec. wt. (kg/m²)*
AIV.1	162	12	Interior	150
AIV.2	163	12	Interior	500
AIV.3	164	12	Interior	750
AIV.4	165	12	Exterior or unshaded	150
AIV.5	166	12	Exterior or unshaded	500
AIV.6	167	12	Exterior or unshaded	750
AIV.7	168	16	Interior	150
AIV.8	169	16	Interior	500
AIV.9	170	16	Interior	750
AIV.10	171	16	Exterior or unshaded	150
AIV.11	172	16	Exterior or unshaded	500
AIV.12	173	16	Exterior or unshaded	750
AIV.13	174	24	Interior	150
AIV.14	175	24	Interior	500
AIV.15	176	24	Interior	750
AIV.16	177	24	Exterior or unshaded	150
AIV.17	178	24	Exterior or unshaded	500
AIV.18	179	24	Exterior or unshaded	750
AIV.19	180	Horizontal glass 12 and 24	Interior	150–750
AIV.20	181	Horizontal glass 12 and 24	Exterior or unshaded	150–750

Fig. AIV.1 Storage load factors for solar radiation through glass; N and S latitudes
12 hour plant cooling, interior shades, specific weight 150 kg/m²

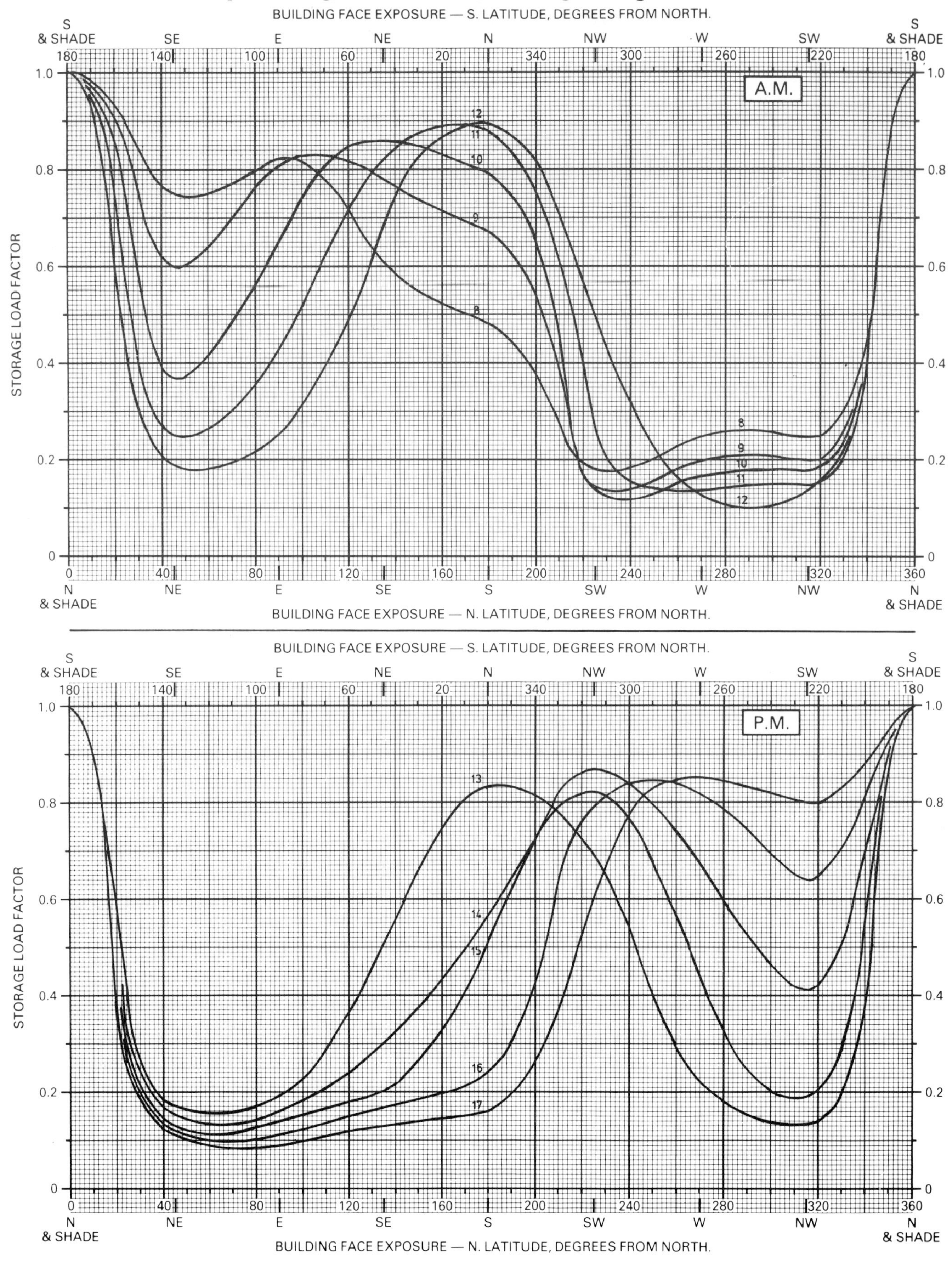

Fig. AIV.2 12-hour plant cooling, interior shades, specific weight 500 kg/m²

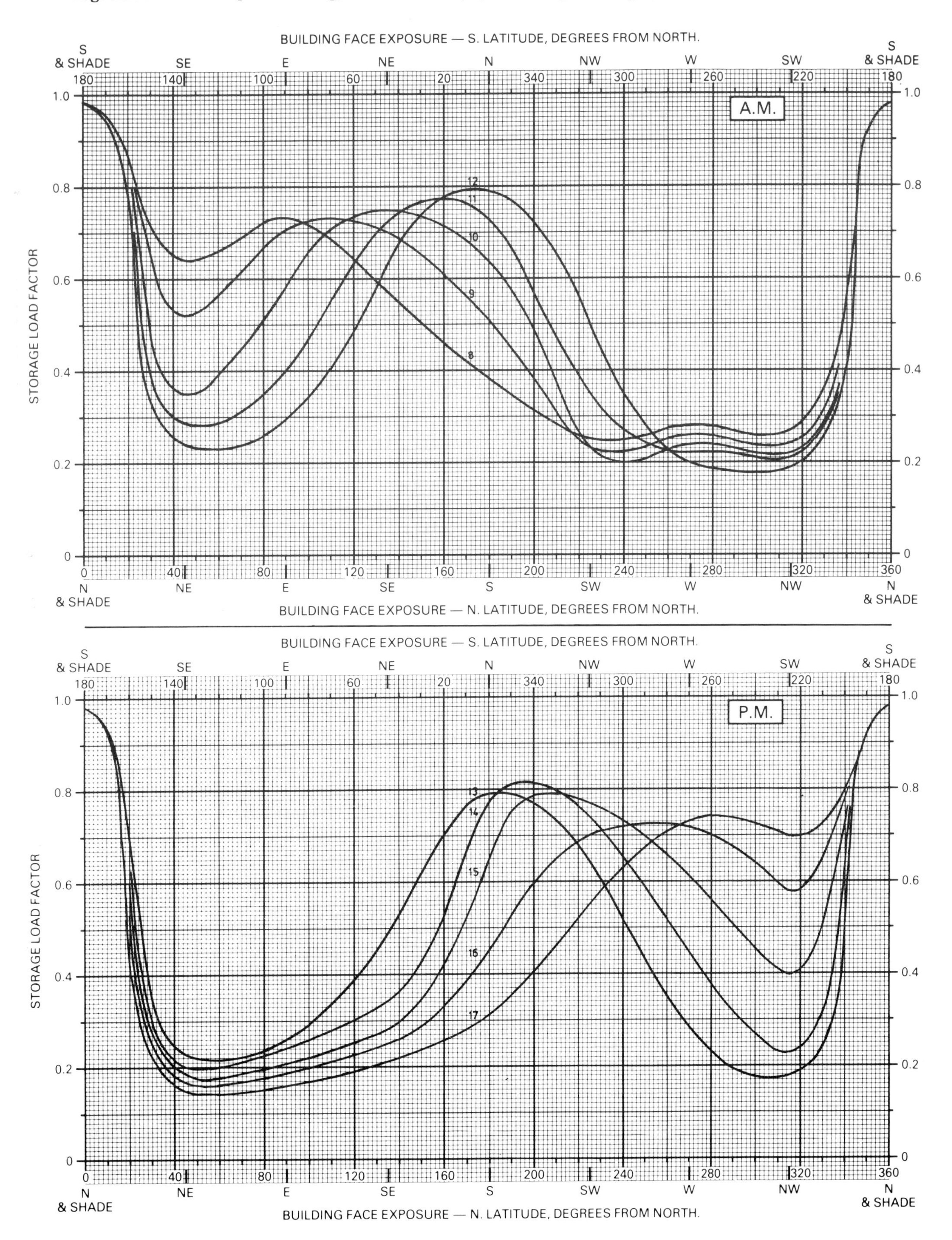

Fig. AIV.3 12 hour plant cooling, interior shades, specific weight 750 kg/m²

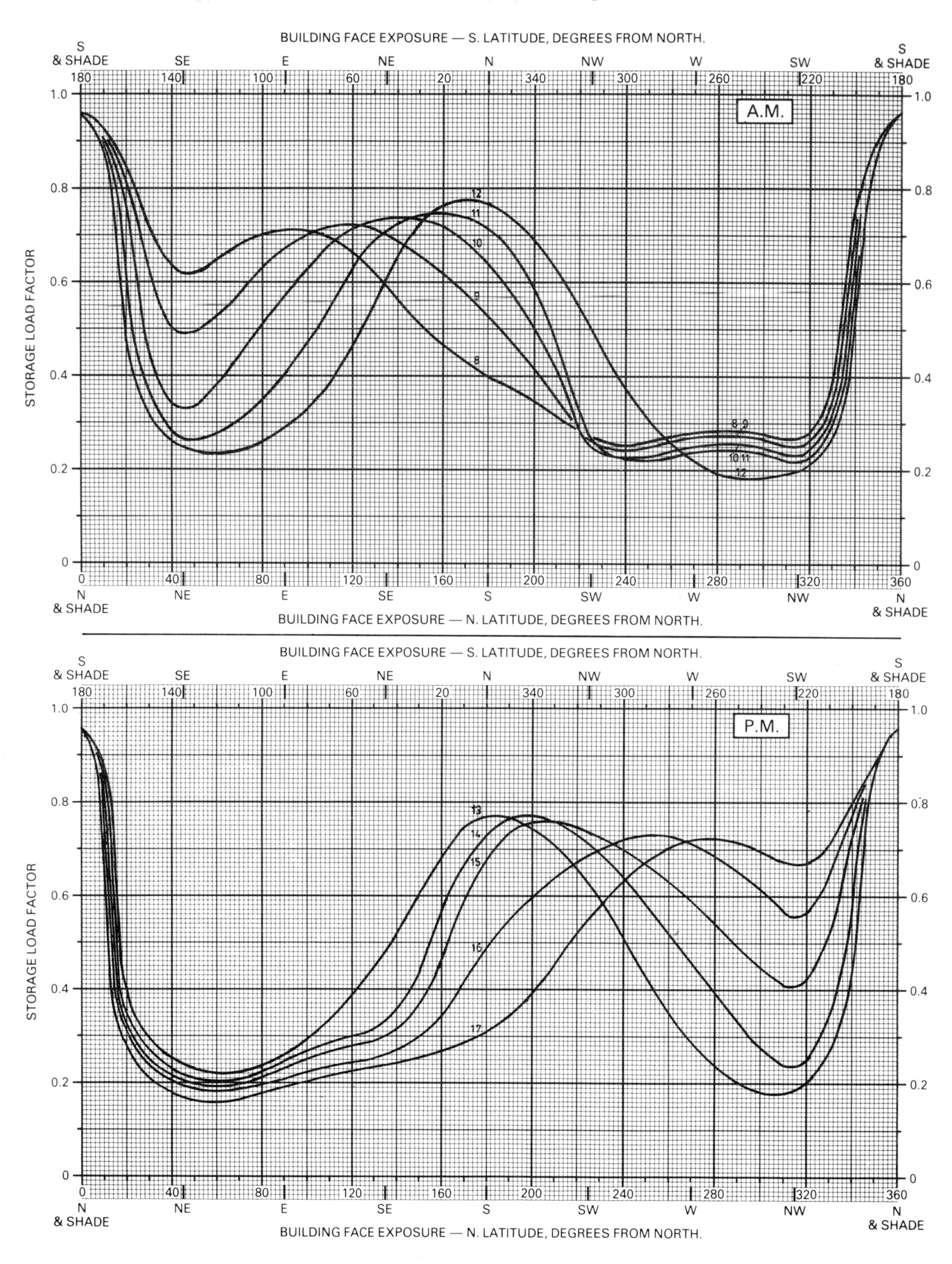

Fig. AIV.4 12 hour plant cooling, exterior shades or unshaded, specific weight 150 kg/m²

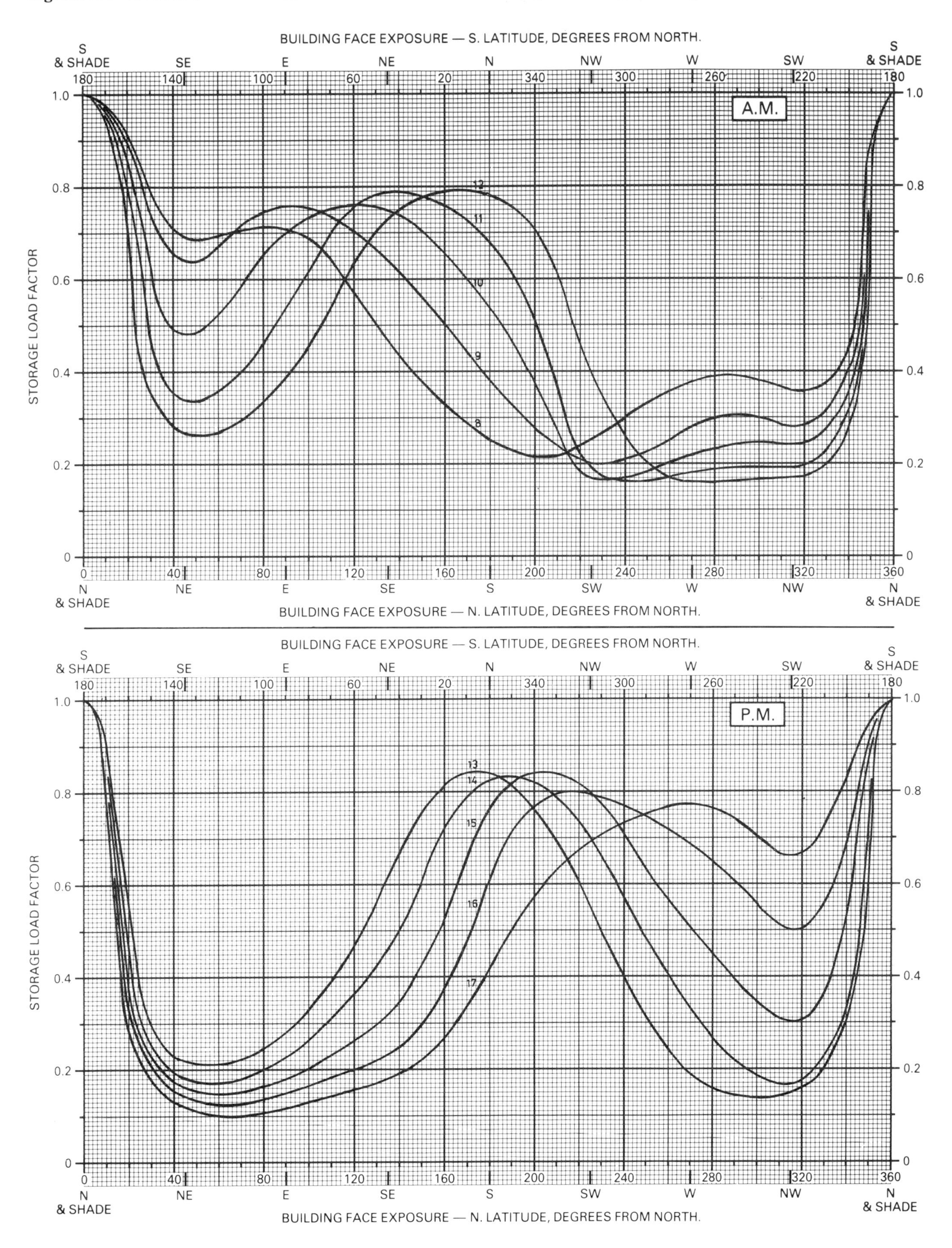

Fig. AIV.5 12 hour plant cooling, exerior shades or unshaded, specific weight 500 kg/m²

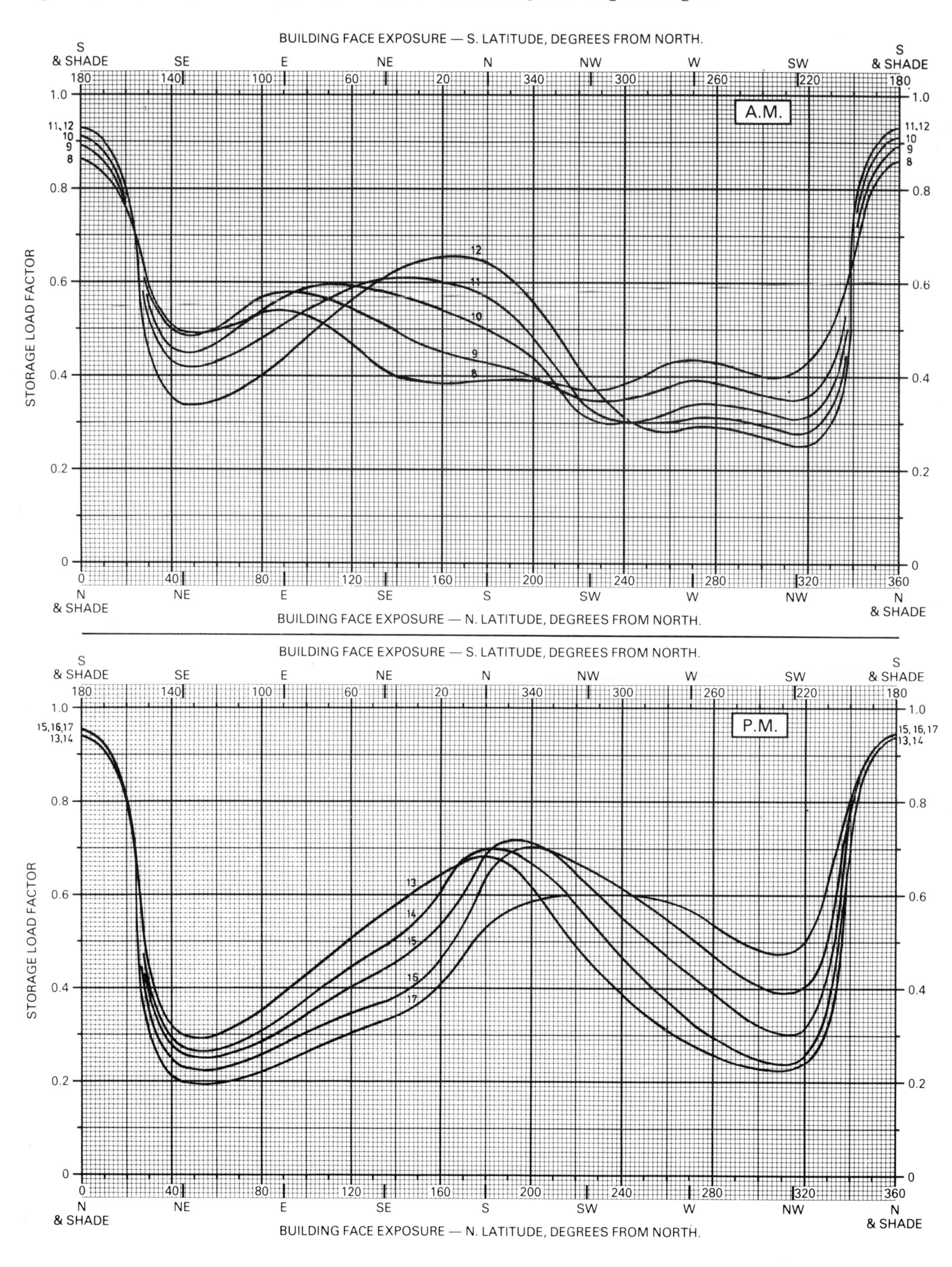

Fig. AIV.6 12 hour plant cooling, exterior shades or unshaded, specific weight 750 kg/m²

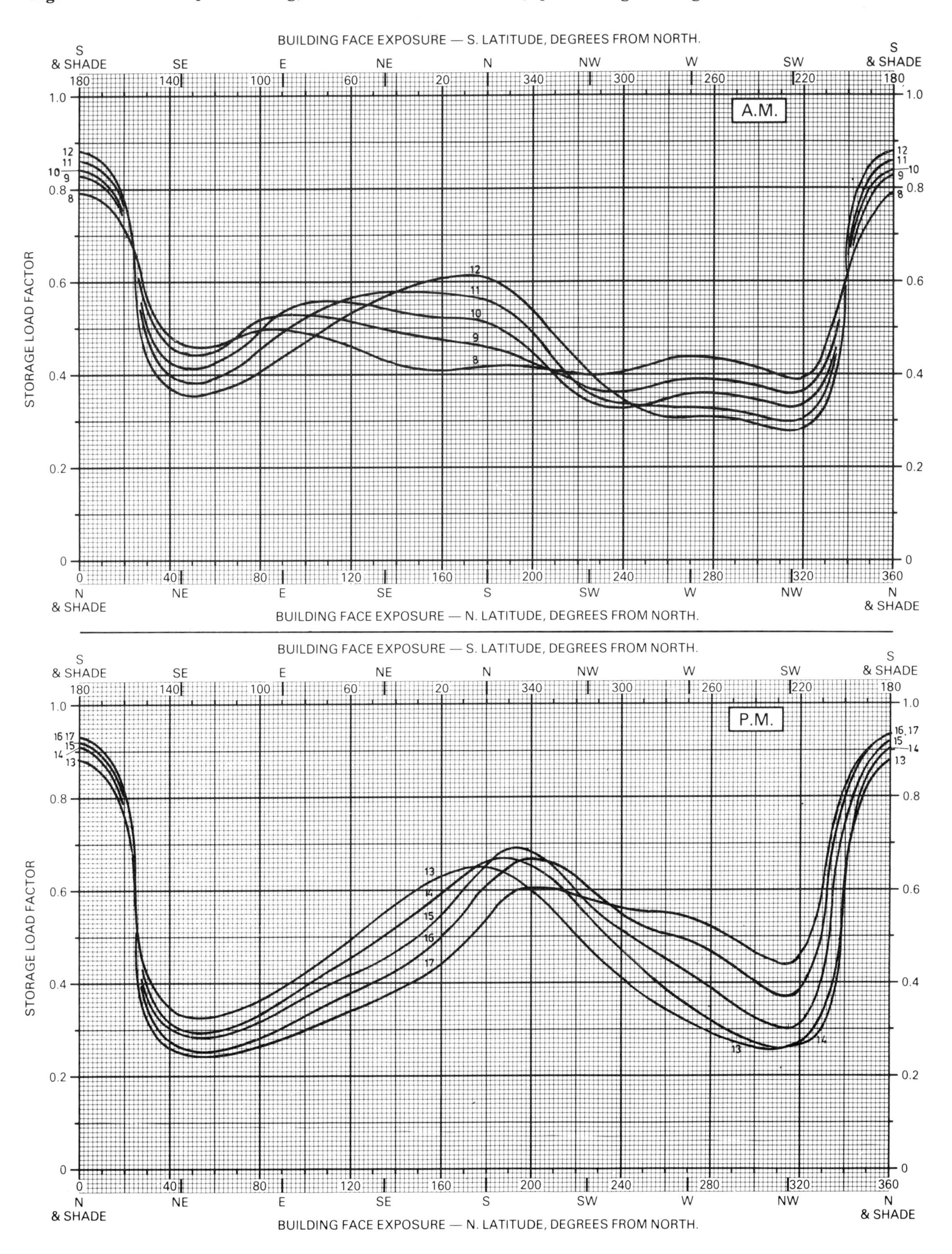

Fig. AIV.7 16 hour plant cooling, interior shades, specific weight 150 kg/m²

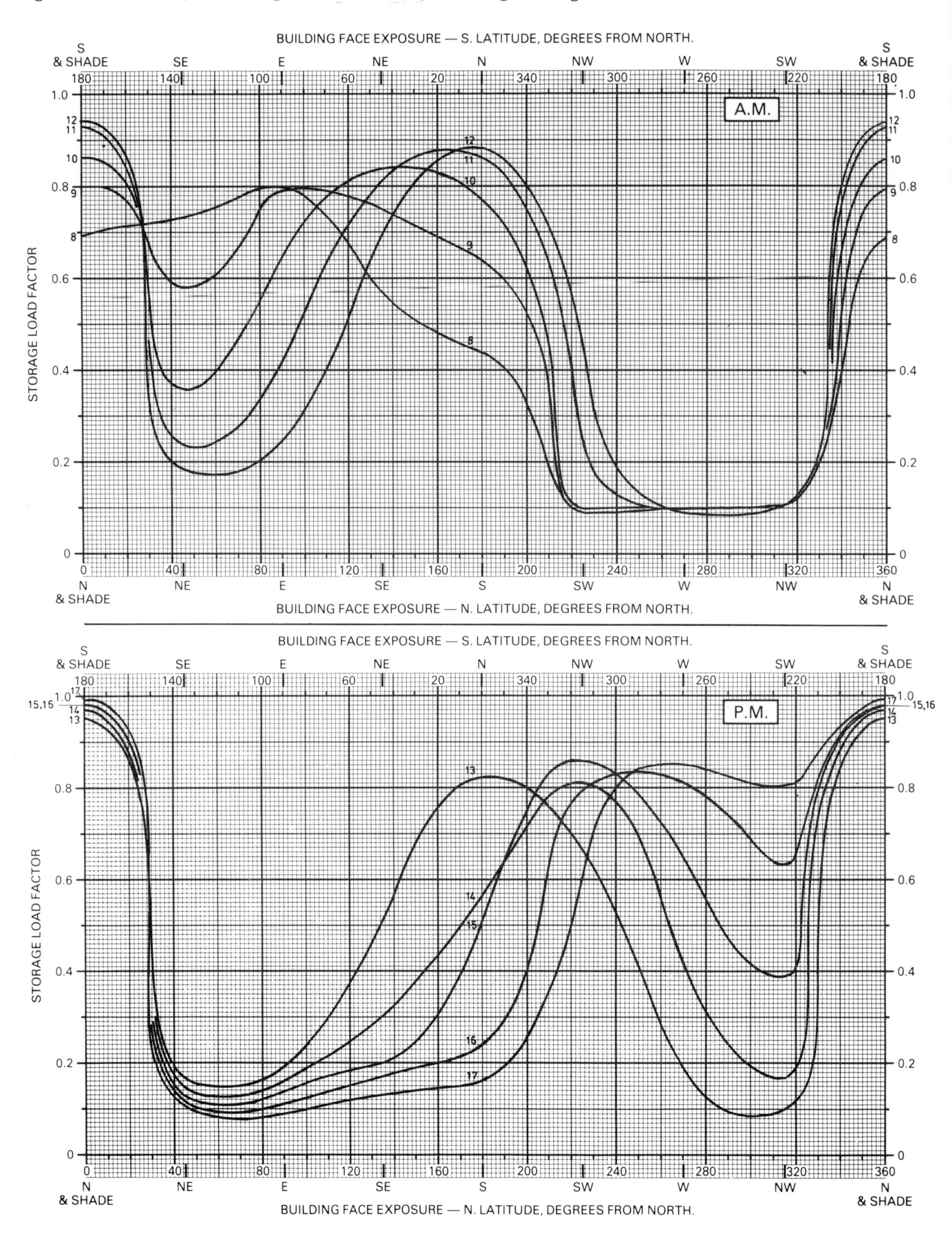

Fig. AIV.8 16 hour plant cooling, interior shades, specific weight 500 kg/m²

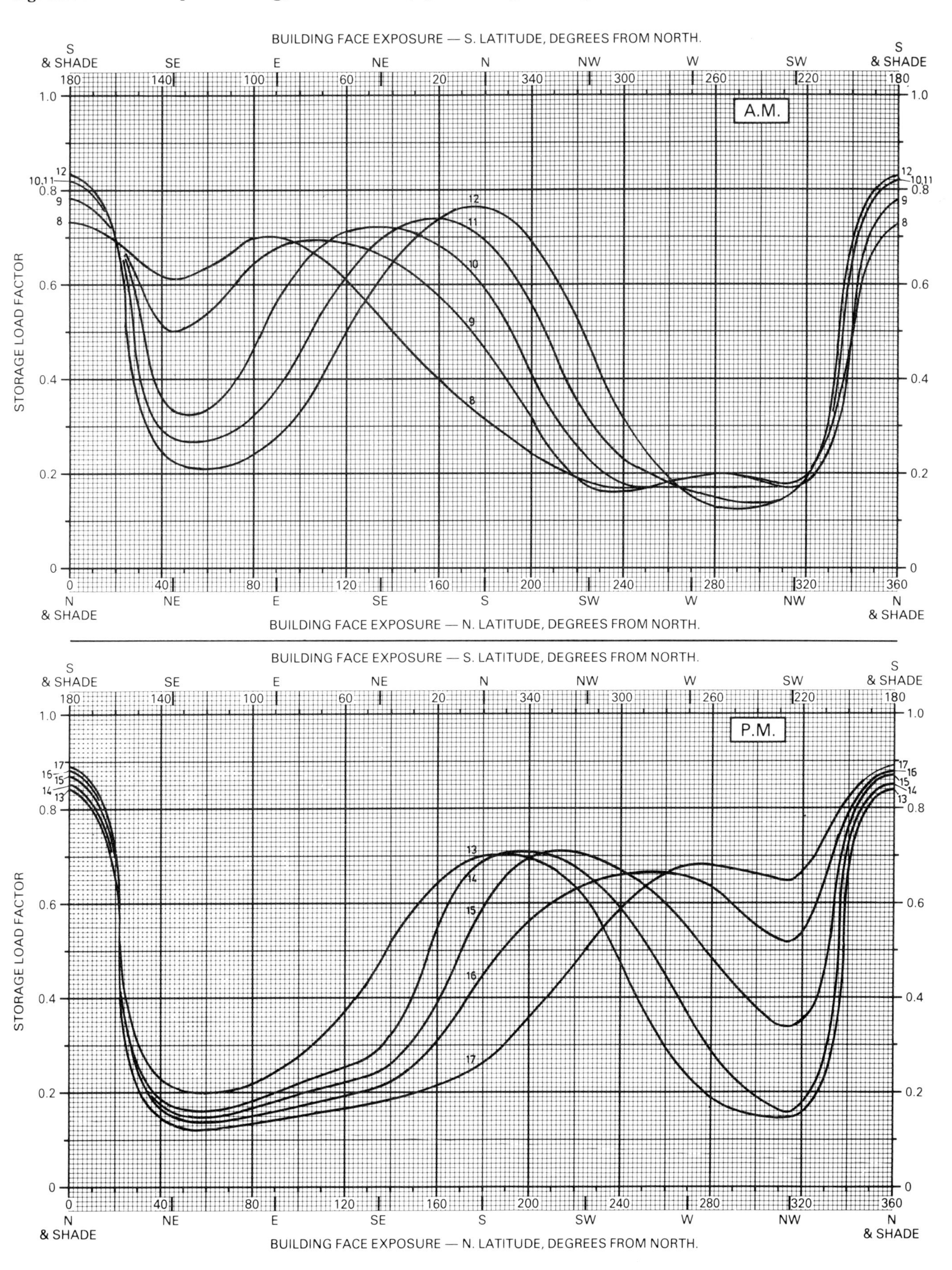

Fig. AIV.9 16 hour plant cooling, interior shades, specific weight 750 kg/m²

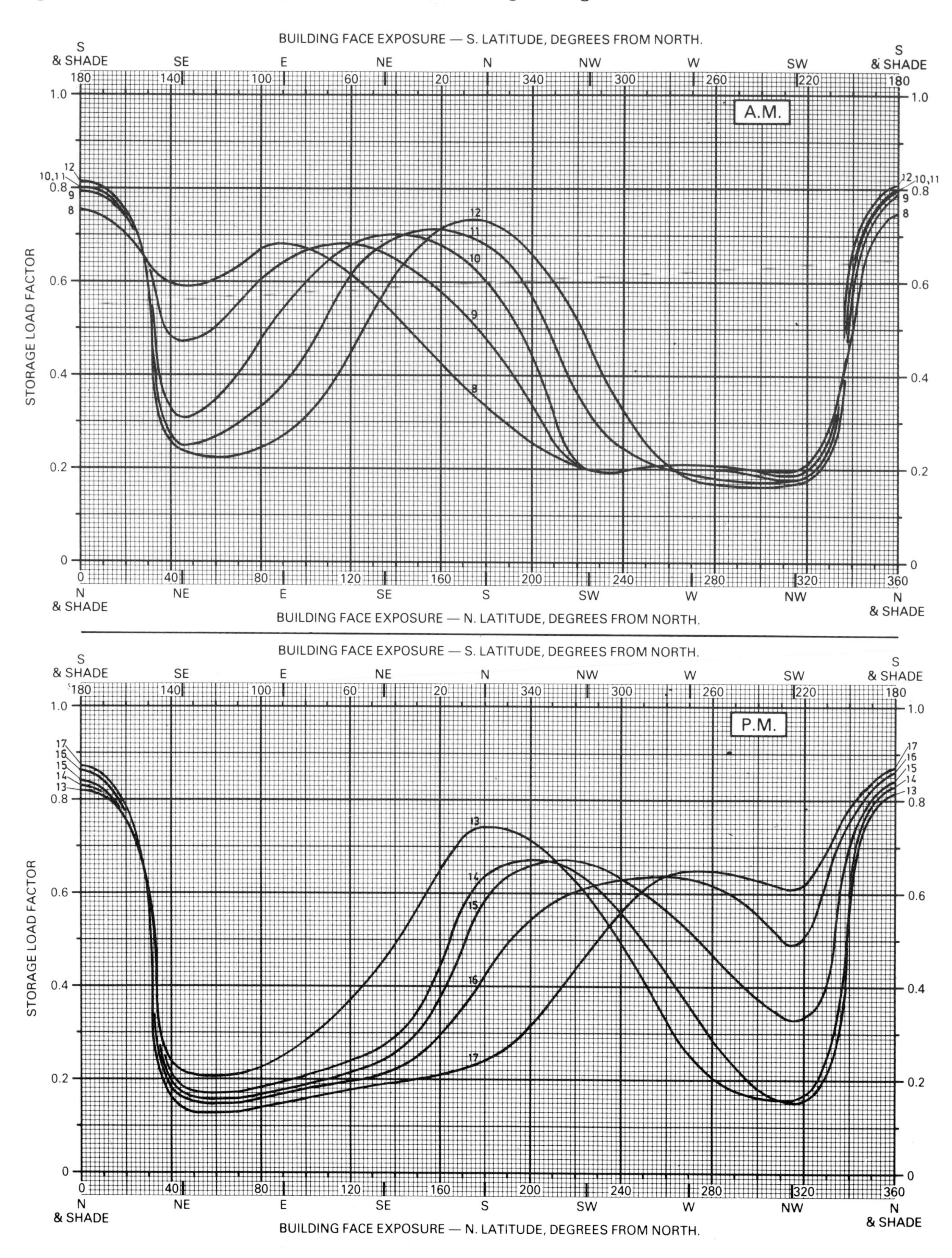

Fig. AIV.10 16 hour plant cooling, exterior shades or unshaded, specific weight 150 kg/m²

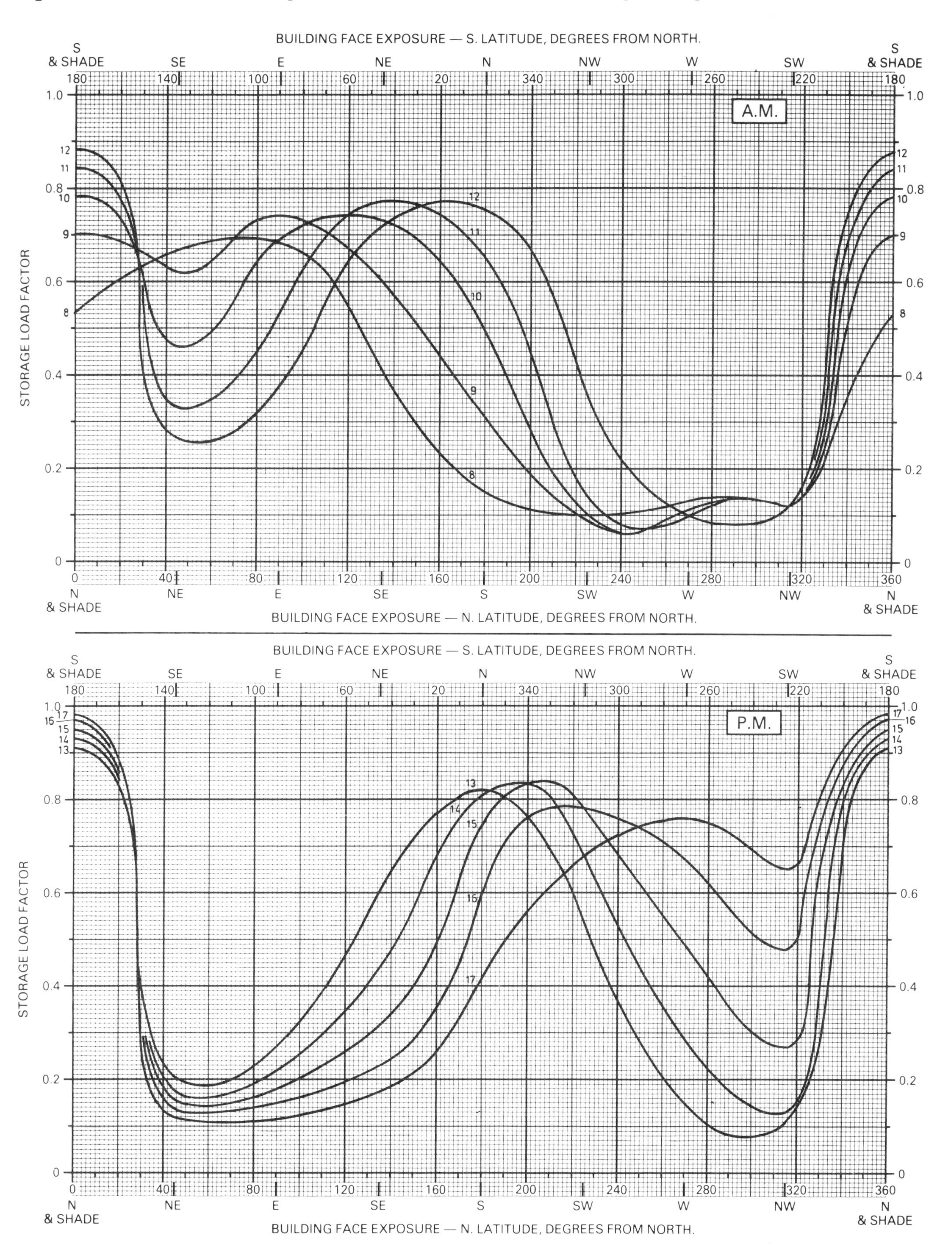

Fig. AIV.11 16 hour plant cooling, exterior shades or unshaded, specific weight 500 kg/m²

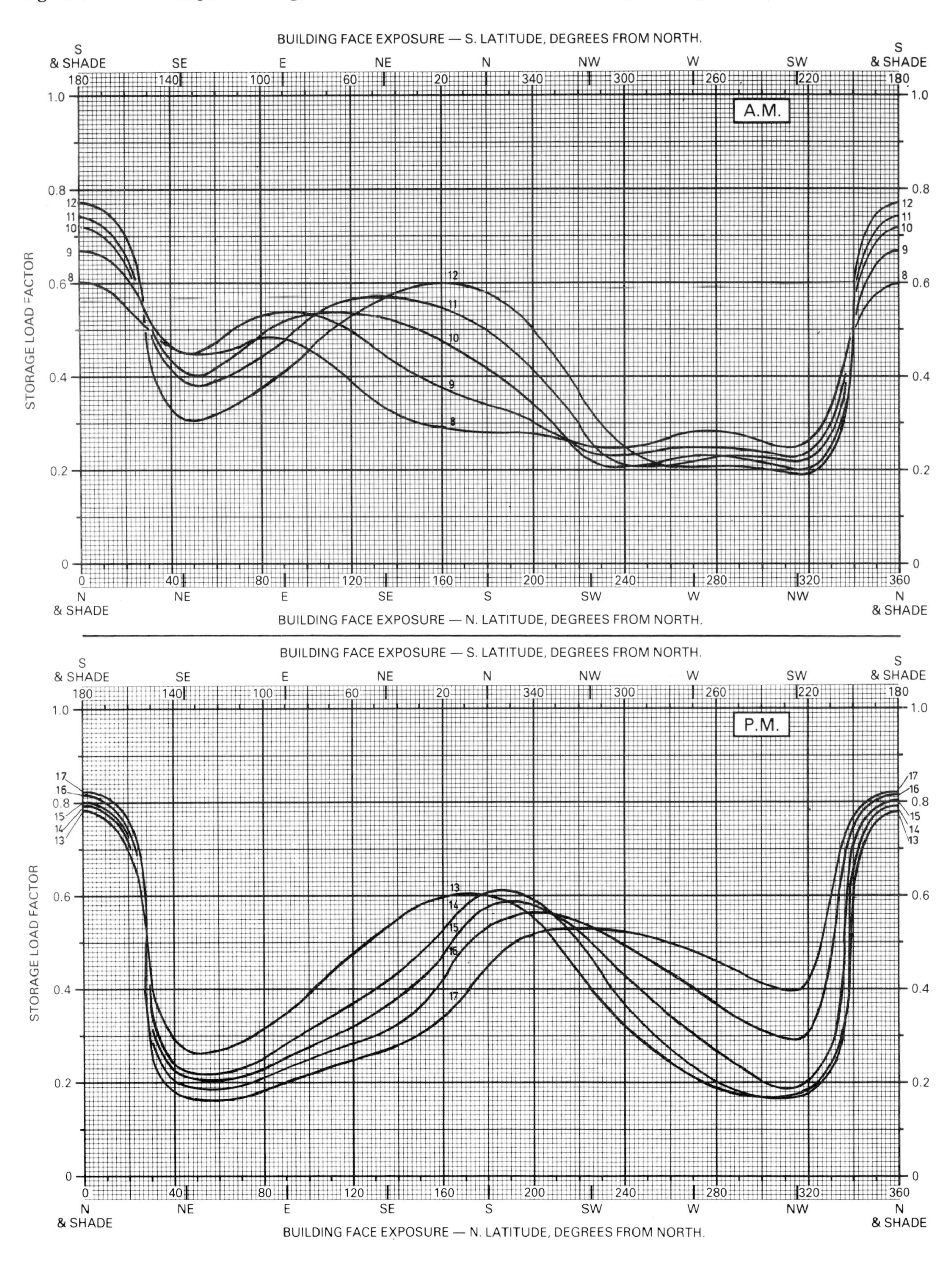

Fig. AIV.12 16 hour plant cooling, exterior shades or unshaded, specific weight 750 kg/m²

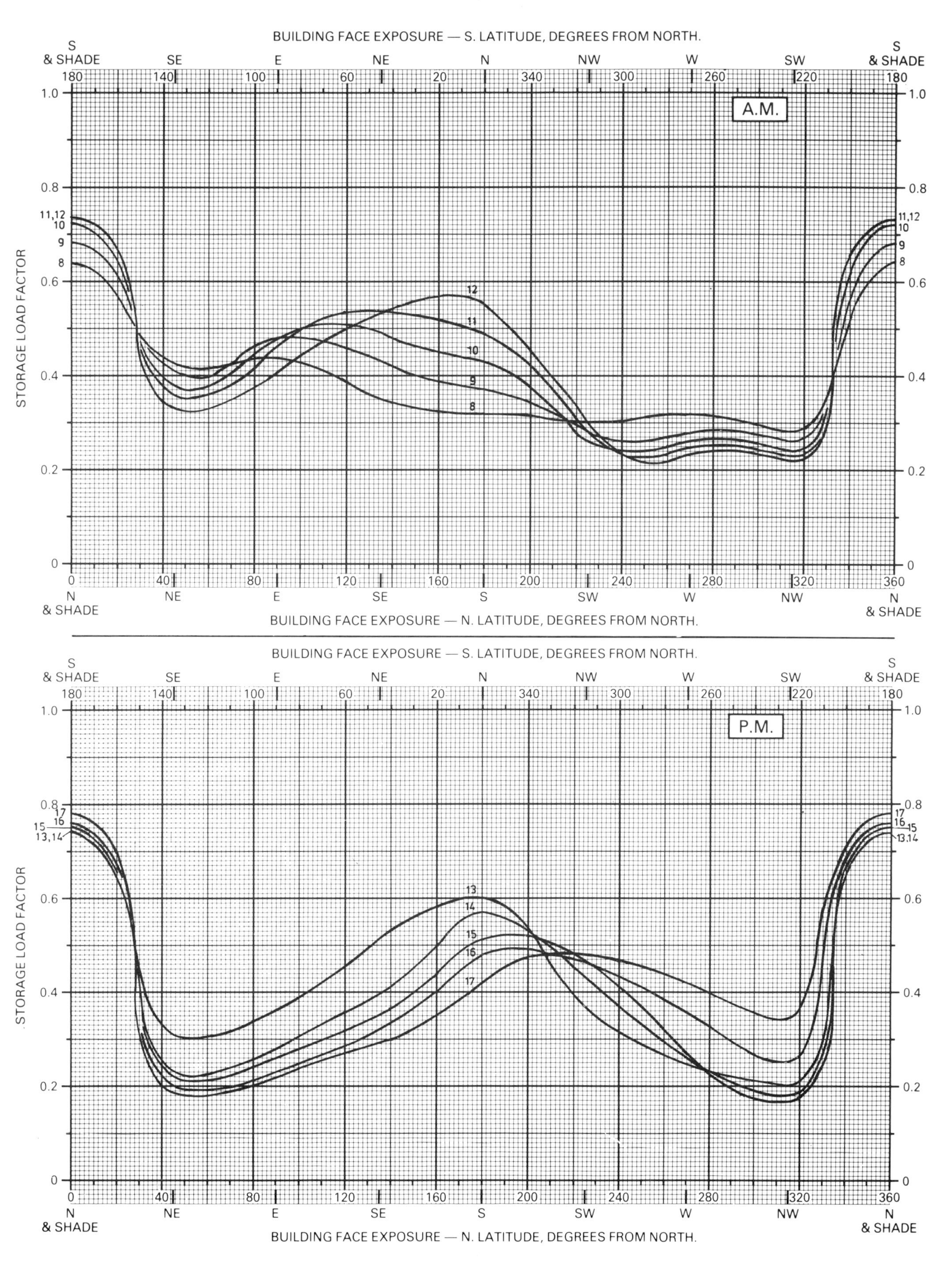

Fig. AIV.13 24 hour plant cooling, interior shades, specific weight 150 kg/m²

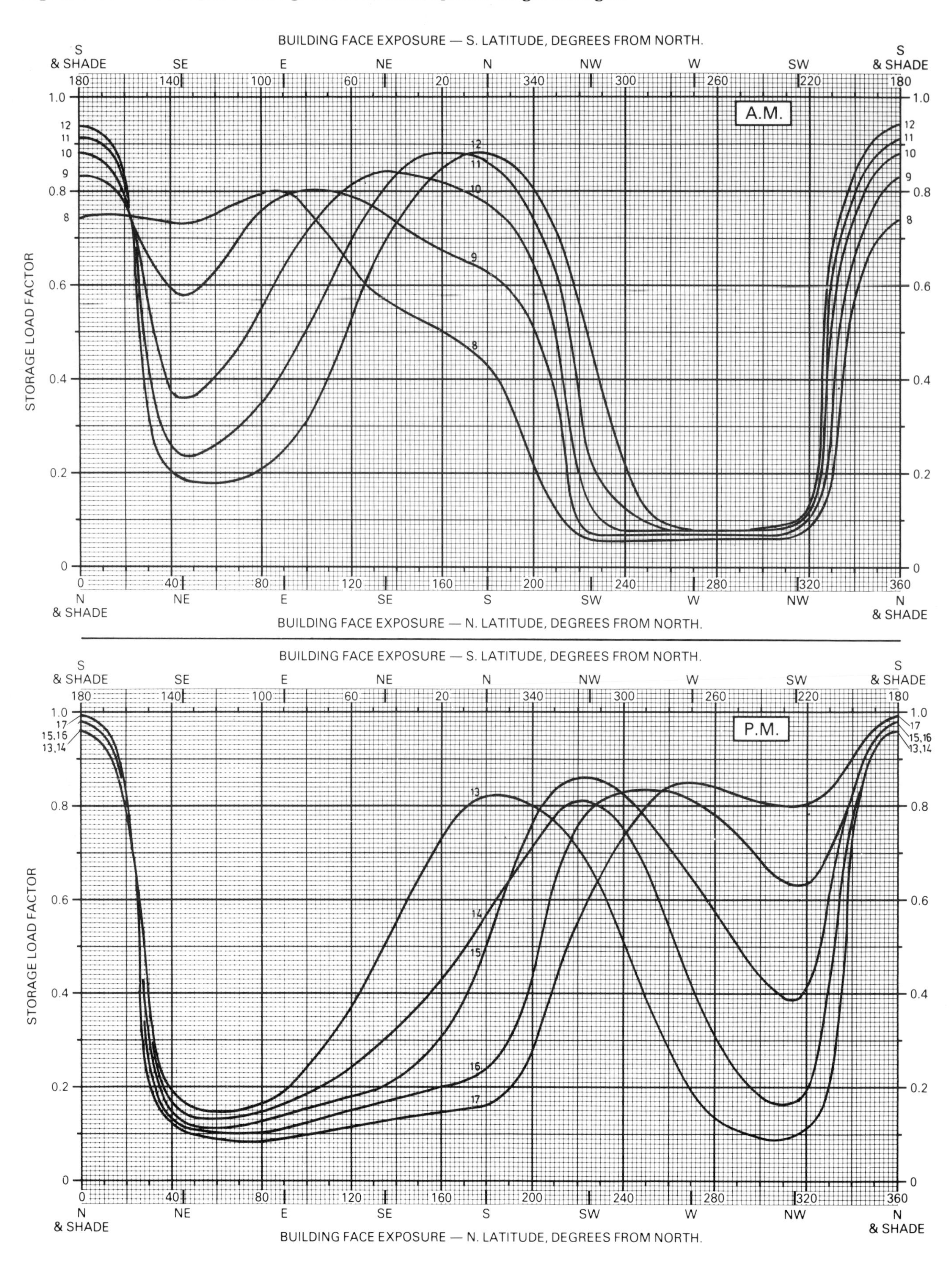

Fig. AIV.14 24 hour plant cooling, interior shades, specific weight 500 kg/m²

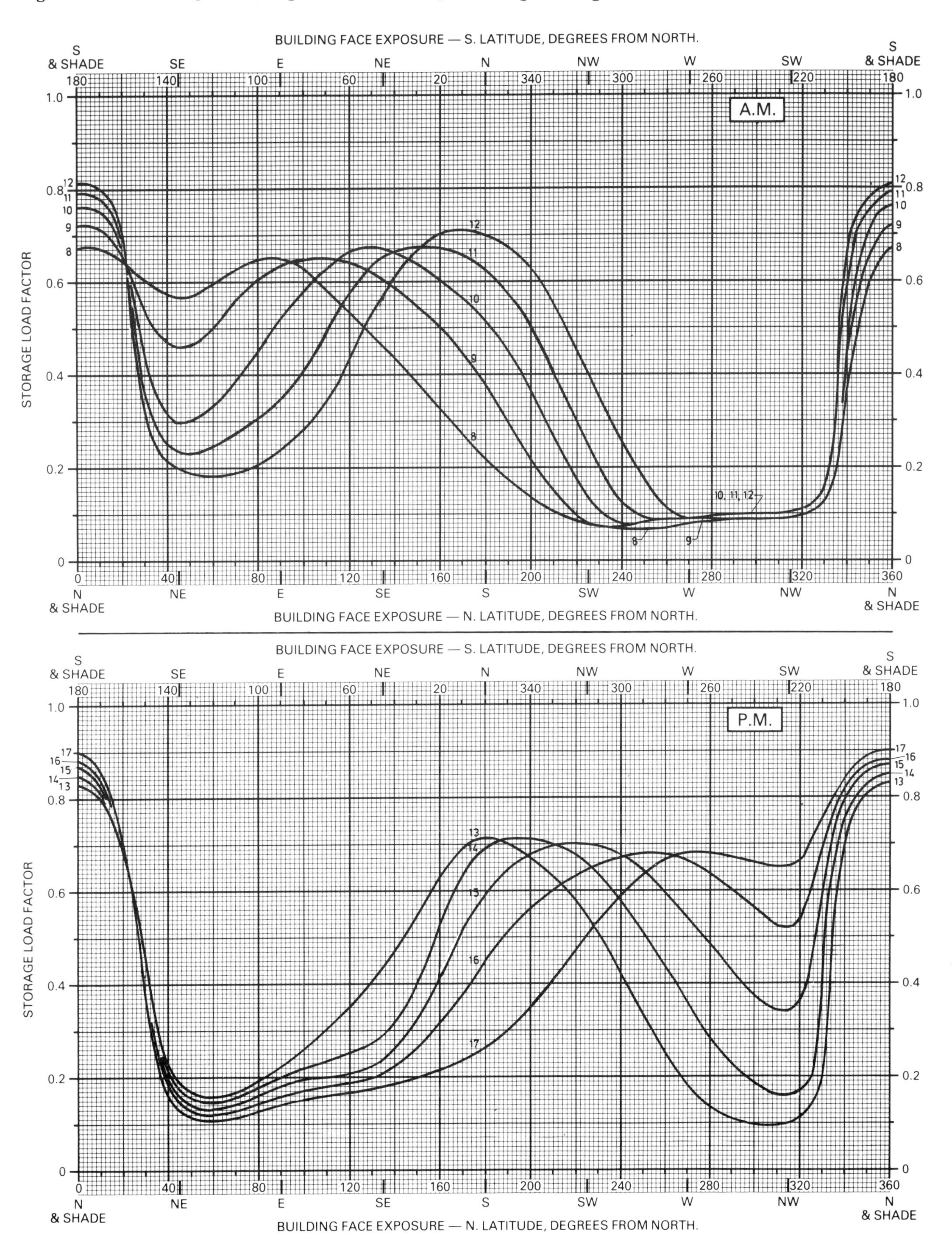

Fig. AIV.15 24 hour plant cooling, interior shades, specific weight 750 kg/m²

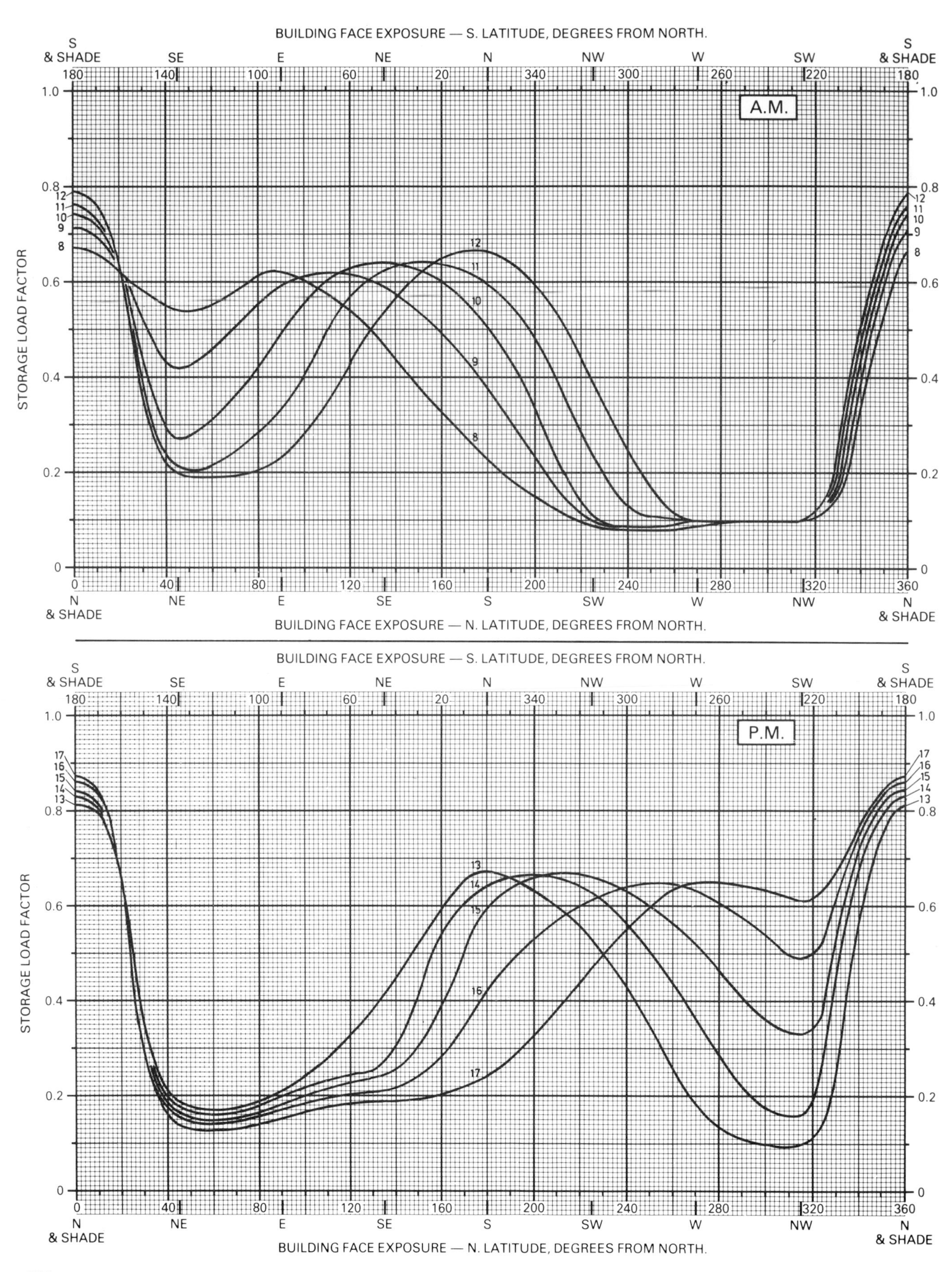

Fig. AIV.16 24 hour plant cooling, exterior shades or unshaded, specific weight 150 kg/m²

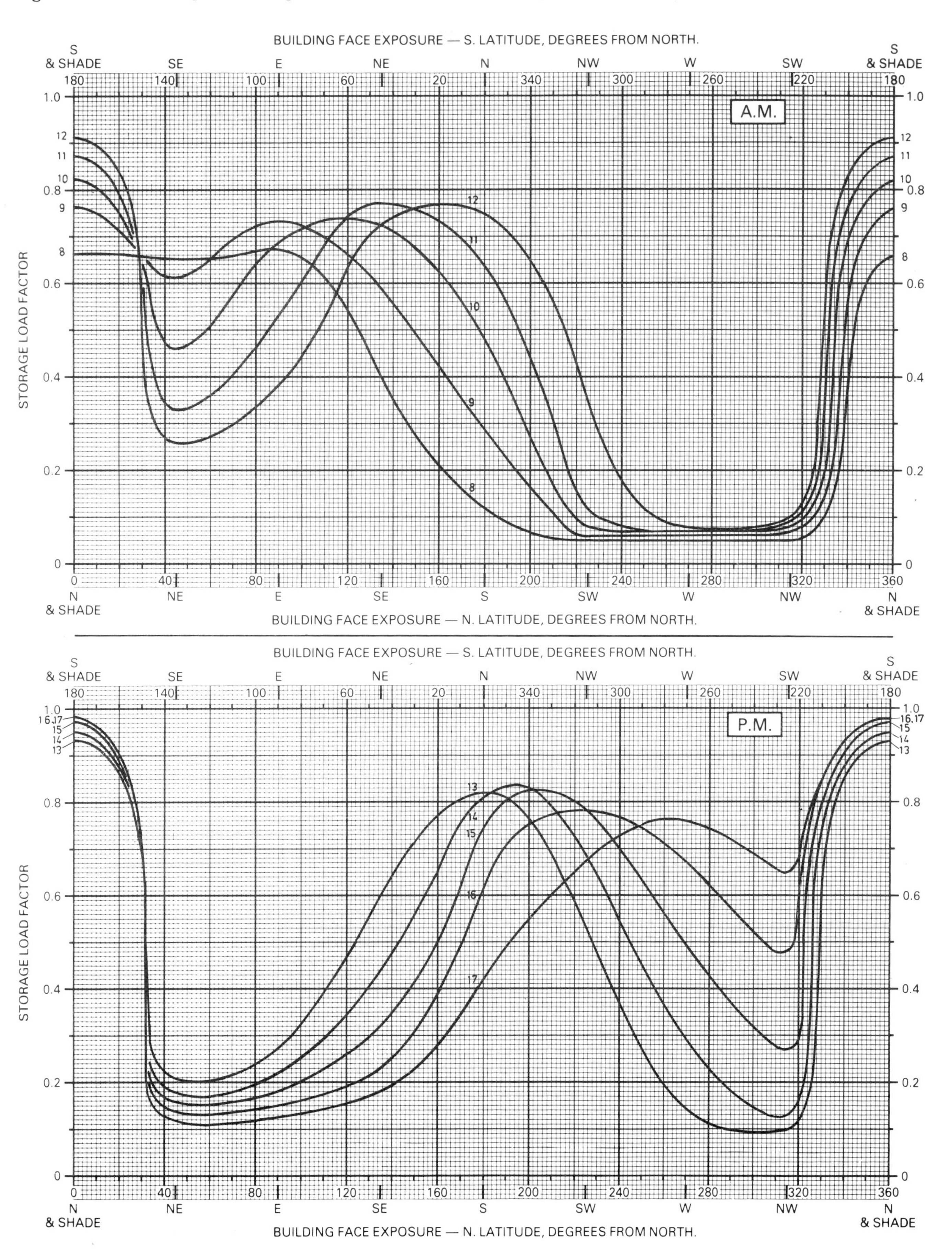

Fig. AIV.17 24 hour plant cooling, exterior shades or unshaded, specific weight 500 kg/m²

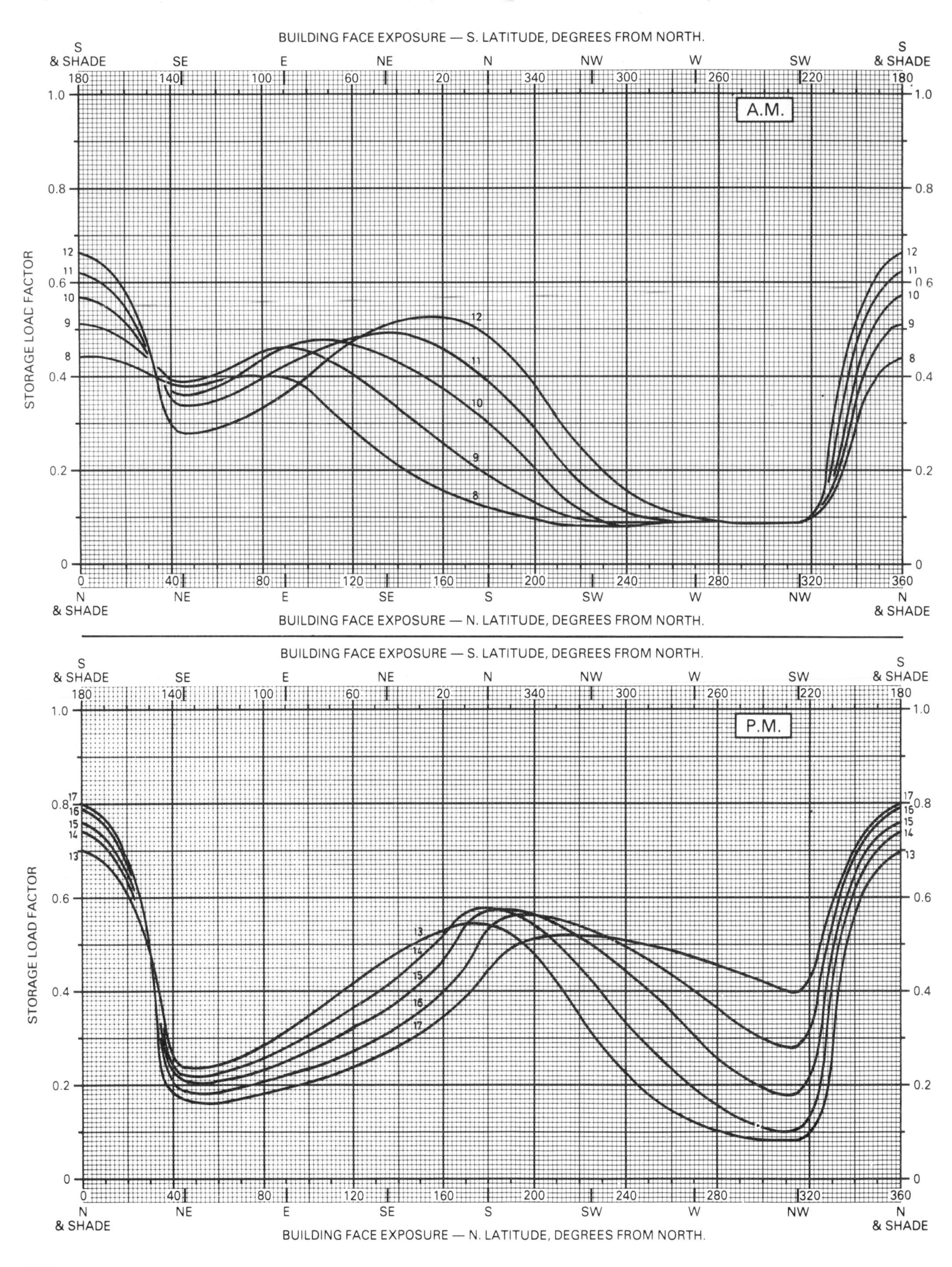

Fig. AIV.18 24 hour plant cooling, exterior shades or unshaded, specific weight 750 kg/m²

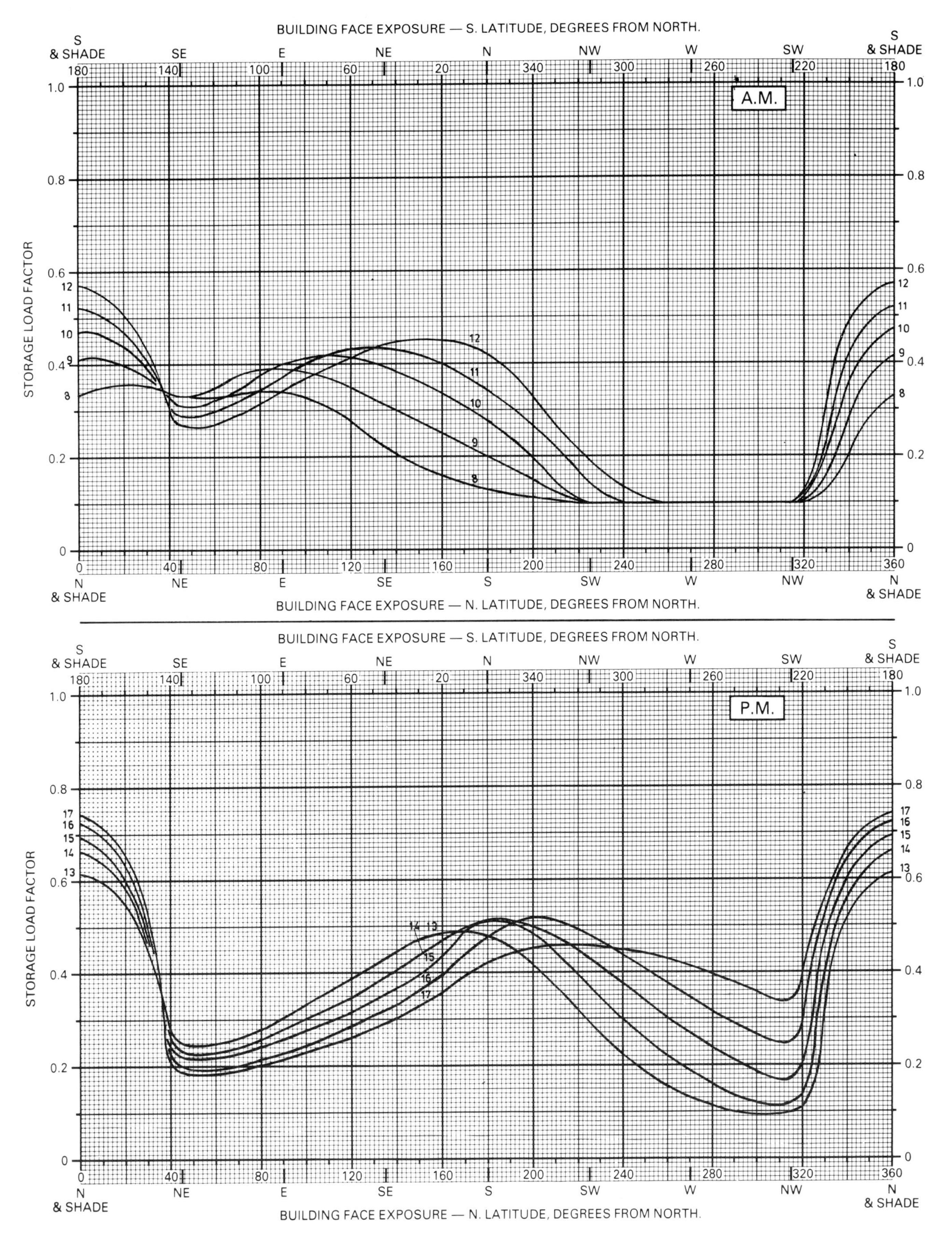

Fig. AIV.19 Storage load factors for horizontal glass with internal shading

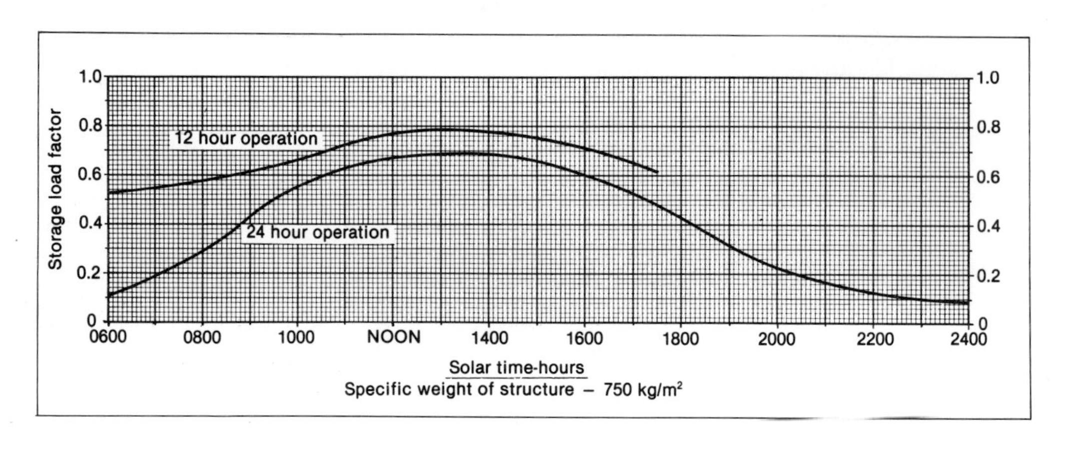

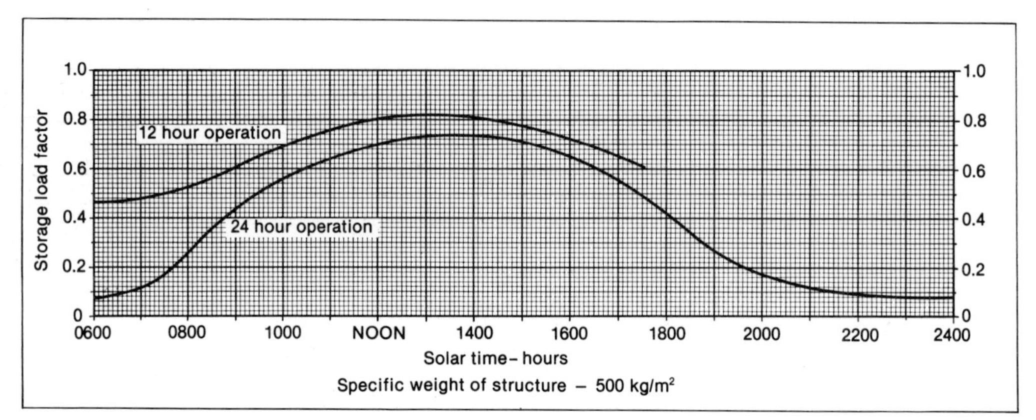

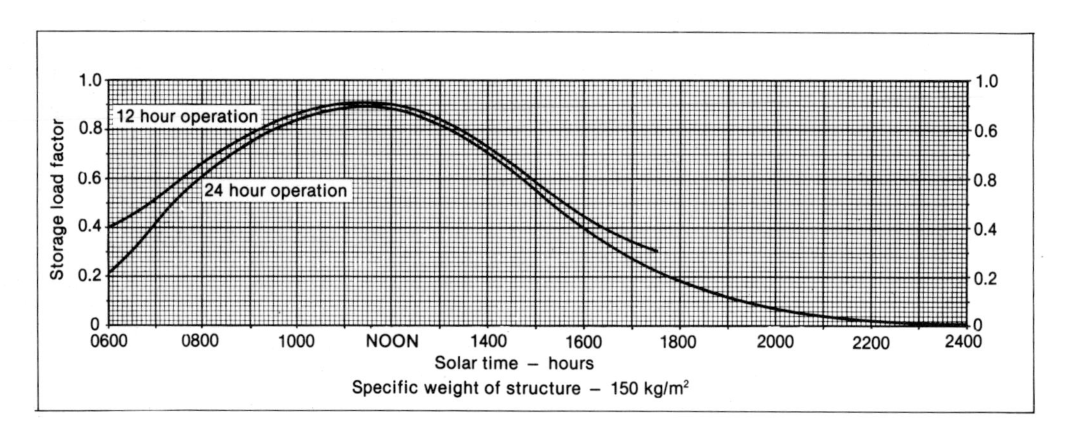

Fig. AIV.20 Storage load factors for horizontal glass unshaded or with external shading

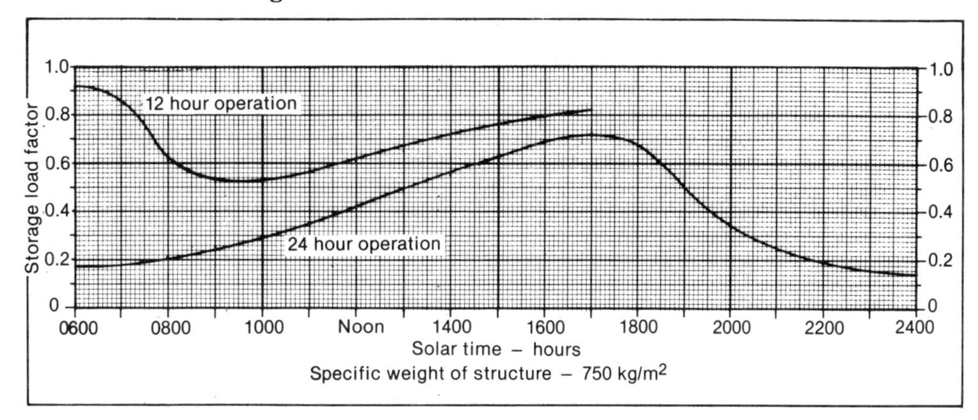

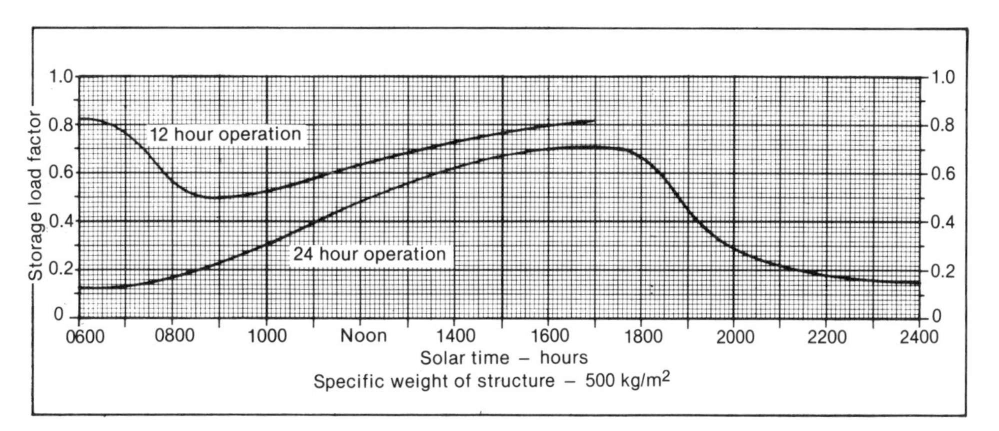

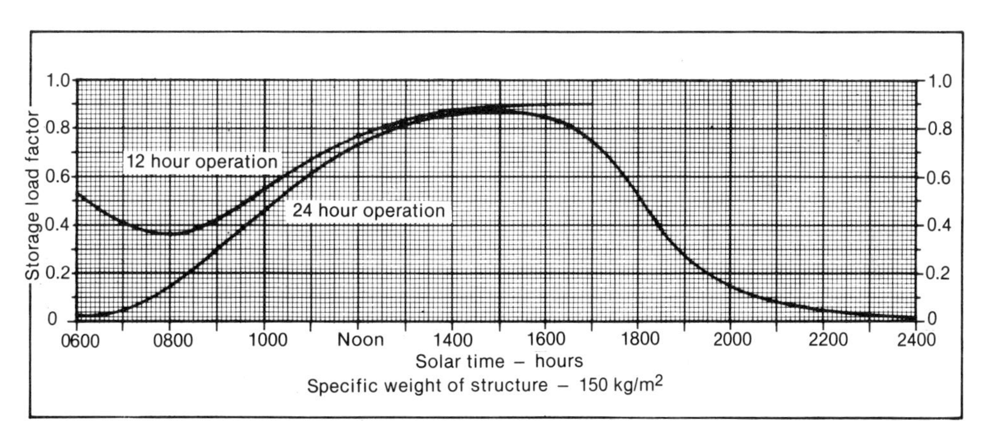

Appendix V
Equivalent temperature differences for sunlit and shaded walls. North and south latitudes

Fig. No.	*Page*	*Wt. of wall construction (kg/m²)*
AV.1	183	500
AV.2	184	100
AV.3	185	300
AV.4	186	700

Fig. AV.1 Equivalent temperature differences for sunlit and shaded walls, N and S latitudes

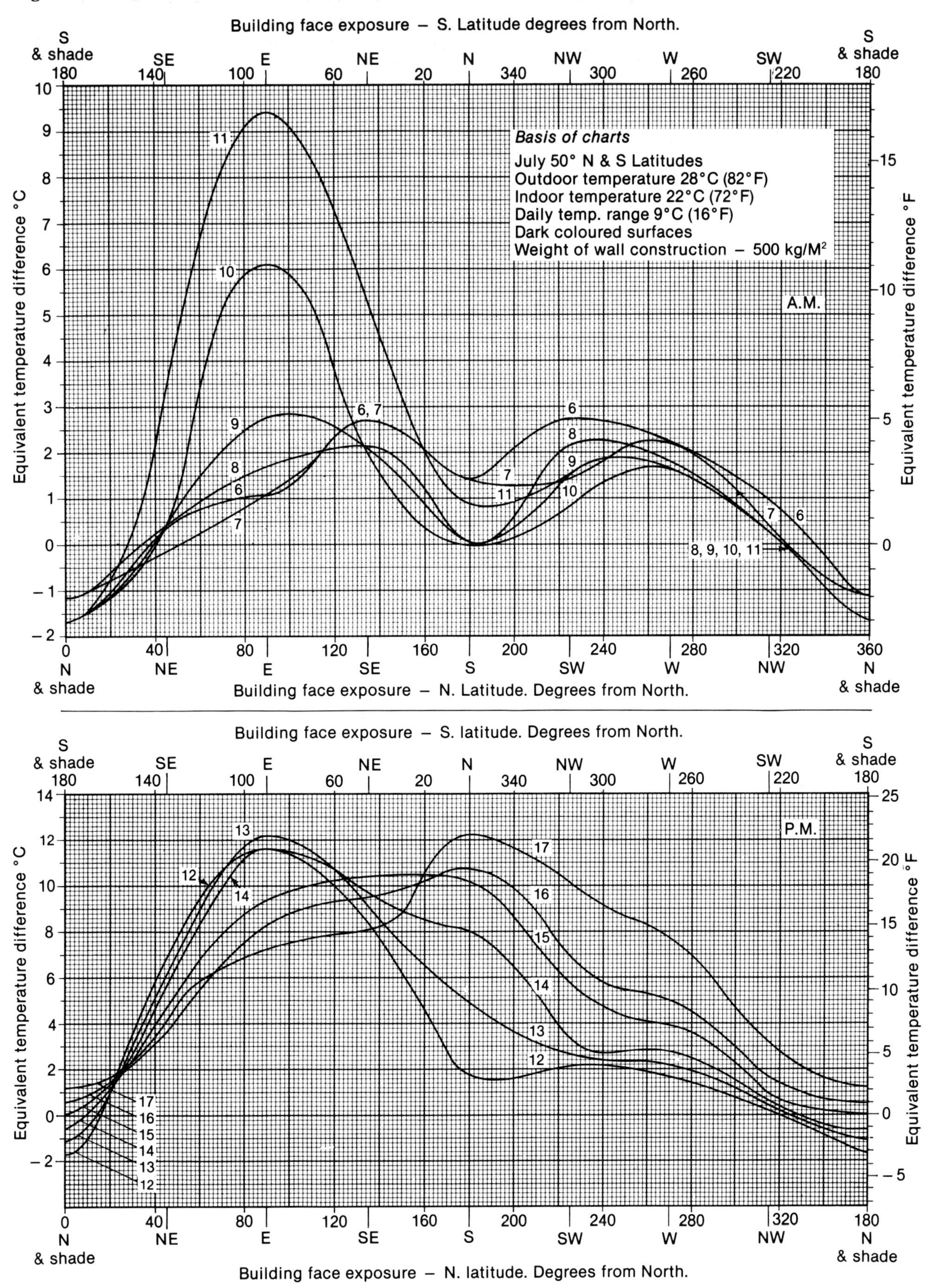

Fig. AV.2 Equivalent temperature differences for sunlit and shaded walls, N and S latitudes

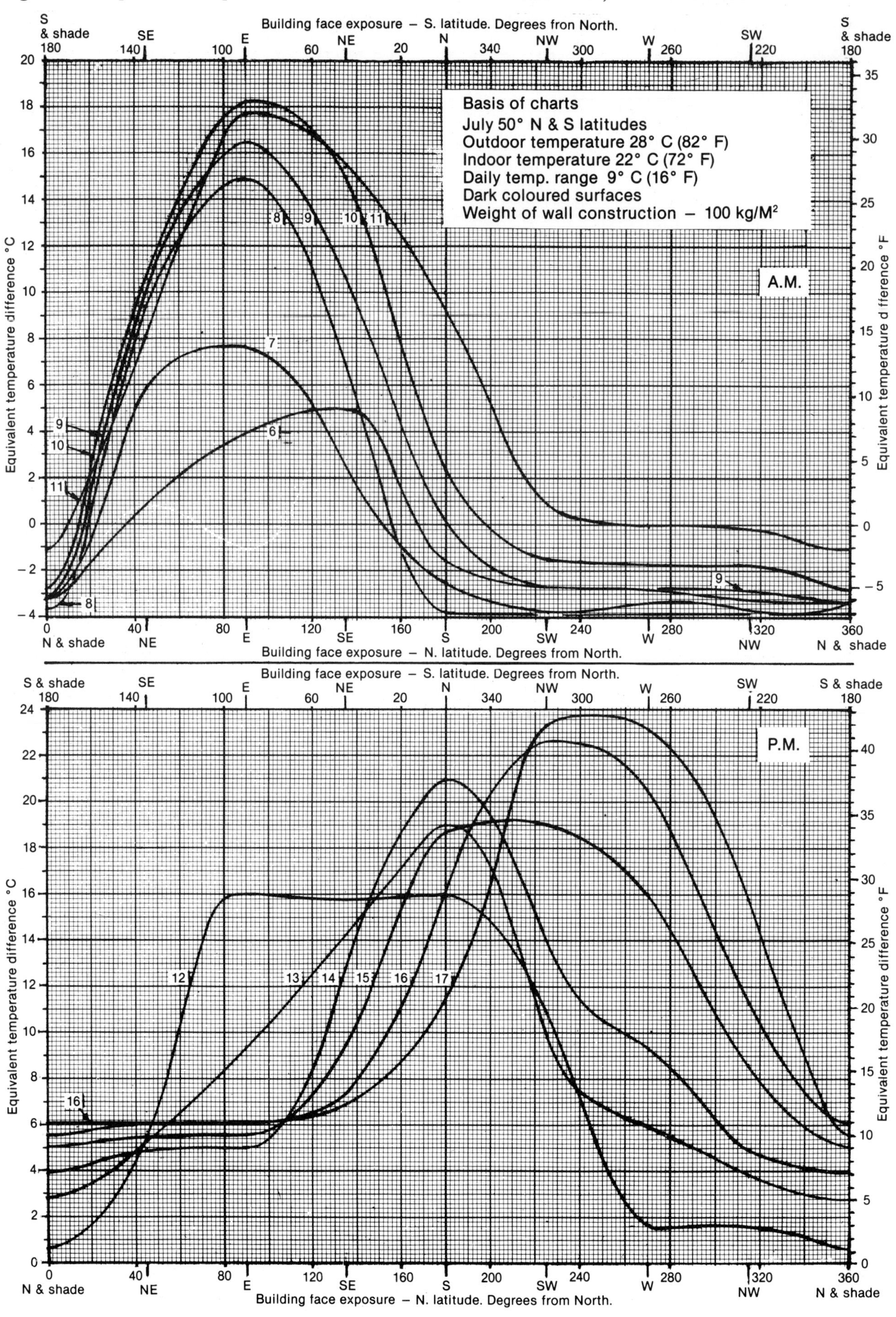

Fig. AV.3 Equivalent temperature differences for sunlit and shaded walls, N and S latitudes

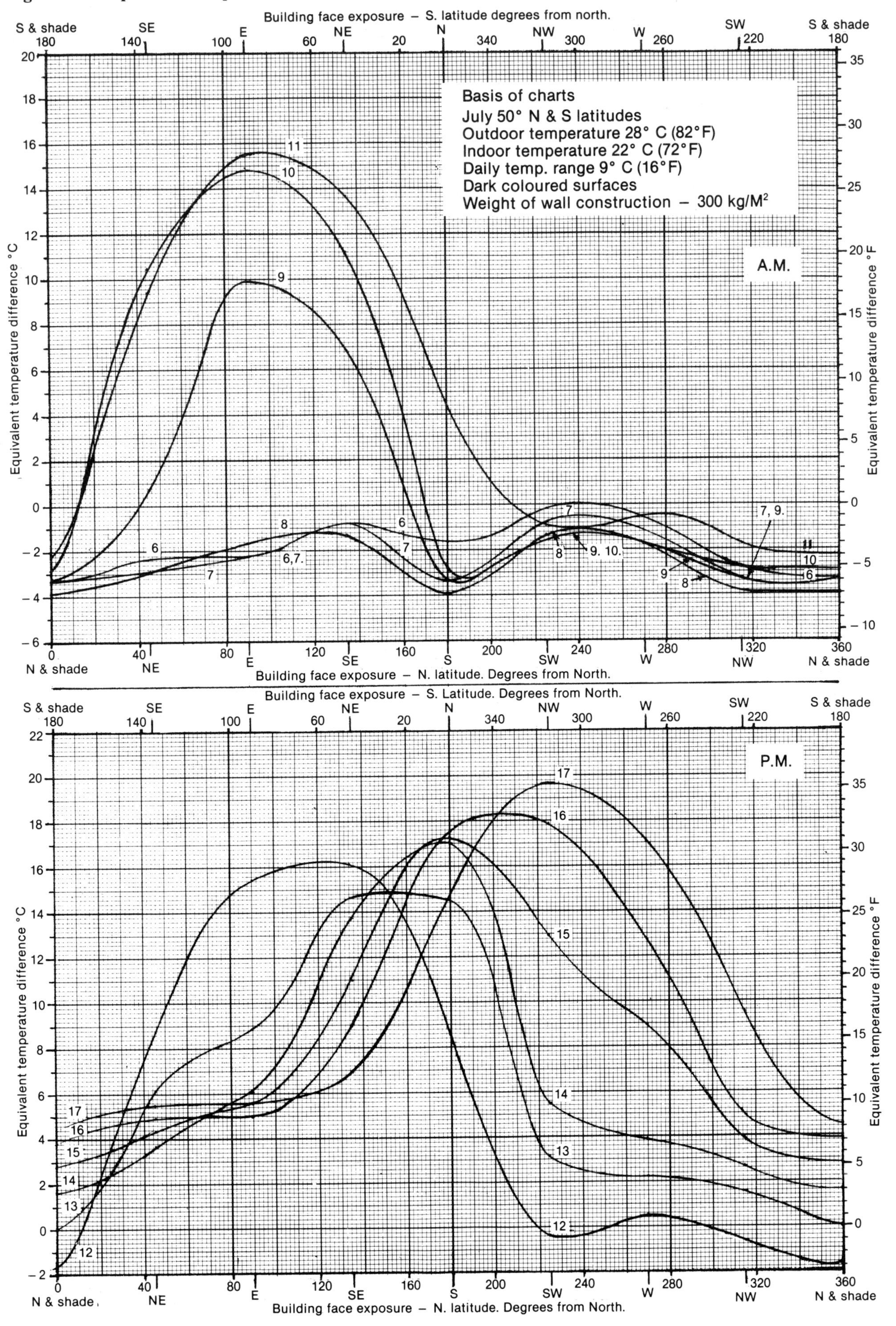

Fig. AV.4 Equivalent temperature differences for sunlit and shaded walls, N and S latitudes

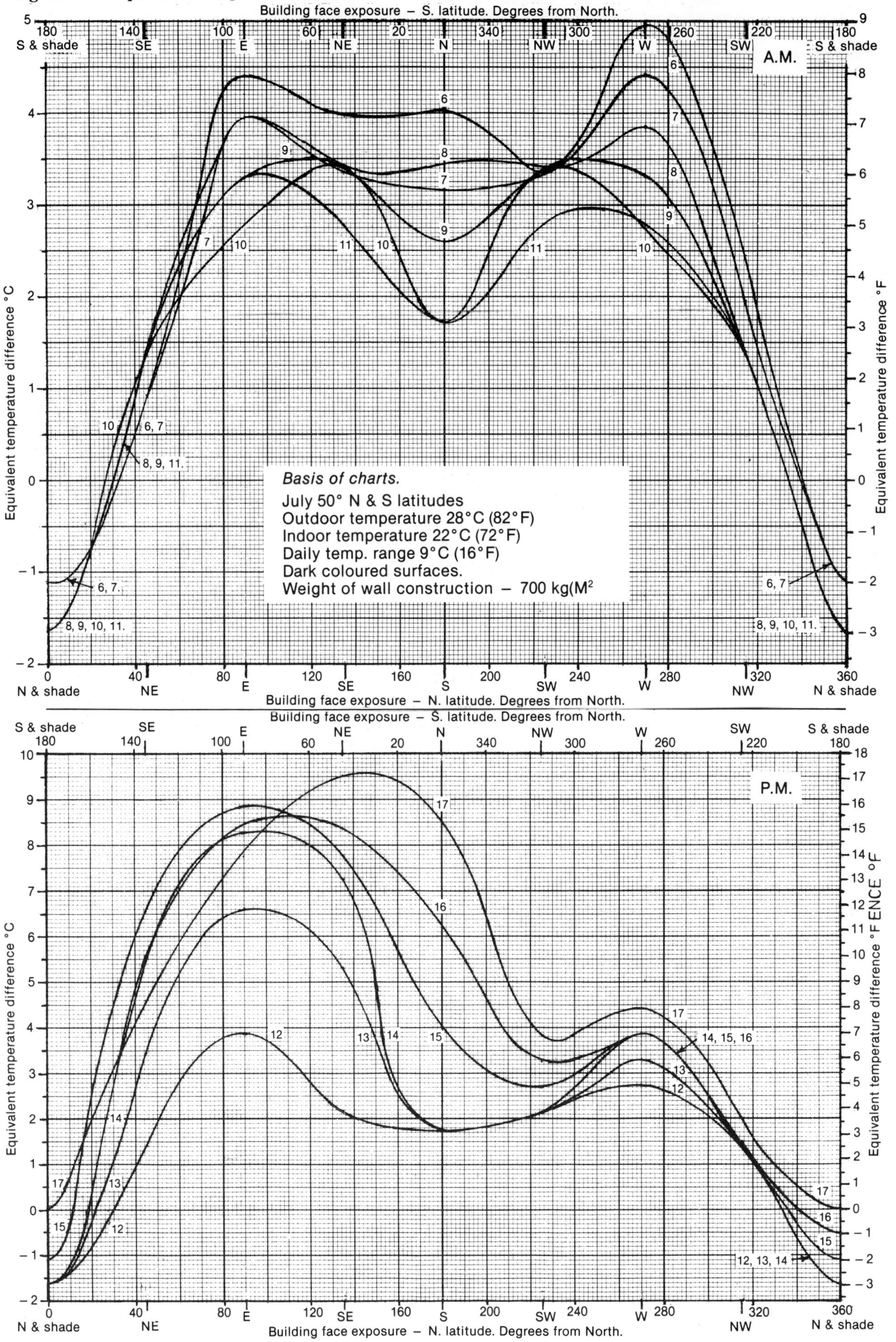

Building face exposure – S. latitude. Degrees from North.

A.M.

Equivalent temperature difference °C

Equivalent temperature difference °F

Basis of charts.

July 50° N & S latitudes
Outdoor temperature 28°C (82°F)
Indoor temperature 22°C (72°F)
Daily temp. range 9°C (16°F)
Dark coloured surfaces.
Weight of wall construction – 700 kg(M²

Building face exposure – N. latitude. Degrees from North.

Building face exposure – S. latitude. Degrees from North.

P.M.

Equivalent temperature difference °C

Equivalent temperature difference °F

Building face exposure – N. latitude. Degrees from North.

Appendix VI
Storage load factors for lighting, equipment and occupants for structural specific weights of 150, 500 and 750 kg/m²

Fig. No.	*Page*	*Application*	*Usage time (hours)*	*Cooling plant operating time (hours)*
AVI.1	188	Exposed fluorescent lights,	5 and 10	12
AVI.2	189	equipment and building	5, 10, and 15	16
AVI.3	190	occupants	5, 10 and 15	24
AVI.4	191	Fluorescent lights recessed	5 and 10	12
AVI.5	192	into unventilated ceiling	5, 10 and 15	16
AVI.6	193	voids and exposed tungsten lights; and equipment	5, 10 and 15	24
AVI.7	194	Fluorescent and tungsten	5 and 10	12
AVI.8	195	lights recessed into	5, 10 and 15	16
AVI.9	196	ventilated ceiling voids; and equipment	5, 10 and 15	24

Fig. AVI.1 Storage load factors for lighting, equipment and occupants

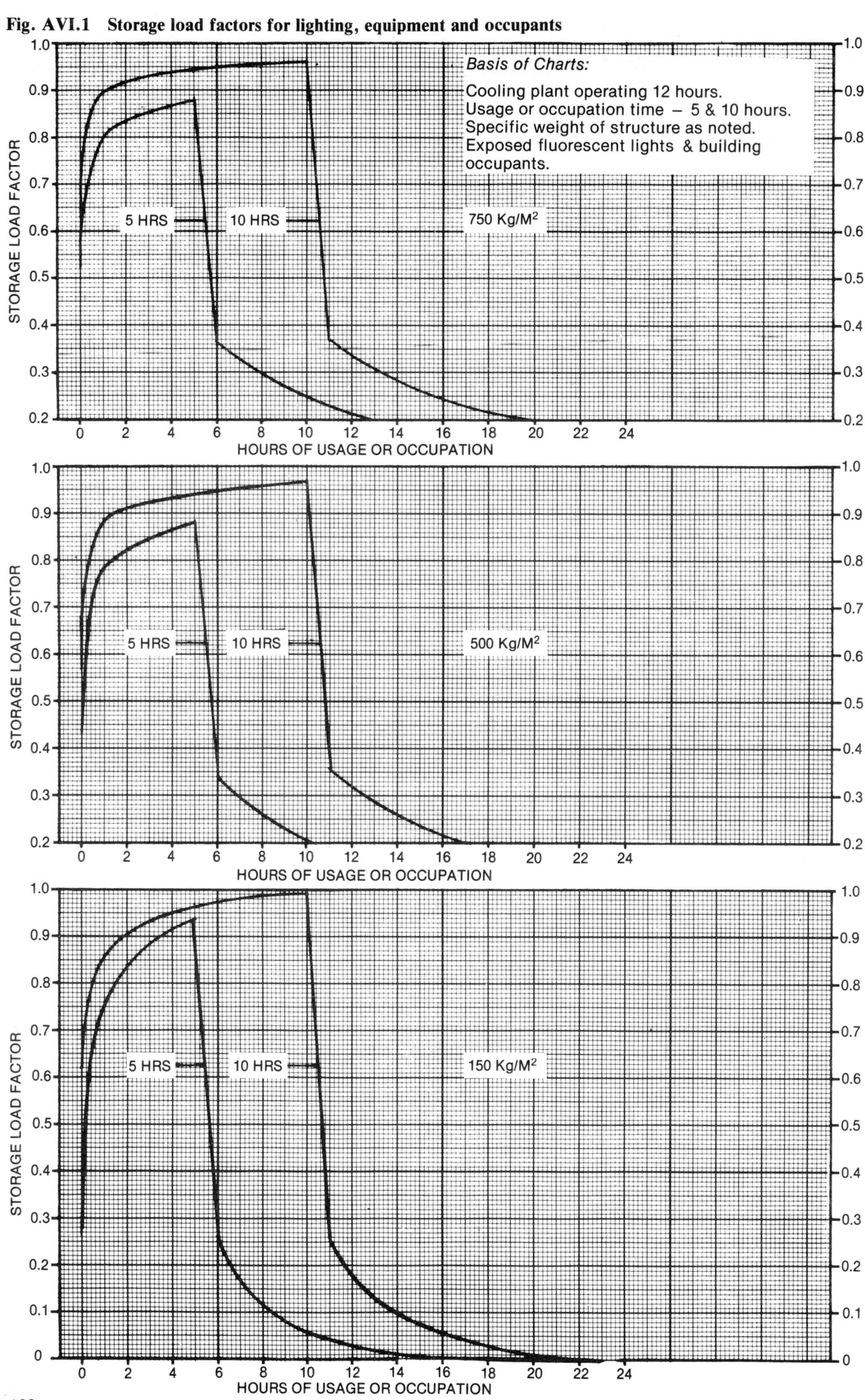

Fig. AVI.2 Storage load factors for lighting, equipment and occupants

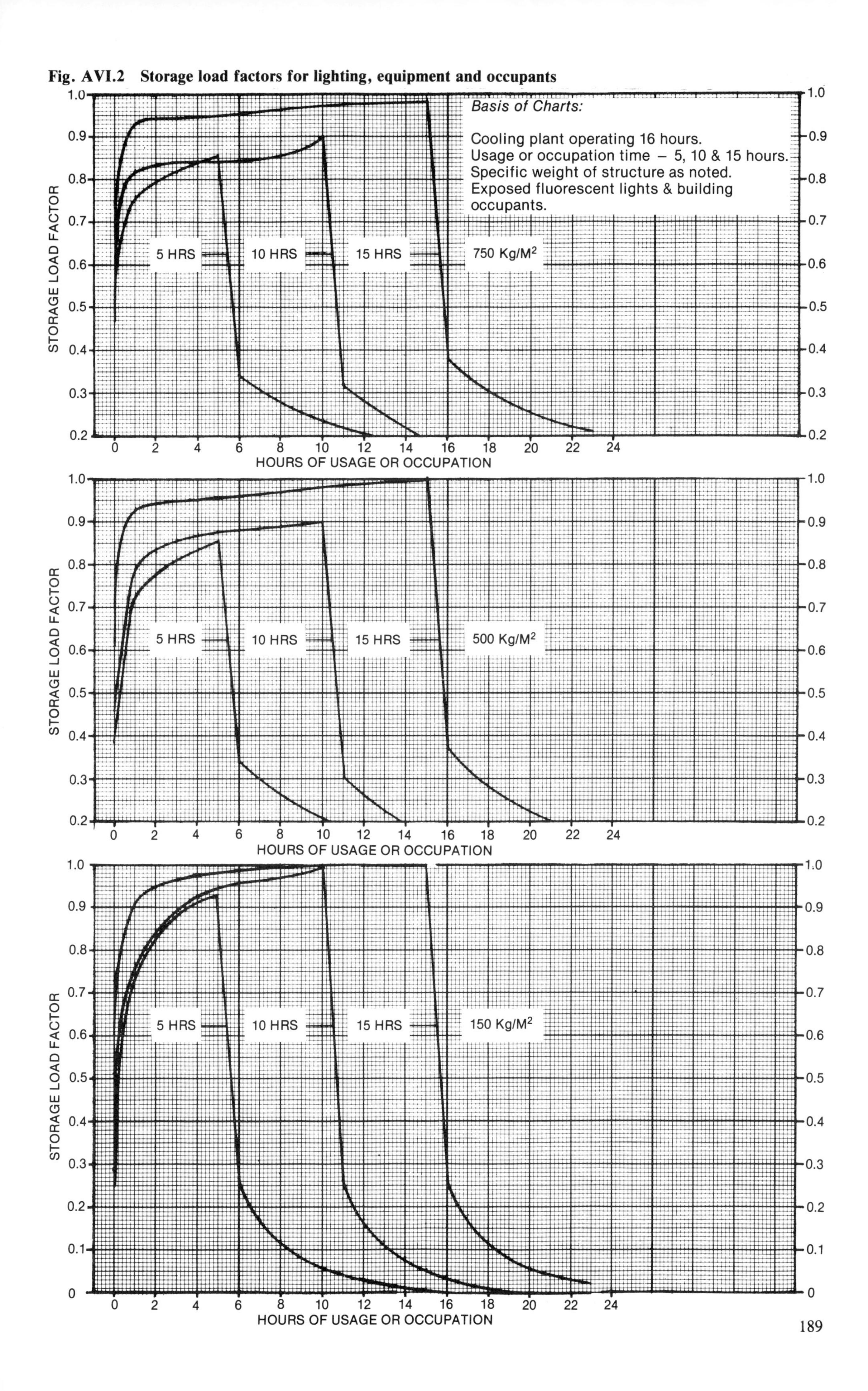

Fig. AVI.3 Storage load factors for lighting, equipment and occupants

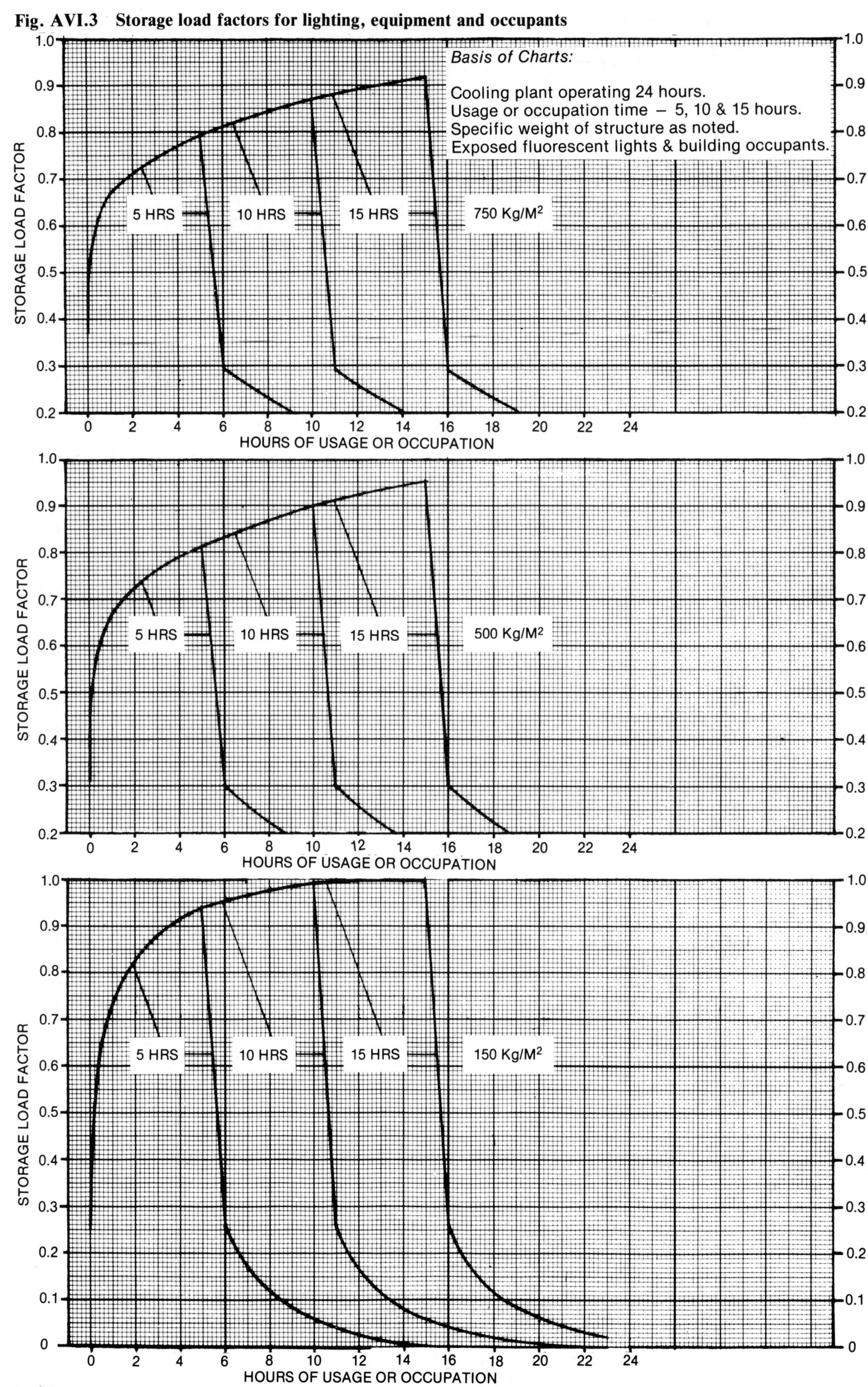

Fig. AVI.4 Storage load factors for lighting and equipment

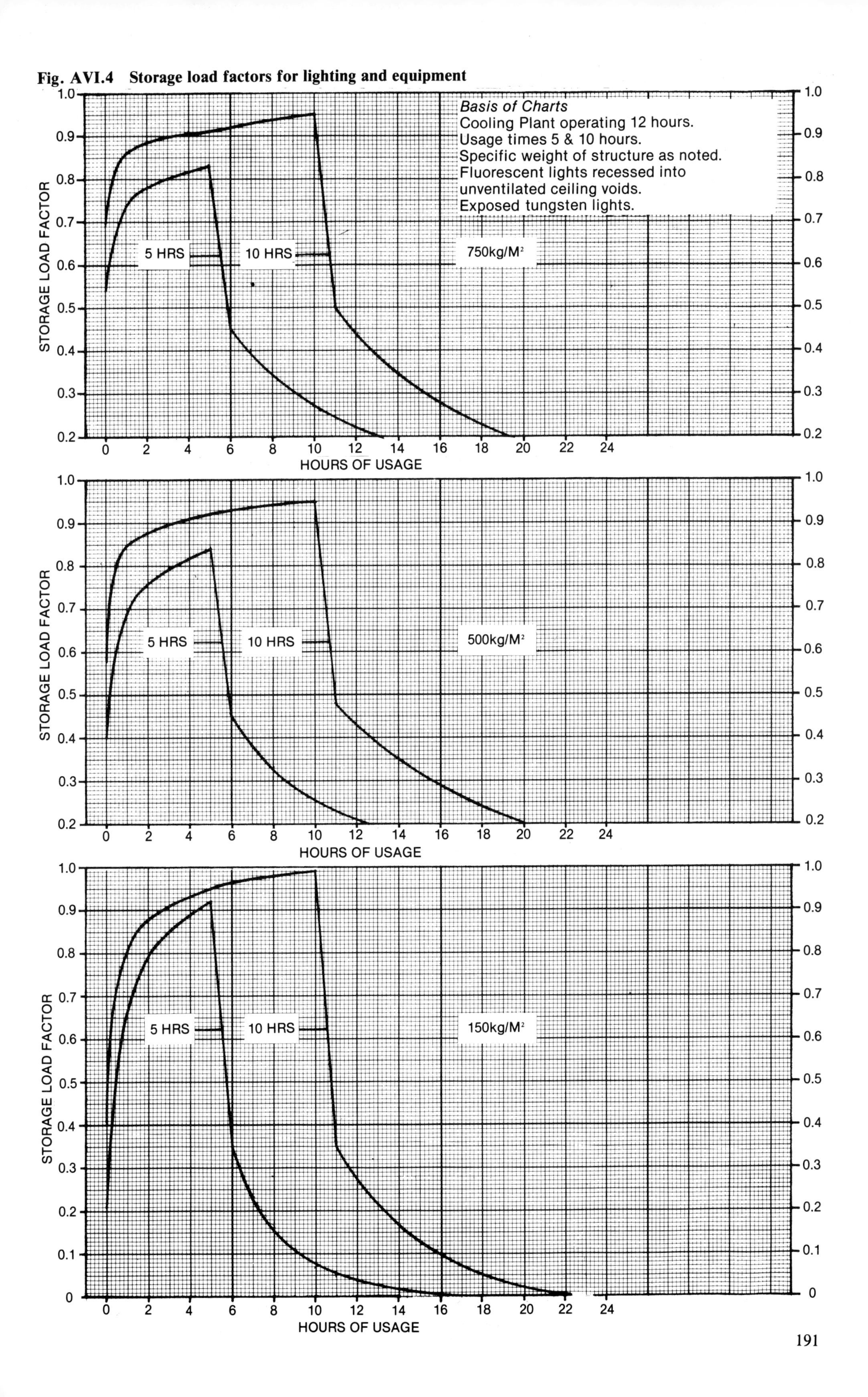

Fig. AVI.5 Storage load factors for lighting and equipment

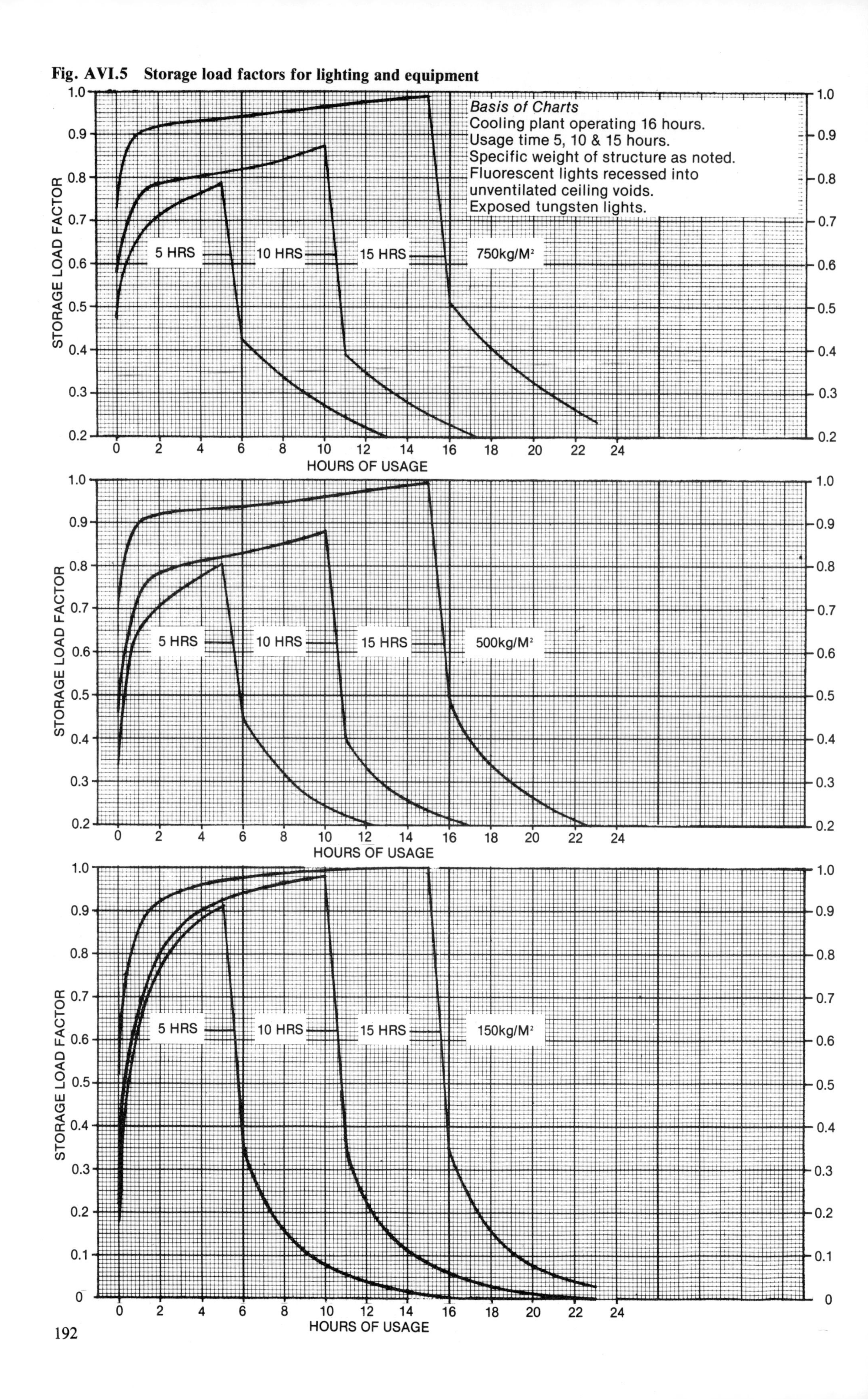

Fig. AVI.6 Storage load factors for lighting and equipment

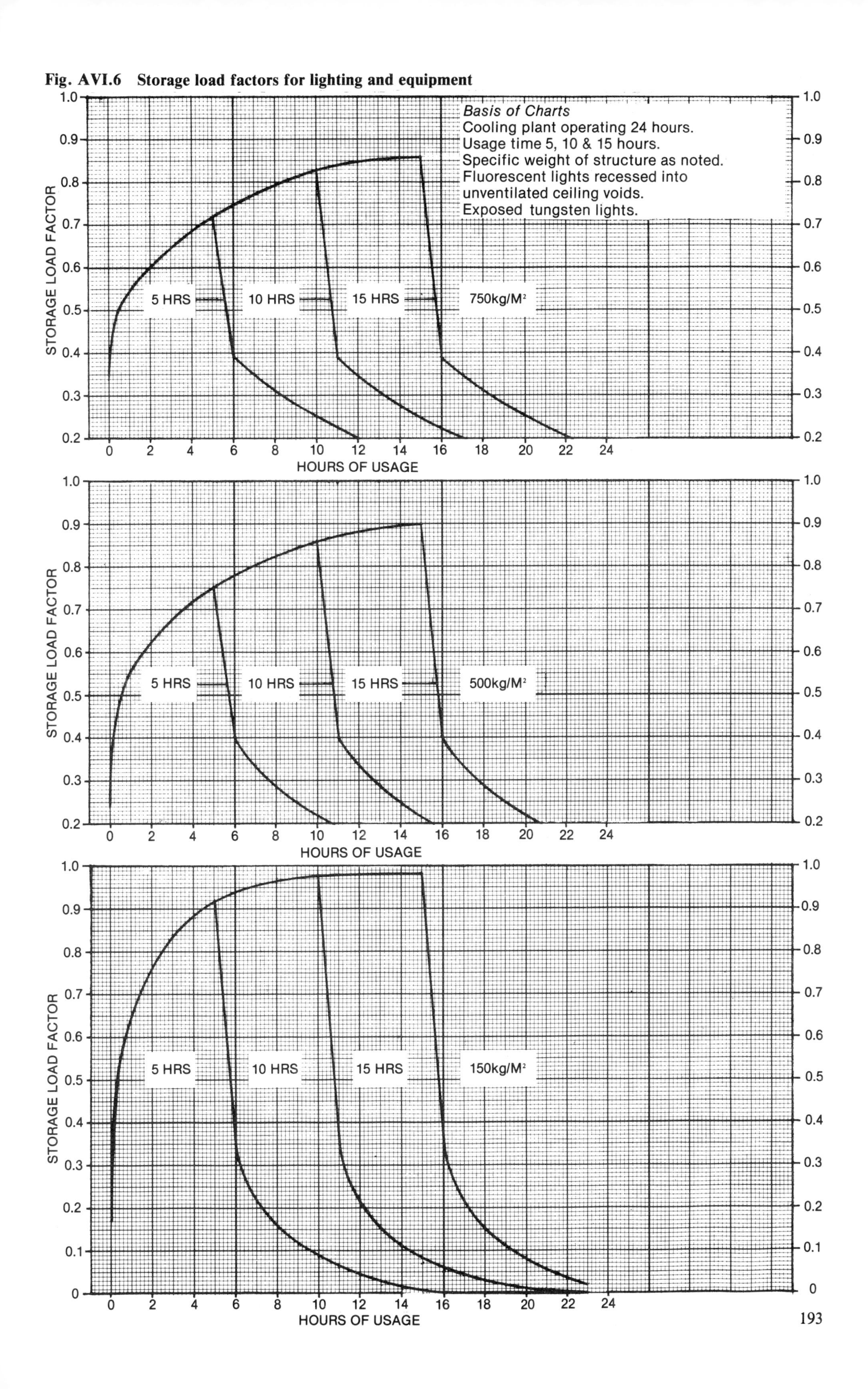

Fig. AVI.7 Storage load factors for lighting and equipment

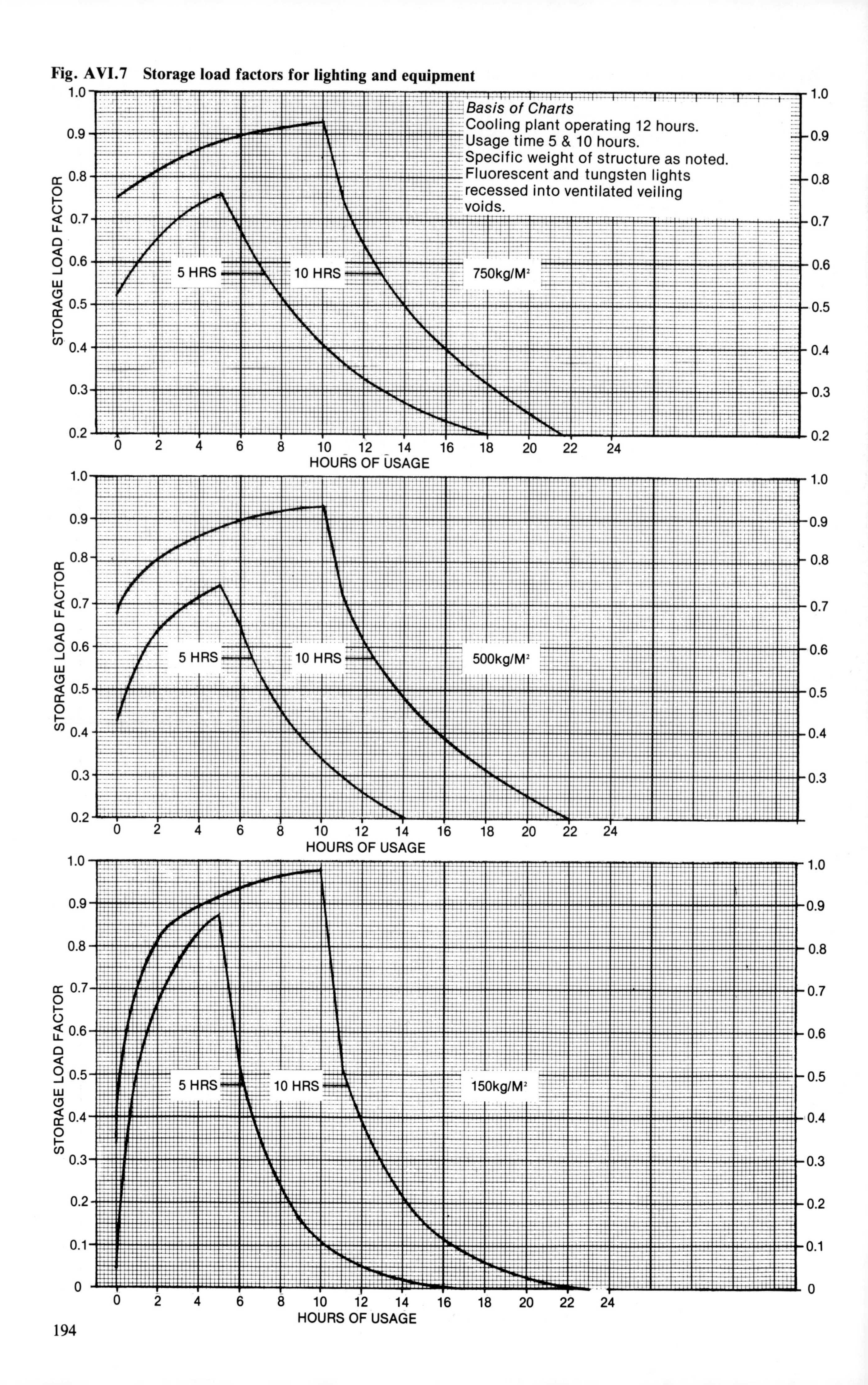

Fig. AVI.8 Storage load factors for lighting and equipment

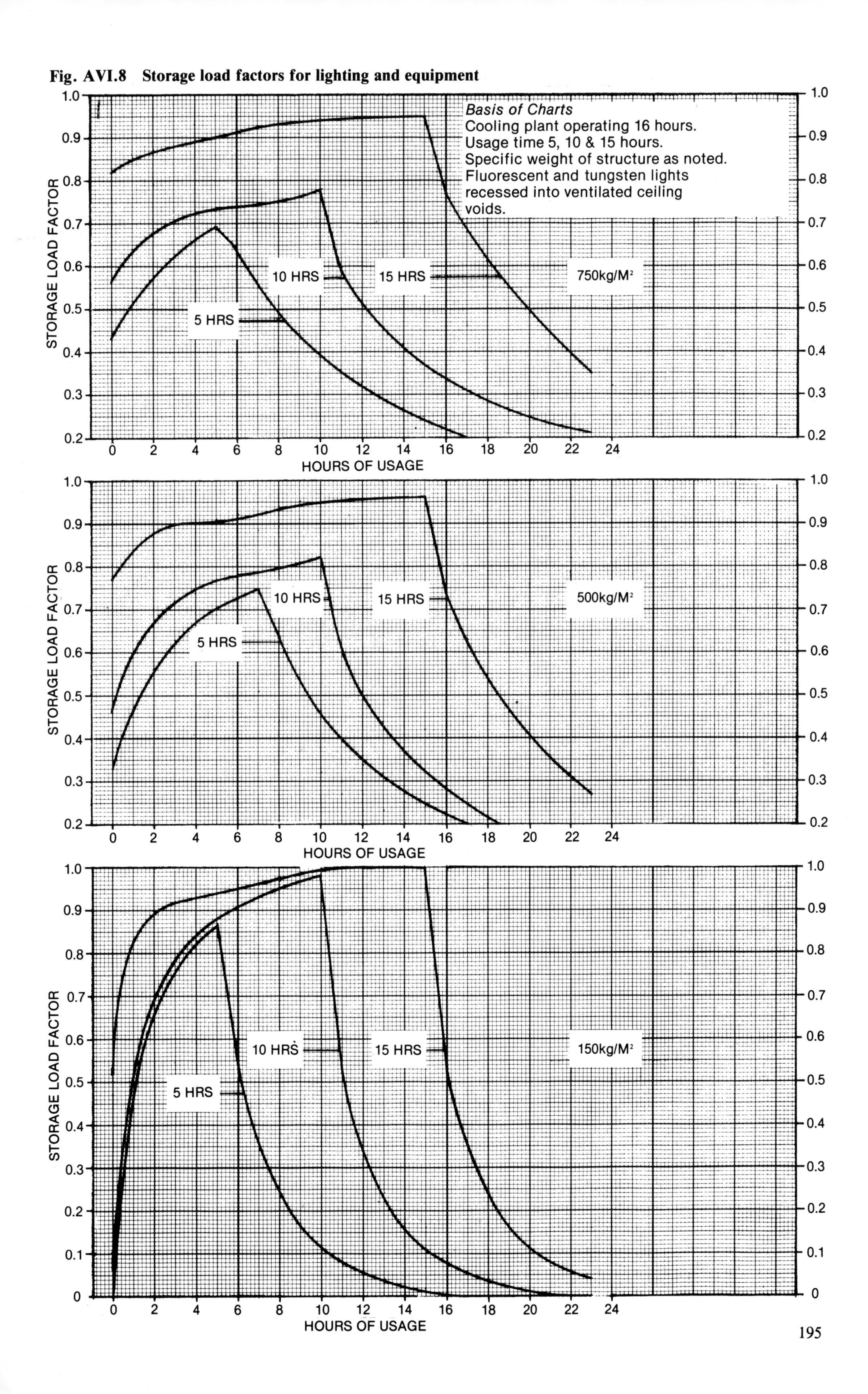

Fig. AVI.9 Storage load factors for lighting and equipment

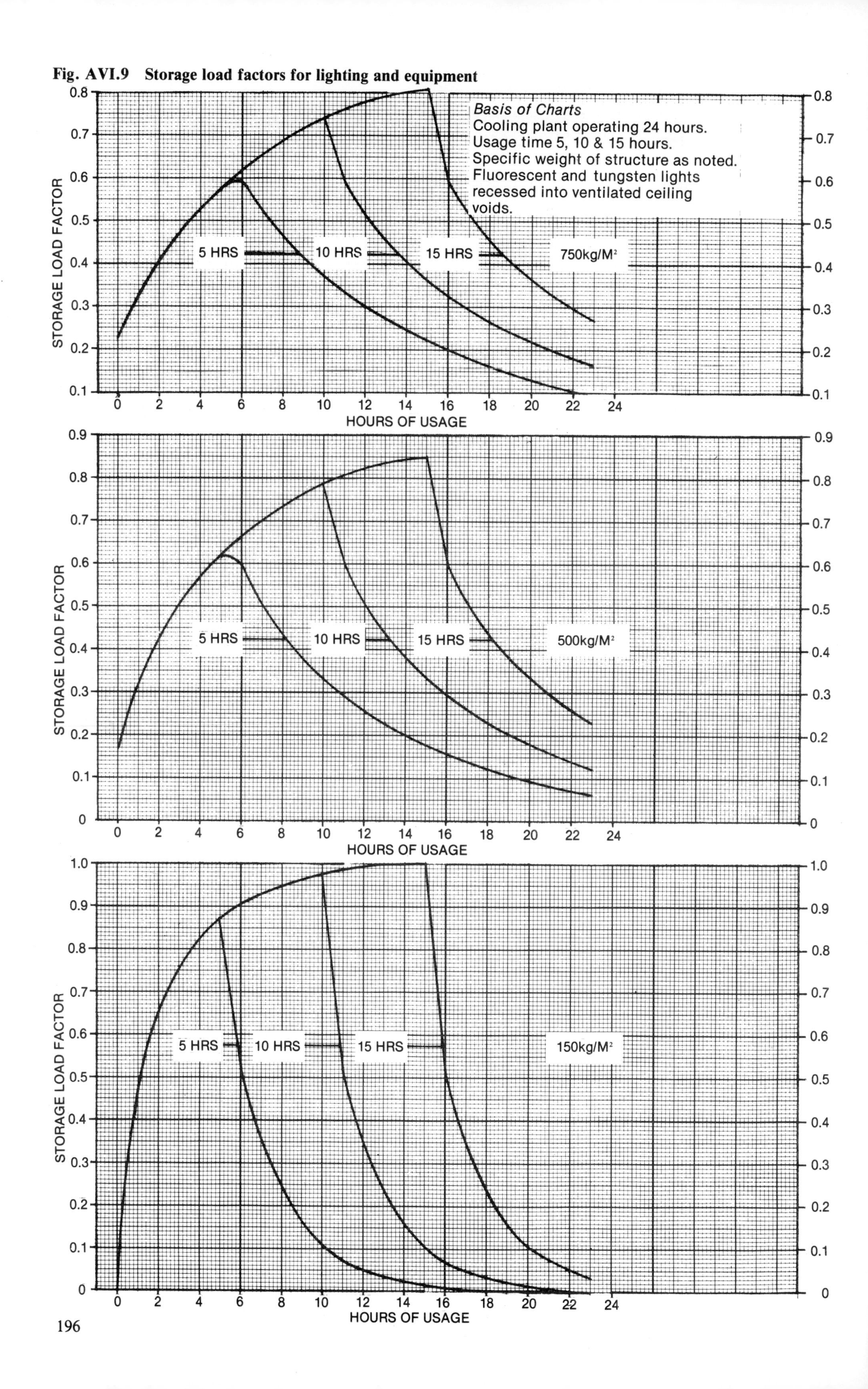

Appendix VII
Solar altitude and azimuth angles

North latitude	Sun time	21 Jan		20 Feb		22 Mar		20 Apr		21 May		21 June		23 July		24 Aug		22 Sept		23 Oct		21 Nov		22 Dec		Sun time
		Alt	*Az*	*Alt*	*Az*	*Alt*	*Az*	*Alt*	*Az*	*Alt*	*Az*	*Alt*	*Az*	*Alt*	*Az*	*Alt*	*Az*	*Alt*	*Az*	*Alt*	*Az*	*Alt*	*Az*	*Alt*	*Az*	
	06.00		110		101		90		79		70		67		70		79		90		101		110		113	06.00
	07.00	14	111	15	102	15	90	15	78	14	69	14	66	14	69	15	78	15	90	15	102	14	111	14	114	07.00
	08.00	28	113	29	103	30	89	29	77	28	67	27	63	28	67	29	77	30	89	29	103	28	113	27	117	08.00
	09.00	42	117	44	106	45	89	44	74	42	63	40	58	42	63	44	74	45	89	44	106	42	117	40	122	09.00
	10.00	54	126	58	112	60	89	58	68	54	54	53	49	54	54	58	68	60	89	58	112	54	126	53	131	10.00
	11.00	65	145	71	127	75	88	71	53	65	35	62	32	65	35	71	53	75	88	71	127	65	145	62	148	11.00
	12.00	70	180	79	180	89	0	79	0	70	0	67	0	70	0	79	0	89	0	79	180	70	180	67	180	12.00
Lat. 0°																										
	13.00	65	215	71	233	75	272	71	307	65	325	62	328	65	325	71	307	75	272	71	233	65	215	62	212	13.00
	14.00	54	234	58	248	60	271	58	292	54	306	53	311	54	306	58	292	60	271	58	248	54	234	53	229	14.00
	15.00	42	243	44	254	45	271	44	286	42	297	40	302	42	297	44	286	45	271	44	254	42	243	40	238	15.00
	16.00	28	247	29	257	30	271	29	283	28	293	27	297	28	293	29	283	30	271	29	257	28	247	27	243	16.00
	17.00	14	249	15	258	15	270	15	282	14	291	14	294	14	291	15	282	15	270	15	258	14	249	14	246	17.00
	18.00		250		259		270		281		290		293		290		281		270		259		250		247	18.00
	06.00						90		79	2	70	2	67	2	70		79		90							06.00
	07.00	12	112	14	103	15	81	16	80	16	71	16	67	16	71	16	80	15	91	14	103	12	112	12	115	07.00
	08.00	26	115	28	105	30	92	30	80	30	70	29	66	30	70	30	80	30	92	28	105	26	115	25	119	08.00
	09.00	39	121	42	110	45	94	45	79	44	67	43	62	44	67	45	79	45	94	42	110	39	121	38	125	09.00
	10.00	51	131	56	118	60	98	60	76	57	60	56	54	57	60	60	76	60	98	56	118	51	131	49	135	10.00
	11.00	61	150	68	137	74	106	74	65	69	44	67	37	69	44	74	65	74	106	68	137	61	150	58	153	11.00
	12.00	65	180	74	180	85	180	83	0	75	0	71	0	75	0	83	0	85	180	74	180	65	180	61	180	12.00
Lat. 5°																										
	13.00	61	210	68	223	74	254	74	295	69	316	67	323	69	316	74	295	74	254	68	223	61	210	58	207	13.00
	14.00	51	229	56	242	60	262	60	284	57	300	56	306	57	300	60	284	60	262	56	242	51	229	48	225	14.00
	15.00	39	239	42	250	45	266	45	281	44	293	43	298	44	293	45	281	45	266	42	250	39	239	38	235	15.00
	16.00	26	245	28	255	30	268	30	280	30	290	29	294	30	290	30	280	30	268	28	255	26	245	25	241	16.00
	17.00	12	248	14	257	15	269	16	281	16	289	16	293	16	289	16	280	15	269	14	257	12	248	12	245	17.00
	18.00						270		281	2	290	2	293	2	290		281		270							18.00
	06.00						90	2	79	3	70	4	67	3	70	2	79		90							06.00
	07.00	10	113	13	104	15	92	17	81	17	72	18	68	17	72	17	81	15	92	13	104	10	113	9	116	07.00
	08.00	24	117	27	108	30	95	31	83	31	73	31	68	31	73	31	83	30	95	27	108	24	117	22	121	08.00
	09.00	37	124	41	114	44	99	46	84	46	72	45	67	46	72	46	84	44	99	41	114	37	124	35	128	09.00
	10.00	48	136	54	124	59	106	61	84	59	67	58	61	59	67	61	84	59	106	54	124	48	136	45	139	10.00
	11.00	57	154	64	144	72	122	75	83	72	53	70	45	72	53	75	83	72	122	64	144	57	154	53	157	11.00
	12.00	60	180	69	180	80	180	88	0	80	0	77	0	80	0	88	0	80	180	69	180	60	180	57	180	12.00
Lat. 10°																										
	13.00	57	206	64	216	72	238	75	277	72	307	70	315	72	307	75	277	72	238	64	216	57	206	53	203	13.00
	14.00	48	224	54	236	59	254	61	276	59	293	58	299	59	293	61	276	59	254	54	236	48	224	45	221	14.00
	15.00	37	236	41	246	44	261	46	276	46	288	45	293	46	288	46	276	44	261	41	246	37	236	35	232	15.00
	16.00	24	243	27	252	30	265	31	277	31	287	31	292	31	287	31	277	30	265	27	252	24	243	22	239	16.00
	17.00	10	247	13	256	15	268	17	279	17	288	18	292	17	288	17	279	15	268	13	256	10	247	9	244	17.00
	18.00						270	2	281	3	290	4	293	3	290	2	281		270							18.00
	06.00						90	3	79	6	71	6	67	6	71	3	79		90							06.00
	07.00	8	113	11	105	15	94	17	82	19	74	19	70	19	74	17	82	15	94	11	105	8	113	7	117	07.00
	08.00	22	119	25	110	29	98	32	86	33	76	33	71	33	76	32	86	29	98	25	110	22	119	20	122	08.00
	09.00	33	127	38	118	43	104	46	88	47	77	47	71	47	77	46	88	43	104	38	118	33	127	32	130	09.00
	10.00	44	139	51	129	57	113	60	93	61	76	60	69	61	76	60	93	57	113	51	129	44	139	42	142	10.00
	11.00	52	157	60	148	69	133	75	102	75	69	73	57	75	69	75	102	69	133	60	148	52	157	49	159	11.00
	12.00	55	180	64	180	75	180	86	180	85	0	81	0	85	0	86	180	75	180	64	180	55	180	51	180	12.00
Lat. 15°																										
	13.00	52	203	60	212	69	227	75	258	75	291	73	303	75	291	75	258	69	227	60	212	52	203	49	201	13.00
	14.00	44	221	51	231	57	247	60	267	61	284	60	291	61	284	60	267	57	247	51	231	44	221	42	218	14.00
	15.00	33	233	38	242	43	256	46	272	47	283	47	289	47	283	46	272	43	256	38	242	33	233	32	230	15.00
	16.00	22	241	25	250	29	262	32	274	33	284	33	289	33	284	32	274	29	262	25	250	22	241	20	239	16.00
	17.00	8	247	11	255	15	266	17	278	19	286	19	290	19	286	17	278	15	266	11	255	8	247	7	243	17.00
	18.00						270	9	281	6	289	6	293	6	289	3	281		270							18.00
South* latitude	Sun time	23 July		24 Aug		22 Sept		23 Oct		21 Nov		22 Dec		21 Jan		20 Feb		22 Mar		20 Apr		21 May		21 June		Sun time

* Use months indicated at top for north latitudes; and use months at bottom for south latitudes.

		21 Jan		*20 Feb*		*22 Mar*		*20 Apr*		*21 May*		*21 June*		*23 July*		*24 Aug*		*22 Sept*		*23 Oct*		*21 Nov*		*22 Dec*		
North latitude	*Sun time*	*Alt*	*Az*	*Alt*	*Az*	*Alt*	*Az*	*Alt*	*Az*	*Alt*	*Az*	*Alt*	*Az*	*Alt*	*Az*	*Alt*	*Az*	*Alt*	*Az*	*Alt*	*Az*	*Alt*	*Az*	*Alt*	*Az*	*Sun time*
	06.00						90	4	79	7	71	8	68	7	71	4	79		90							06.00
	07.00	6	114	10	106	14	95	18	84	20	75	21	72	20	75	18	84	14	95	10	106	6	114	5	117	07.00
	08.00	19	121	23	112	28	101	32	89	34	79	35	75	34	79	32	89	28	101	23	112	19	121	17	124	08.00
	09.00	30	130	36	121	42	108	46	94	48	82	48	77	48	82	46	94	42	108	36	121	30	130	28	133	09.00
	10.00	40	142	47	134	55	120	60	102	62	85	62	77	62	85	60	102	55	120	47	134	40	142	38	145	10.00
	11.00	47	159	56	153	66	141	73	118	76	87	76	73	76	87	73	118	66	141	56	153	47	159	44	161	11.00
	12.00	50	180	59	180	70	180	81	180	89	0	86	0	89	0	81	180	70	180	59	180	50	180	47	180	12.00
Lat. 20°																										
	13.00	47	201	56	207	66	219	73	242	76	273	76	287	76	273	73	242	66	219	56	207	47	201	44	199	13.00
	14.00	40	218	47	226	55	240	60	258	62	275	62	283	62	275	60	258	55	240	47	226	40	218	38	215	14.00
	15.00	30	230	36	239	42	252	46	266	48	278	48	283	48	278	46	266	42	252	36	239	30	230	28	227	15.00
	16.00	19	239	23	248	28	259	32	271	34	281	35	285	34	281	32	271	28	259	23	248	19	239	17	236	16.00
	17.00	6	246	10	254	14	265	18	276	20	285	21	288	20	285	18	276	14	265	10	254	6	246	5	243	17.00
	18.00						270	4	281	7	289	8	292	7	289	4	281		270							18.00
	06.00						90	5	80	8	72	10	68	8	72	5	80		90							06.00
	07.00	4	114	9	106	14	96	18	86	21	77	23	74	21	77	18	86	14	96	9	106	4	114	3	118	07.00
	08.00	16	122	21	114	27	103	32	92	35	82	36	78	35	82	32	92	27	103	21	114	16	122	14	125	08.00
	09.00	27	132	33	124	40	112	45	99	48	88	49	82	48	88	45	99	40	112	33	124	27	132	25	134	09.00
	10.00	36	144	44	137	52	126	59	110	62	94	63	87	62	94	59	110	52	126	44	137	36	144	33	147	10.00
	11.00	43	161	51	156	62	147	70	131	75	107	76	83	75	107	70	131	62	147	51	156	43	161	39	162	11.00
	12.00	45	180	54	180	65	180	76	180	85	180	88	180	85	180	76	180	65	180	54	180	45	180	41	180	12.00
Lat. 25°																										
	13.00	43	199	51	204	62	213	70	229	75	253	76	267	75	253	70	229	62	213	51	204	43	199	39	198	13.00
	14.00	36	216	44	223	52	234	59	250	62	266	63	273	62	266	59	250	52	234	44	223	36	216	33	213	14.00
	15.00	27	228	33	236	40	248	45	261	48	272	49	278	48	272	45	261	40	248	33	236	27	228	25	226	15.00
	16.00	16	238	21	246	27	257	32	268	35	278	36	282	35	278	32	268	27	257	21	246	16	238	14	235	16.00
	17.00	4	246	9	254	14	264	18	274	21	283	23	286	21	283	18	274	14	264	9	254	4	246	3	242	17.00
	18.00						270	5	280	8	288	10	292	8	288	5	280		270							18.00
	06.00							6	80	10	72	11	69	10	72	6	80									06.00
	07.00	2	115	7	107	13	97	19	87	22	79	24	76	23	79	19	87	13	97	7	107	2	115			07.00
	08.00	13	123	19	116	26	106	31	95	35	86	36	82	35	86	31	95	26	106	19	116	13	123	11	126	08.00
	09.00	24	133	30	120	38	116	44	104	48	93	50	88	48	93	44	104	38	116	30	126	24	133	21	136	09.00
	10.00	32	146	40	140	49	130	57	117	61	103	62	96	61	103	57	117	49	130	40	140	32	146	29	148	10.00
	11.00	38	162	47	158	57	151	67	140	73	123	75	112	73	122	67	140	57	151	47	158	38	162	35	163	11.00
	12.00	40	180	49	180	60	180	71	180	80	180	83	180	80	180	71	180	60	180	49	180	40	180	37	180	12.00
Lat. 30°																										
	13.00	38	198	47	202	57	209	67	220	73	237	75	248	73	238	67	220	57	209	47	202	38	198	35	197	13.00
	14.00	32	214	40	220	49	230	57	243	61	257	62	264	61	257	57	243	49	230	40	220	32	214	29	212	14.00
	15.00	24	227	30	234	38	244	44	256	48	267	50	272	48	267	44	256	38	244	30	234	24	227	21	224	15.00
	16.00	13	234	19	244	26	254	31	265	35	274	36	278	35	274	31	265	26	254	19	244	13	237	11	234	16.00
	17.00	2	245	7	253	13	263	19	273	23	281	24	284	23	281	19	273	13	263	7	253	2	245			17.00
	18.00							6	280	10	288	11	291	10	288	6	280									18.00
	06.00						90	7	81	11	73	13	70	11	73	7	81		90							06.00
	07.00	0	115	6	108	13	98	19	89	23	81	25	78	23	81	19	89	13	98	6	108	0	115			07.00
	08.00	11	124	17	117	24	108	31	98	35	89	37	85	35	89	31	98	24	108	17	117	11	124	8	127	08.00
	09.00	20	135	27	129	36	119	43	109	48	99	49	94	48	99	43	109	36	119	27	129	20	135	18	137	09.00
	10.00	28	148	36	143	46	134	54	123	60	112	62	106	60	112	54	123	46	134	36	143	28	148	25	150	10.00
	11.00	33	163	42	160	53	155	63	146	70	135	73	127	70	135	63	146	53	155	42	160	33	163	30	164	11.00
	12.00	35	180	44	180	55	180	66	180	75	180	78	180	75	180	66	180	55	180	44	180	35	180	81	180	12.00
Lat. 35°																										
	13.00	33	197	42	200	53	205	63	214	70	225	73	233	70	225	63	214	53	205	42	200	33	197	30	196	13.00
	14.00	28	212	36	217	46	226	54	237	60	248	62	254	60	248	54	237	46	226	36	217	28	212	25	210	14.00
	15.00	20	225	27	231	36	241	43	251	48	261	49	266	48	261	43	251	36	241	27	231	20	225	18	223	15.00
	16.00	11	236	17	243	24	252	31	262	35	271	37	275	35	271	31	262	24	252	17	243	11	236	8	233	16.00
	17.00	0	245	6	252	13	262	19	271	23	279	25	282	23	279	19	271	13	262	6	252	0	245			17.00
	18.00						270	7	279	11	287	13	290	11	287	7	279		270							18.00
South latitude*	*Sun time*	*23 July*		*24 Aug*		*22 Sept*		*23 Oct*		*21 Nov*		*22 Dec*		*21 Jan*		*20 Feb*		*22 Mar*		*20 Apr*		*21 May*		*21 June*		*Sun time*

* Use months indicated at top for north latitudes; and use months at bottom for south latitudes.

North latitude	Sun time	21 Jan		20 Feb		22 Mar		20 Apr		21 May		21 June		23 July		24 Aug		22 Sept		23 Oct		21 Nov		22 Dec		Sun time
		Alt	Az	Alt	Az	Alt	Az	Alt	Az	Alt	Az	Alt	Az	Alt	Az	Alt	Az	Alt	Az	Alt	Az	Alt	Az	Alt	Az	
	06.00							7	81	13	74	15	72	13	74	7	81									06.00
	07.00			4	108	12	99	19	91	24	83	26	80	24	83	19	91	12	99	4	108					07.00
	08.00	8	125	15	119	23	110	30	101	35	93	37	89	35	93	30	101	23	110	15	119	8	125	5	127	08.00
	09.00	17	136	24	131	33	122	41	113	47	104	49	100	47	104	41	113	33	122	24	131	17	136	14	138	09.00
	10.00	24	149	32	145	42	138	51	129	57	119	60	114	57	119	51	129	42	138	32	145	24	149	20	151	10.00
	11.00	28	164	37	161	48	157	59	151	66	143	69	138	66	143	59	151	48	157	37	161	28	164	25	165	11.00
	12.00	30	180	39	180	50	180	61	180	70	180	73	180	70	180	61	180	50	180	39	180	30	180	27	180	12.00
Lat. 40°																										
	13.00	28	196	37	199	48	203	59	209	66	217	69	222	66	217	59	209	48	203	37	199	28	196	25	195	13.00
	14.00	24	211	32	215	42	222	51	231	57	241	60	246	57	241	51	231	42	222	32	215	24	211	20	209	14.00
	15.00	17	224	24	229	33	238	41	247	47	256	49	260	47	256	41	247	33	238	24	229	17	224	14	222	15.00
	16.00	8	235	15	241	23	250	30	259	35	267	37	271	35	267	30	259	23	250	15	241	8	235	5	233	16.00
	17.00			4	252	12	261	19	269	24	277	26	280	24	277	19	269	12	261	4	252					17.00
	18.00							7	279	13	286	15	288	13	286	7	279									18.00
	06.00						90	8	82	14	76	16	73	14	76	8	82		90							06.00
	07.00			3	108	11	100	19	92	24	86	27	83	24	86	19	92	11	100	3	108					07.00
	08.00	5	125	12	120	21	112	29	104	35	96	37	93	35	96	29	104	21	112	12	120	5	125	2	127	08.00
	09.00	13	137	21	132	30	125	39	117	45	109	48	105	45	109	39	117	30	125	21	132	13	137	10	139	09.00
	10.00	19	150	28	146	38	140	48	133	55	125	58	121	55	125	48	133	38	140	28	146	19	150	16	162	10.00
	11.00	24	165	32	163	44	159	54	154	62	149	65	145	62	149	54	154	44	159	32	163	24	165	20	165	11.00
	12.00	25	180	34	180	45	180	56	180	65	180	68	180	65	180	56	180	45	180	34	180	25	180	21	180	12.00
Lat. 45°																										
	13.00	24	195	32	197	44	201	54	206	62	211	65	215	62	211	54	206	44	201	32	197	24	195	20	195	13.00
	14.00	19	210	28	214	38	220	48	227	55	235	58	239	55	235	48	227	38	220	28	214	19	210	16	208	14.00
	15.00	13	223	21	228	30	235	39	243	44	251	48	255	45	251	39	243	30	235	21	228	13	223	10	221	15.00
	16.00	5	235	12	240	21	248	29	256	35	264	37	267	35	264	29	256	21	248	12	240	5	235	2	233	16.00
	17.00			3	252	11	260	19	268	24	274	27	277	24	274	19	268	11	260	3	252					17.00
	18.00						270	8	278	14	284	16	287	14	284	8	278		270							18.00
	06.00						90	9	83	15	77	18	74	15	77	9	83		90							06.00
	07.00			1	108	10	101	18	94	25	88	27	85	25	88	18	94	10	101	1	108					07.00
	08.00	2	125	10	120	19	114	28	106	34	100	37	97	34	100	28	106	19	114	10	120	2	125			08.00
	09.00	10	138	17	133	27	127	37	120	44	114	46	110	44	114	37	120	27	127	17	133	10	138	6	139	09.00
	10.00	15	151	24	148	34	143	44	137	52	131	55	128	52	131	44	137	34	143	24	148	15	151	12	152	10.00
	11.00	19	165	28	163	39	161	50	157	58	153	61	151	58	153	50	157	39	161	28	163	19	165	15	166	11.00
	12.00	20	180	29	180	40	180	51	180	60	180	63	180	60	180	51	180	40	180	29	180	20	180	17	180	12.00
Lat. 50°																										
	13.00	19	195	28	197	39	199	50	203	58	207	61	209	58	207	50	203	39	199	28	197	19	195	15	194	13.00
	14.00	15	209	24	212	34	217	44	223	52	229	55	232	52	229	44	223	34	217	24	212	15	209	12	208	14.00
	15.00	10	222	17	227	27	233	37	240	44	246	46	250	44	246	37	240	27	233	17	227	10	222	6	221	15.00
	16.00	2	234	10	240	19	246	28	254	34	260	37	263	34	260	28	254	19	246	10	240	2	234			16.00
	17.00			1	252	10	259	18	266	25	272	27	275	25	272	18	266	10	259	1	252					17.00
	18.00						270	9	277	15	283	18	286	15	283	9	277		270							18.00
	06.00						90	9	83	16	78	19	76	16	78	9	83		90							06.00
	07.00					9	103	18	96	25	90	28	88	25	90	18	86	9	103							07.00
	08.00			7	121	18	115	26	109	33	103	36	101	33	103	26	109	18	115	7	121					08.00
	09.00	6	138	14	134	24	129	34	123	41	118	44	115	41	118	34	123	24	125	14	134	6	138	3	140	09.00
	10.00	11	151	19	149	30	145	41	140	48	135	51	133	48	135	41	140	30	145	19	149	11	151	7	152	10.00
	11.00	14	166	23	164	34	162	45	159	53	156	57	154	53	156	45	159	34	162	23	164	14	166	10	166	11.00
	12.00	15	180	24	180	35	180	46	180	55	180	58	180	55	180	46	180	35	180	24	180	15	180	11	180	12.00
Lat. 55°																										
	13.00	14	194	23	196	34	198	45	201	53	204	57	206	53	204	45	201	34	198	23	196	14	194	10	194	13.00
	14.00	11	209	19	211	30	215	41	220	48	225	51	227	48	225	41	220	30	215	19	211	11	209	7	208	14.00
	15.00	6	222	14	226	24	231	34	237	41	242	44	245	41	242	34	237	24	231	14	226	6	222	3	220	15.00
	16.00			7	239	18	245	26	251	33	257	36	259	33	257	26	251	18	245	7	239					16.00
	17.00					9	257	18	264	25	270	28	272	25	270	18	264	9	257							17.00
	18.00						270	9	277	16	282	19	284	16	282	9	277		270							18.00
South* latitude	Sun time	23 July		24 Aug		22 Sept		23 Oct		21 Nov		22 Dec		21 Jan		20 Feb		22 Mar		20 Apr		21 May		21 June		Sun time

* Use months indicated at top for north latitudes; and use months at bottom for south latitudes.

Bibliography

1. CIBS, *Guide of the Chartered Institution of Building Services*; Sections A1, A2, A3, A5, A6, A7, A9, A9 Supplement, C1

2. ASHRAE, *Guide of the American Society of Heating, Refrigerating and Air-Conditioning Engineers*; Section F (Fundamentals).

3. Carrier Air Conditioning Corporation, *Handbook of Air-Conditioning System Design*, McGraw-Hill.

4. London Meteorological Office, *Tables of Temperature, Relative Humidity and Precipitation for the World, Parts I–IV.*

5. *Thermal Transmission of Windows, Pilkington Glass Ltd.*

6. Practical Building Services Design, Vol. One, George Godwin.

7. *The Building (Second Amendment) Regulations 1974*, SI 1974 No. 1944, HMSO.

8. *The Building (First Amendment) Regulations 1978*, SI 1978 No. 723, HMSO.

9. *KF&P Design Manual*, Kenneth Fowler & Partners.

Index